Gene Therapy

A Primer for Physicians

SECOND EDITION
Revised and Expanded

Kenneth W. Culver, M.D.

*Director of Gene Therapy Research
and Clinical Affairs
OncorPharm, Inc.
Gaithersburg, MD*

Mary Ann Liebert, Inc. publishers

To the many patients, families and physicians who have had the courage to participate in these early pioneering gene therapy trials. Their enormous gift will benefit all humanity by providing a critical part of the research program that will allow gene therapy to become a reality.

To

G. Terry Sharrer, Ph.D., who has brought the history of medicine to life for me through his friendship and enthusiasm for gene therapy.

And to

Cynthia Alloway, who has proven to be the exceptional wife and mother I knew she would be when I married her 17 years ago. Thank you for your support, encouragement, and love.

CONTENTS

Acknowledgments   *ix*

Foreword-First Edition   *xi*

Foreword-Second Edition   *xiii*

Introduction   *xv*

Chapter 1   ***The Historical Development of Recombinant DNA and Gene Therapy***   ***1***

    Step 1: Identification and Application of Genes to Human Disease   *1*

    Gene Mapping and Diagnosis   *1*

    Production of Recombinant DNA Pharmaceuticals   *2*

    Step 2: Development of Gene Delivery and Repair Methods   *7*

    Step 3: Regulation of Gene Expression   *8*

    Potential Applications of Gene Therapy   *9*

    Gene Transfer   *9*

    Antisense Genes and Oligonucleotides   *10*

    Biotechnology and Gene Therapy: The Development of a New Pharmaceutical Industry   *10*

    The Potential Economic Impact of Gene Therapy   *11*

    Summary   *12*

Chapter 2   ***Identification of Genes in the Human Genome***   ***15***

    Summary   *18*

Chapter 3   ***Methods for Gene Transfer and Repair***   ***19***

    General Concepts   *19*

    Gene Transfer In Vitro   *19*

    Methods to Improve Cell Survival In Vivo   *20*

    Gene Transfer for In Vivo *and* In Vitro *Applications*   *21*

    Direct Injection of Recombinant DNA In Vivo   *21*

    Human Artificial Chromosomes   *23*

    Receptor-Mediated Gene Transfer   *23*

    Recombinant Virus Vectors   *25*

    Moloney Murine Leukemia Virus (MoMLV) Vectors   *25*

    Adenovirus Vectors   *28*

    Adeno-Associated Virus (AAV) Vectors   *30*

    Herpes Simplex Virus (HSV) Vectors   *32*

    Poxvirus Vectors   *33*

    Human Immunodeficiency Virus (HIV) Vectors   *34*

    Other Types of Viral Vectors   *35*

    Gene Replacement and Repair   *35*

    Summary   *37*

Chapter 4 *The First Human Gene Therapy Experiment* **47**
    The Genetics of ADA Deficiency 47
    Current Clinical Treatments for ADA Deficiency 48
    The Development of Gene Therapy for ADA Deficiency 49
    The First Gene Therapy Trial 50
    The Next Steps in the Genetic Treatment of ADA Deficiency 53
    Summary 53

Chapter 5 *Applications of Gene Therapy to Nonneoplastic*
Disorders **57**
    Disorders of Hematopoietic Cells 57
    Immunologic Disorders (Lymphocytes and Granulocytes) 57
    Lysosomal Storage Disorders (Macrophages) 60
    Hematologic System (Erythrocytes and Platelets) 60
    Human Immunodeficiency Virus (HIV) Infection 62
    Recombinant Vaccines 65
    Direct DNA Injection 66
    Genetically Engineered Microorganisms 66
    Vaccination with Viral Vectors 67
    Conclusions 67
    Hepatic System 67
    Blood-Clotting System 69
    Pulmonary System 70
    Cystic Fibrosis 70
    Other Pulmonary Disorders 72
    Cardiovascular System (CVS) 72
    Hypercholesterolemia, Hyperlipidemia, and
      Atherosclerosis 72
    Marfan Syndrome 73
    Vascular Occlusive Disease 73
    Hypertension 74
    Cardiac Gene Transfer 74
    Muscle 74
    Muscular Dystrophy 75
    Other Potential Applications 75
    Skin, Bone, and Joints 76
    Fibroblasts and Keratinocytes 76
    Use in Bone Disease 77
    Treatment of Arthritis 77
    Endocrine System 78
    Diabetes Mellitus 78
    Gastrointestinal (GI) Tract 78
    Urinary System 79
    Nervous System and the Eye 79
    Summary 81

Chapter 6   *Applications of Gene Therapy to Cancer*   **97**
     Hematopoietic Stem Cell Gene Marking and Therapy
          Protocols   *100*
     Hematopoietic Stem Cells: Marking Experiments   *100*
     Hematopoietic Stem Cells: MDR Gene Experiments   *102*
     Hematopoietic Stem Cells: Other Potential Uses for Cancer
          Therapy   *102*
     T Lymphocyte Gene Marking and Therapy Protocols   *104*
     T Lymphocytes: Marking Experiments   *104*
     T Lymphocytes: Therapy Experiments   *104*
     The Genetic Alteration of Tumor Cells (and Fibroblasts)   *105*
     Cytokine Gene Transfer into Tumor Cells and Fibroblasts   *106*
     Transfer of Foreign MHC Genes into Tumor Cells   *109*
     Making the Tumor "Visible" to T Lymphocytes   *111*
     Expression of Tumor Antigens on the Surface of Skin and
          Muscle Cells   *112*
     Transfer of Sensitivity Genes   *112*
     Insertion of Tumor Suppressor Genes   *120*
     Insertion of Antisense Oncogenes and Intracellular
          Antibody Genes   *121*
     Other Cancer Gene Therapy Methods in Development   *122*
     Induction of Apoptosis   *122*
     Enhancement of Chemotherapeutic and Radiation
          Activity   *123*
     The Genetic Prevention of Cancer   *123*
     Summary   *124*

Chapter 7   *Regulatory and Ethical Considerations in Human*
                Gene Therapy
     Regulatory Issues   *137*
     Ethical Issues   *138*

Conclusions   **141**

Appendix A   *Resources for Further Information*   **143**

Appendix B   *Gene Therapy Protocols Approved by the RAC*   **145**
     Reference List of Published Clinical Trial Protocols from
          the U.S. and Europe   *155*

Appendix C   *Glossary*   **161**

Appendix D   *Index of Health Disorders and*
                Chromosome Locations   **167**

Appendix E   *Points to Consider in the Design and Submission of*
                Protocols for the Transfer of Recombinant DNA
                Molecules into the Genome of One or More Human
                Subjects   **175**

Index   **193**

ACKNOWLEDGMENTS

I would like to thank the following individuals for their thoughtful review of all or part of this manuscript: Ken Allen, Cynthia Alloway, B.S.N., Vicki Cohn, Linda Fried, Jay George, Ph.D., Karim Calis, Pharm.D., Mary Ann Liebert, Paula Masi, Michael Seidman, Ph.D. and G. Terry Sharrer, Ph.D. I want to also thank Odile Cohen-Haguenauer, M.D., Becky Lawson, Clyde White, and Nelson Wivel, M.D. for providing information critical to completing a comprehensive presentation of the current status of gene therapy research.

FOREWORD FOR THE FIRST EDITION

Editor's Note: The foreword for the first edition is included to give readers a more complete perspective on how the field has grown over the past three years.

All societies recall some golden age when people supposedly were wiser or more virtuous. Seeing the past in this light seems to arise from confusion over the future. Yet, history does hold epochal moments. The last two decades of the nineteenth century were such a time—when Pasteur, Koch, Lister, and others introduced the germ theory of disease to medicine. Most of the twentieth century's accomplishments would have been inconceivable without the knowledge that microbes cause tuberculosis, cholera, typhoid, septicemia, and the like. Germ theory's golden age—a pioneering time—made health a more achievable goal and so conditioned all subsequent hopes and achievements.

Today, the molecular theory of disease and gene therapy suggest a parallel to the medical progress of Pasteur's time. The recombinant DNA process, patented in 1980, opened stunning possibilities that, in a single decade, brought the concepts of "inborn errors of metabolism," "one gene–one enzyme," DNA as "the transforming principle," "molecular disease," and "the double helix" to the bedside of a critically sick little girl. On September 14, 1990, at 12:52 in the afternoon, Dr. Culver inserted a needle into the left hand of that child, started the infusion of genetically repaired cells, and, quite possibly, defined a fundamental change in the human potential for health. Since that historic day, the use of gene therapy has spread to several types of cancer, cystic fibrosis, and familial hypercholesterolemia. Researchers here and abroad are designing protocols as "platforms" to attack AIDS and a number of primary immune deficiencies. They even have begun to imagine how certain devastating neurological disorders might be approached. Running concurrently with gene therapy, the Human Genome Mapping Project aims in the next dozen years to locate and sequence all of the genes that make up a human being. As recently as 1971, only 15 of the estimated 100,000 human genes had been located. Now, several thousand are known. Together, genome mapping and gene therapy represent a systematic search for health.

So, is a new golden age at hand? Time will tell for sure, but it is not too early to wonder if history has come to a notable turning point.

Terry Sharrer, Ph.D.
Curator of Health Sciences
The National Museum of American History
Smithsonian Institition
Washington, DC

FOREWORD FOR THE SECOND EDITION

Max Planck, the renowned German physicist, once remarked that an important scientific innovation rarely proceeds by converting opponents. Instead, opponents gradually die out and the succeeding generation adopts the idea as an assumption.

The idea of gene therapy is not quite as new as it seems. Nobel Laureate Edward Tatum first raised the prospects 30 years ago. At the dedication of the new research facilities of Merck, Sharp and Dohme in May 1966, he predicted developments in molecular biology for the next two decades. Among other things, he said, ". . . it can be anticipated that viruses will be effectively used for man's benefit, in theoretical studies in somatic-cell genetics and possibly in genetic therapy." And regarding metabolic disorders, he added, "We can even be somewhat optimistic on the long-range possibility of therapy by the isolation or design, synthesis, and introduction of new genes into defective cells of particular organs." Probably even Garrod in 1909 imagined some distant future when a direct genetic intervention might correct "inborn errors of metabolism." But Tatum, in the face of unknown ways and means, talked about a foreseeable future. Recombinant DNA had not yet been invented; only a few genes had been mapped. Still his prediction, astonishingly, was only four years from being right on target.

Between Tatum's remarks and their actualization in 1990, gene therapy became one of the theaters in the "gene-splicing wars." Critics of recombinant DNA proposed dire consequences of genetic manipulations, from man-made pandemics to baby Frankensteins. If nothing else, their arguments illustrate that most of the terrible things that people can imagine happening, never happen. Opposition to proceeding with the first clinical trial climaxed in March 1990, during a particularly contentious RAC meeting at NIH. Six months later though, the experiment that may rank with Pasteur's pioneering trial in the nineteenth century, and Jenner's in the eighteenth century, went ahead.

Today, critics warn not to expect too much too soon from gene therapy, or that perhaps the whole concept has been "over-sold." This is mild stuff compared to earlier invective. No one can know the future, but with close to 200 gene therapy clinical trials worldwide, one senses that this new technology has advanced to the end of its beginning. The next stage is unfolding.

Amid the pending protocols and clinical trials already in progress, the real foundation of gene therapy may be proceeding unnoticed. It is in the number of young scientists now in training around the world who assume that molecular medicine is real enough for them to stake out their careers. Creating this generation has been one of the goals of the Human Genome Project. Soon there may be thousands of "gene" doctors who, quite probably, will think that all the doubts and worries of their parents' generation were curious, in an old-fashioned way—if Planck was right.

G. Terry Sharrer, Ph.D.
Curator of Health Sciences
The National Museum of American History
Smithsonian Institution
Washington, DC

INTRODUCTION

For about 30 years, people have dreamed of the ultimate cure—correction of the gene defect itself. It was only in 1953 that the structure of DNA, the genetic material in chromosomes, was identified by James Watson and Francis Crick. Forty-three years later, approximately 6,000 of the more than 100,000 genes in the human genome have been mapped and more than 1000 people have been treated with gene therapy worldwide. The major events in molecular medicine can be summarized as follows:

1944   DNA is determined to be the hereditary material.

1953   The structure of DNA is determined.

1961–7 The genetic code is deciphered.

1968   Restriction endonucleases are discovered.

1973   The technique for recombining different genes in living cells is established.

1976   The first cancer gene is identified.

1977   Human growth hormone is produced in bacteria with recombinant DNA techniques.

1978   The gene for human insulin is cloned. Humulin is first marketed in 1982.

1983   The polymerase chain reaction is developed; the first paper describing PCR is published in 1985.

1985   The first genetic marker for cystic fibrosis is identified.

1986   Tumor suppressor genes are identified.

1990   The international human genome project is created.

1990   The first human gene therapy experiment is initiated.

1991   The first human gene therapy experiments for cancer are initiated.

1992   The first gene therapy experiments for cystic fibrosis are approved.

1992   The first gene therapy trial using *in vivo* gene transfer for cancer is initiated.

1993   The first gene therapy trials for autoimmune and vascular disease are approved.

1994   More *in vivo* gene transfer trials than *ex vivo* methods are approved this year.

1995   More than 1000 individuals have received experimental gene therapy treatment.

Advances in molecular biology, which encompasses the study of the genetic basis of disease, have produced new diagnostic methods (e.g., DNA tests for the rapid detection of microorganisms) and drug therapies for congenital diseases (e.g., recombinant erythropoietin for anemia) and acquired diseases (e.g., granulocyte-macrophage colony-stimulating factor (GM-CSF) for chemotherapy-induced neutropenia). The growth in the understanding of human genetics also led to the initiation of the first human gene therapy experiment on September

14, 1990 at the National Institutes of Health. With more than 4,000 known genetic diseases, many of which have no satisfactory therapy, the prospect of a genetic cure using "gene therapy" stands as a great monument of hope for patients, families, and healthcare providers because it offers the possibility to eliminate the underlying basis of disease.

EXPECTED HEALTH BENEFITS OF RECOMBINANT DNA RESEARCH

Two of the promises of recombinant DNA research are improved methods of diagnosis and new pharmaceuticals for the treatment of human disease. Research at the molecular level will provide an improved understanding of how and why inborn metabolic disorders and acquired disorders such as AIDS, autoimmune diseases, and cancers occur. Already possible is earlier and more accurate diagnosis of diseases; examples include the rapid identification of infectious microorganisms such as *Mycoplasma* and the prenatal diagnosis of genetic diseases. Recombinant DNA research will also enable the prevention of acquired diseases through the production of recombinant vaccines such as the genetic alteration of Bacillus Calmette-Guerin (BCG) to express proteins from Schistosomiasis parasites or by fusion of antigens with cytokines to increase their immunogenicity and the possibility for gene therapy.

WHAT IS GENE THERAPY?

Gene therapy is the insertion of a functioning gene into the cells of a patient to correct an inborn error of metabolism (i.e., genetic abnormality or birth defect) or to provide a new function in a cell (e.g., insertion of an immuno-stimulatory gene into cancer cells to vaccinate a patient against their own cancer). This is a very broad definition that includes the potential treatment of essentially all types of human disease including all genetic disorders, cancer, infectious diseases, cardiovascular diseases, and autoimmune disorders through the genetic modification of cells of the human body to prevent or eliminate disease.

SOMATIC CELL VERSUS GERM-LINE THERAPY

Somatic cells are the nonreproductive cells of the body (e.g., skin, muscle, bone, brain, and cells of the blood). Gene therapy that would alter the reproductive cells (sperm or ova) is called germ-line gene therapy. At this time in the evolution of human gene therapy, somatic cell gene therapy is the only form that is technically feasible and ethically acceptable for human use. Somatic cell gene therapy can correct hereditary diseases, but only for one generation. Germ-line gene therapy, which is practiced in animals, can eliminate a disease for successive generations, but at this time it is neither technically feasible nor ethically resolved. See Chapter 7 for a further discussion.

WHY THIS BOOK?

The first edition of this book was written in response to the many physicians and patients who called me in an effort to find a gene therapy trial in which to enroll their patients or themselves. Because much of the medical community was educated before these recent advances in molecular biology, I wrote the first edition with a pragmatic approach to facilitate easy learning. Extensive references were added throughout for those who desired additional information.

The field of gene therapy has continued to grow in numbers and in breadth (see Fig. I–1), and it was clear that an update was needed. Thus, this second edition has an expanded section on genetic diagnosis, gene transfer systems, a new section on gene repair, and updates on all 122 approved therapeutic clinical trials have been added. The appendices list all of the cloned genes as of September, 1995, all of the approved trials, and places to call for additional information. I truly hope that this primer will provide a valuable resource for you and your patients while we all work to remain knowledgeable and current as the field of molecular medicine blossoms into a new clinical discipline.

Kenneth W. Culver, M.D.

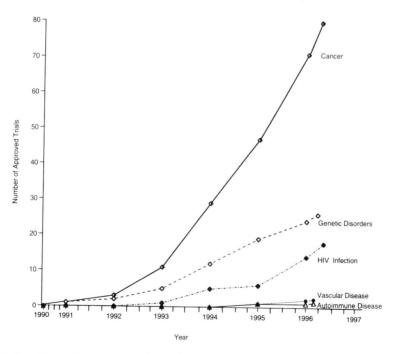

Fig. I–1.   Growth in the number of RAC-approved gene therapy protocols.

THE HISTORICAL DEVELOPMENT OF RECOMBINANT DNA AND GENE THERAPY

This handbook does not attempt to review the entire history of genetics; instead, it is an overview, providing a discussion of the most significant aspects of genetics as they relate to gene therapy. There have been a number of significant advances in our understanding of the molecular basis of disease during the past 20 years that are responsible for the seeming explosion in the number of research centers initiating human gene therapy programs. The genes, machines, and reagents for building gene transfer vectors now are readily available, allowing most universities to initiate human clinical trials. These are commonly physician-sponsored trials instead of the more traditional pharmaceutical company-sponsored trials. In addition, there has been a large investment in start-up biotechnology companies that has contributed to the initiation of 122 therapeutic and 27 marking trials in the United States in the past 7 years.

STEP 1: IDENTIFICATION AND APPLICATION OF GENES TO HUMAN DISEASE

Gene Mapping and Diagnosis

Defining the location, structure, and function of genes has been a long-term goal for many investigators. The pace of unraveling the human genome has hastened with the initiation of the Human Genome Project in 1990 (see Chapter 2). The possibility of mapping all of the genes in our cells and using this information to treat disease is the result of a generation of scientists working together toward a common goal. As of the end of 1995, about 6,000 genes have been identified, compared to about 3,500 genes in 1993 and only 15 genes in 1971. (See Appendix D for a listing of mapped disease genes.) However, there have been only 10 genetic diseases for which gene therapy experiments have been approved (Table 1-1). The identification of a normal gene and the development of an understanding of how the gene functions are clearly essential; yet, until there is a suitable gene delivery system, the gene cannot be used for *in vivo* gene correction.

However, after a gene is identified, it may be used for diagnostic screening. Diagnostic products are being developed, but none are currently on the market for inherited genetic diseases although a number are available through reference laboratories. The largest clinical applications during the next several years are likely to be for cancer diagnosis and risk determination. There is one FDA-ap-

Table 1–1. The First Gene Therapy Experiments for Genetic Diseases

Genetic diseases	No. of trials	Tissue	Gene (year initiated)
Adenosine deaminase deficiency	1	T cells and HSC	ADA (1990)
α_1-Antitrypsin deficiency	1	Respiratory epithelium[a]	α_1AT (1995)
Chronic granulomatous disease	1	HSC	p47phox (1995)
Cystic fibrosis	13	Respiratory epithelium[a]	CFTR (1993)
Familial hypercholesterolemia	1	Hepatocytes	LDLr (1992)
Fanconi anemia	1	HSC	Compl. Grp C (1995)
Gaucher disease	3	HSC	Glucocerebrosidase (1995)
Mucopolysaccharidosis type II (Hunters syndrome)	1	T cells	Iduronate-2-sulfatase (P)
Ornithine transcarbamylase (OTC) deficiency (partial)	1	Hepatocytes	OTC (P)
Purine nucleoside phosphorylase deficiency	1	T cells	PNP (P)

(P) = pending.

proved DNA diagnostic for cancer (distinguishes T and B cell subtypes in null cell leukemias/lymphomas), with several others under review by the FDA. Early clinical DNA diagnostics under development typically focus on molecular correlates to guide therapy, such as the diagnosis of erbB2 oncogene amplification in breast cancer cells as an indicator of more aggressive disease that warrants systemic chemotherapy. At our current state of technological advancement, the development of DNA diagnostics is much easier than the development of genetic therapeutics. Therefore, many diseases will have an approved or investigational DNA diagnostic test available long before an experimental gene therapy protocol is available. In the case of common diseases (e.g., genetic abnormalities in cancer), these tests will be readily available. In the case of rare disorders, the DNA diagnostics will likely remain with the academic laboratories that are working to define these diseases and develop therapeutics.

Production of Recombinant DNA Pharmaceuticals

Knowledge of the genetic defect may allow the production of the gene product for use as a pharmaceutical. The process by which genes from different species are combined with the DNA of another organism results in "recombinant DNA" (Fig. 1–1). The transfer of recombinant DNA molecules into microorganisms or cells has been used to produce a variety of drugs (Table 1–2). Figures 1–2, 1–3, and 1–4 depict examples of how bacteria, yeast, and mammalian cells can be genetically engineered to produce pharmaceuticals for human use.

Another possible method for the production of recombinant pharmaceuticals is the introduction of genes into plants and animals. For instance, a gene can be transferred into a fertilized ovum of a dairy animal. The genetically altered ovum is reimplanted and allowed to develop to term. The resulting offspring are called transgenic animals, because they contain a foreign gene in each of their cells. If a gene encoding a drug such as a clotting factor has been inserted with mammary gland specificity, the clotting factor will be secreted in large quantities into the milk and can subsequently be purified (Maga and Murray, 1995). This has been accomplished with several genes including those for clotting factors VIII and IX, anti-thrombin III, fibrinogen, tPA, serum albumin, and α_1-antitrypsin. One advantage of this process can be significantly reduced costs of purification of large amounts of protein, but this method is currently limited by production of insufficient quantities of protein to be cost-effective.

Plants offer the opportunity to package a biologically active substance into the stem, leaf, or seed. The gene product might theoretically be taken orally directly from the plant without the need for purification or repackaging. Examples include the ingestion of plants expressing vaccine antigens such as tetanus, polio, and diphtheria. Feeding mice fresh potato tubers that were genetically altered with bacterial antigens has shown that induction of an antigen-specific mucosal and systemic immune response is possible (Haq et al., 1995). I anticipate

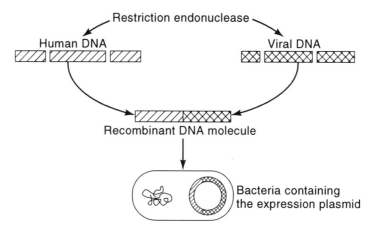

Fig. 1–1.   Production of recombinant DNA and protein in bacteria. DNA can be cut into pieces with restriction endonucleases (enzymes that cut DNA at specific nucleotide sequences). If human DNA and viral DNA are cut with the same restriction endonuclease, the cut ends will match and the two different species of DNA can be "recombined" or ligated together. This procedure creates recombinant DNA. This human–viral recombinant DNA (plasmid) can then be inserted (transfected) into bacteria, viruses, fungi, and plant or animal cells. As the bacteria grow in culture, the recombinant DNA is duplicated, producing billions of copies of the recombinant DNA molecules and the protein expressed from the inserted gene in 24 hr. The bacteria can then be disrupted and the recombinant DNA and proteins can be isolated for further studies.

Table 1–2. FDA-Approved Recombinant Drugs and Vaccines

Anemia
  Erythropoietin (Epogen; Procrit)
Cancer
  GM-CSF (Leukine). To enhance myeloid reconstitution after a bone marrow
    transplant
  G-CSF (Neupogen). To enhance myeloid reconstitution after a bone marrow
    transplant and treatment of neutropenia following chemotherapy
  Interferon α-2a (Roferon-A). Hairy cell leukemia; AIDS-related Kaposi's sarcoma
  Interferon α-2b (Intron A). Hairy cell leukemia; AIDS-related Kaposi's sarcoma
  Interleukin-2 (Proleukin). Renal cell carcinoma
Chronic severe neutropenia
  G-CSF (Neupogen)
Gauchers disease
  Glucocerebrosidase (Cerezyme)
Genital warts
  Interferon α-2b (Intron A)
Growth failure in children with renal insufficiency
  Growth hormone (Nutropin)
Hemophilia factor replacement
  Factor VIII (Bioclate; Recombinate; KoGENate)
  Factor IX (Mono IX)
Hepatitis B and C infections
  Interferon α-2b (Intron A)
Hormone replacement
  Insulin (Humulin; Novolin)
  Growth hormone (Humatrope; Nutropin; Protropin)
Infections in patients with chronic granulomatous disease
  Interferon γ-1b (Actimmune)
Multiple sclerosis
  Interferon β-1b (Betaseron)
Prevention of kidney, heart, and liver transplant rejection
  Anti-CD3 monoclonal antibody (Orthoclone OKT3)
Pulmonary disease in patients with cystic fibrosis
  Deoxyribonuclease I (Pulmozyme)
Thrombolytic agents
  Tissue plasminogen activator (Activase)
Vaccines
  Hepatitis B vaccine (Recombivax HB; Engerix-B)

that the use of plants as a vehicle for large-scale vaccination can be expected in the future.

In addition to the production of new drugs, molecular biology techniques can be used to redesign existing drugs. One example has been demonstrated with the cytokine, tumor necrosis factor (TNF). TNF is an immune regulatory factor secreted locally by T lymphocytes in response to infection and tumors. When the recombinant form of this cytokine is infused into patients, the toxicities are so significant that sufficient antitumor therapeutic levels cannot be reached. A single alteration in the amino acid sequence of TNF improves the cell binding specificity, resulting in significantly decreased toxicity without loss of antitumor activity (Van Ostade et al., 1993). The redesign of pharmaceuticals to eliminate undesirable side effects, while maintaining or enhancing their therapeutic effects, offers exciting new possibilities for therapy. The benefits of recombinant DNA technology, which is now only 20 years old, are new techniques for diagnosis, the production of new pharmaceuticals, the improvement of currently used pharmaceuticals, and the opportunity for gene therapy.

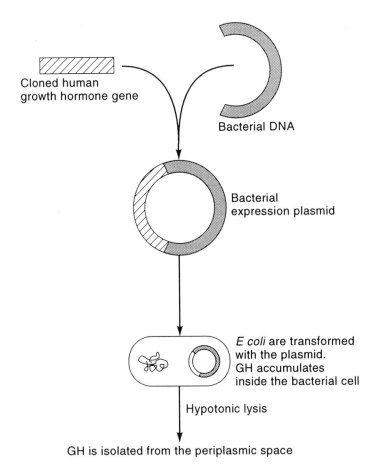

Fig. 1–2. Production of recombinant human growth hormone (hGH) in bacteria. The gene for human growth hormone is isolated with restriction endonucleases and ligated into a bacterial expression plasmid. The recombinant plasmid is transfected into the bacterium *E. coli*. The plasmid produces hGH, which accumulates within the periplasmic space. Using hypotonic lysis, the bacterial wall is ruptured and the hGH is purified from the bacterial extract.

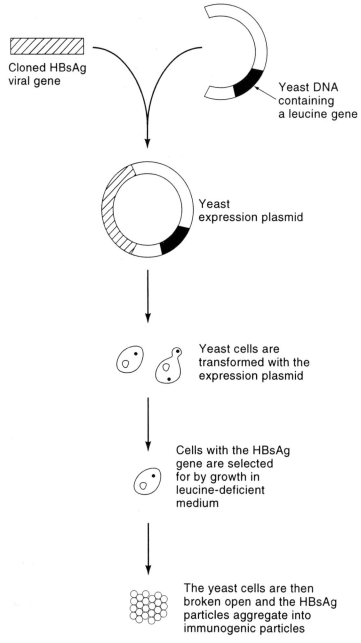

Cloned HBsAg
viral gene

Yeast DNA
containing
a leucine gene

Yeast
expression plasmid

Yeast cells are
transformed with the
expression plasmid

Cells with the HBsAg
gene are selected
for by growth in
leucine-deficient
medium

The yeast cells are then
broken open and the HBsAg
particles aggregate into
immunogenic particles

Fig. 1–3. Production of a hepatitis B subunit vaccine in yeast. The HBsAg gene is obtained from the virus, inserted into an expression plasmid, and transfected into bakers' yeast. The recombinant yeast produces large amounts of intracellular HBsAg. The organisms are disrupted, and the HBsAg is collected and purified.

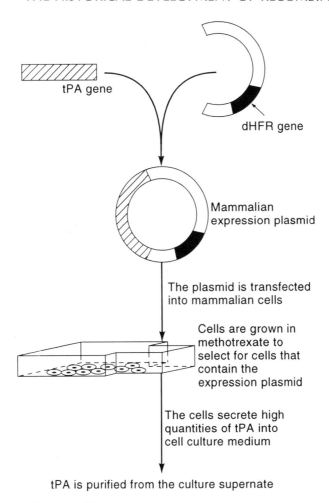

tPA gene

dHFR gene

Mammalian expression plasmid

The plasmid is transfected into mammalian cells

Cells are grown in methotrexate to select for cells that contain the expression plasmid

The cells secrete high quantities of tPA into cell culture medium

tPA is purified from the culture supernate

Fig. 1–4. Production of human tissue plasminogen activator (tPA) by mammalian cells. The human tPA gene is isolated, inserted into an expression plasmid containing the dihydrofolate reductase (dHFR) gene, and transfected into mammalian cells. Cells are grown in methotrexate, which destroys all plasmid-negative cells. The tPA is secreted into the cell culture medium and then purified. Because human tPA is a large, complex protein, it must be produced in mammalian cells instead of bacteria.

STEP 2: DEVELOPMENT OF GENE DELIVERY AND REPAIR METHODS

Methods for transferring genes into living cells have been available since 1974. The early techniques were inefficient and not practical for clinical use. In addition, the transferred gene did not replace the defective gene, but added to the total quantity of DNA in the cell. However, during the last 10–15 years, several new and far more efficient techniques for the transfer of genes into living cells have been developed. Techniques that replace the defective gene with the normal gene, a process termed "homologous recombination," or that repair small mutations, remain too inefficient for use in clinical trials (see Chapter 3). In the past 5 years, the development of methods for both *ex vivo* and *in vivo* gene transfer have progressed into use in clinical trials. Despite these advances, efficient gene delivery remains the primary limitation to the widespread, successful use of gene therapy. Methods used for gene transfer and repair are discussed in Chapter 3.

STEP 3: REGULATION OF GENE EXPRESSION

All genes are under some form of genetic control (Fig. 1–5). The control, or regulatory genes may induce a gene to express its gene product continuously, such as an enzyme required for cellular metabolism. For others, the control elements will modulate a gene's expression to match the physiologic needs of the body (e.g., insulin). In circumstances where variable expression is required, insertion of a normal copy of a gene alone, without the appropriate regulatory sequences, would be inappropriate. Our understanding of the factors that regulate gene ex-

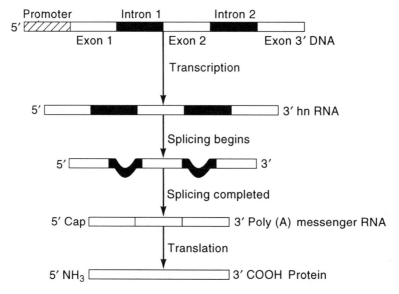

Fig. 1–5. Gene expression and regulation. The protein-encoding portion of a gene is controlled by regulatory elements (promoters, enhancers, etc.). The expression of a gene is initiated by the binding of RNA polymerase to the promoter region. RNA polymerase produces a large primary transcript, (hnRNA), containing both coding sequences (exons) and noncoding intervening sequences (introns). The primary transcript is then posttranscriptionally modified by splicing out the introns and the addition of a 5′ cap and 3′ polyadenylated tail. This modified transcript is called messenger RNA (mRNA). The mRNA then leaves the nucleus of the cell, moving to the cytoplasm, where the mRNA is translated into protein.

pression is less developed than the structural mapping of the human genome. For several diseases, such as the thalassemias and diabetes mellitus (DM), the lack of a complete understanding of the regulatory mechanisms is another limiting factor for the application of gene therapy.

POTENTIAL APPLICATIONS OF GENE THERAPY

Gene Transfer

Historically, gene therapy has been thought of as a treatment for classical inherited genetic diseases such as the thalassemias. Current therapies for genetic diseases are poor in general. A random survey of genetic diseases found that only about 15% of genetic diseases currently have therapies that allow restoration of a normal life span, reproductive capacity, and acceptable social adaptation (Valle, 1987). Therefore, the use of genetic correction as a method to correct all of the undesirable consequences related to underlying genetic abnormalities stands as a monument of hope for many thousands of patients with genetic diseases. However, to achieve this goal, the abnormal and normal genes must be isolated, their normal and pathogenic properties elucidated, and an efficient delivery system defined. These elements will be different for each disorder, presenting a tall task with more than 4,000 known genetic diseases. The determinants of gene function vary widely and the requirements for gene delivery to many tissues are completely different. The lack of efficient gene delivery systems that will stably correct diseased tissues in patients with congenital disorders has helped stimulate the broadening of this concept of gene therapy in several ways.

First, gene therapy may be considered a useful treatment for a variety of acquired diseases such as cardiovascular disease, arthritis, and infection by human immunodeficiency virus (HIV), not just for traditional inherited disorders (see Chapter 5). Second, we are no longer limited to the concept that genetic correction can be achieved only by the correction of the specific, defective cell. For instance, the insertion of the insulin gene into skin cells or endothelial cells may be much more practical and efficient than attempting to recover and genetically correct pancreatic islet cells. There is also no reason why one must necessarily insert the hemophilia factor VIII or IX gene into liver cells, where the clotting factors are normally made. Likewise, the insertion of the factor VIII or IX gene into tissues that can be removed from the body and grown in the laboratory (e.g., skin, endothelial cells), instead of surgically removing a piece of liver, may be advantageous for the treatment of hemophilia. Finally, we now know that cancer is a genetic disease, a series of aberrations in the DNA within one cell that result in autonomous, uncontrolled growth. The ability to manipulate the genetic make-up of tumor cells to restore normal cellular growth patterns or to use alterations in the genetic constitution of tumor cells as a means for their selective destruction offers tremendous therapeutic potential (see Chapter 6).

Antisense Genes and Oligonucleotides

Approaches to the direct genetic manipulation of cancer or other diseased tissues may include the use of antisense genes, to inhibit an oncogene, or down-regulate overexpressed disease-producing genes (e.g., HIV genes, inflammatory genes, athrosclerosis-promoting genes). The antisense gene produces a mirror image copy of the (sense) target RNA that binds to the RNA preventing translation into protein (Fig. 1–6). Antisense molecules can be delivered by either gene transfer or oligonucleotides. Oligonucleotides are short nucleotide strands designed to bind specifically to DNA or RNA sequences. This field of oligonucleotide-based therapeutics (infused antisense molecules) has tremendous potential for the direct inhibition of genes for cancer, autoimmune disease, and infectious diseases such as HIV. However, the clinical application of this technology has been limited by an inability to produce molecules that survive sufficiently long in the circulation, by limited entry of these compounds into the target cells, and by insufficient duration of the inhibitory effect.

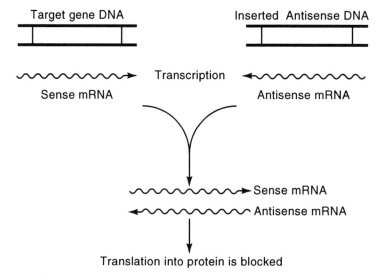

Fig. 1–6. Antisense RNA down-regulation of gene expression. The antisense gene produces a mirror image copy of the mRNA (sense mRNA) produced by the target gene. The sense and antisense mRNA transcripts bind together, preventing translation of the target gene RNA into protein.

BIOTECHNOLOGY AND GENE THERAPY: THE DEVELOPMENT OF A NEW PHARMACEUTICAL INDUSTRY

These recent advances in molecular biology have spawned the creation of another segment of the biotechnology industry, the formation of "gene therapy" companies (Table 1–3). With the commercialization of recombinant DNA, a variety of corporations developed in the late 1970s, notably Genentech and Amgen,

Table 1–3. Biotechnology Companies with RAC-Approved Gene Therapy Clinical Trials in the U.S.A.

Applied Immune Sciences	Santa Clara, CA	Cancer
Canji Inc.	San Diego, CA	Cancer
Cell Genesys Inc.	Foster City, CA	HIV
Chiron Viagene	San Diego, CA	Cancer, HIV
GeneMedicine Inc.	Woodlands, TX	α_1-Antitrypsin deficiency
Genetic Therapy Inc.	Gaithersburg, MD	ADA deficiency, Cancer, Cystic fibrosis, Fanconi anemia, Gaucher disease, HIV
Genzyme	Cambridge, MA	Cystic fibrosis, Gaucher disease
GenVec	Rockville, MD	Cancer, Cystic fibrosis
Immune Response Corp.	San Diego, CA	Cancer
Ingenex Inc.	Menlo Park, CA	Cancer
Introgen Inc.	Austin, TX	Cancer
Pasteur-Merieux Serums et Vaccins	Marcy, France	Cancer
Somatix Therapy Corp.	Alameda, CA	Cancer, Chronic granulomatous disease
Targeted Genetics Corp.	Seattle, WA	Cancer, Cystic fibrosis, HIV
Therion Biologics Corp.	Cambridge, MA	Cancer
Vical	San Diego, CA	Cancer, Cystic fibrosis
Virogenetics	Troy, NY	Cancer

that are major manufacturers of recombinant pharmaceuticals. Now the human genetic revolution turns toward the commercialization of products for the direct genetic manipulation of human tissues. In 1987, the first companies dedicated to the development and commercialization of products for human gene therapy were established. These included Genetic Therapy Inc., Viagene Inc., and Vical Inc. Since 1990, the number of new gene therapy companies has grown to more than 20. In the past 3 years, a number of these companies have been purchased by large pharmaceutical companies. Hopefully, this will provide even greater resources for gene therapy research.

THE POTENTIAL ECONOMIC IMPACT OF GENE THERAPY

As the clinical application of gene therapy becomes more effective, eliminating the need for standard therapies, and the field grows to encompass the treatment of more expensive disorders and common disorders, a cost savings for our health care system should be realized. Table 1–4 lists four examples of diseases that are either in clinical trials (or soon will be) and should be curable with gene therapy in the future. These numbers suggest that a continued focus on research in gene therapy will not only benefit patients, but may also provide substantial savings to the federal government and insurance companies. The time that it

Table 1–4. Estimated Yearly Cost to Care for Individuals with Four Genetic Diseases[a]

Disease	Estimated number of patients in the U.S.	Cost per patient per year	Total cost per disease per year
ADA deficiency	30	$100,000–$200,000	$4,500,000
Cystic fibrosis	30,000	$30,000– $40,000	$1,050,000,000
Gaucher disease (severe form receiving Ceredase®)	1,000	$150,000–$250,000	$200,000,000
Hemophilia A and B (severe form)	13,000	$65,000	$845,000,000
Total	44,030	—	$2,099,500,000

[a]Statistics acquired from members of the Immune Deficiency Foundation, the Cystic Fibrosis Foundation, the Hemophilia Foundation, and the National Organization of Rare Disorders.

will take to realize these cost savings is dependent upon a number of factors, especially funding of biomedical laboratory research and clinical research at academic medical centers. The "Managed Care" phenomenon has not only created chaos, uncertainty, and financial distress in the health care industry, but also in the biomedical research community. Our support of sustained levels of public funding with tax dollars for biomedical research is crucial if gene therapy is to become a reality soon.

SUMMARY

The technologic development of recombinant DNA has had a major impact on medicine in the 20 years since its invention. Human pharmaceuticals produced with this technology can be produced efficiently and are safer than those produced with traditional methods. Examples include the elimination of concerns about slow viral infections in pituitary-derived growth hormone and possible hepatitis or HIV infection related to products derived from blood products (e.g., factors VIII and IX). In addition, recombinant DNA technology produces new drugs, such as erythropoietin and G-CSF, which could not be effectively produced in any other manner. Further advances in recombinant DNA technology will bring us improved "old" drugs and new drugs that will greatly enhance our ability to treat our patients effectively.

Advances in our understanding of the human genome over the past 40 years have provided the foundation for the application of human gene therapy. Expansion of this new clinical discipline is limited in two major ways. First, the identification of genes is occurring at a much faster rate than the development of optimal *in vivo* gene delivery methods and, second, our understanding of gene expression remains limited. Further technological advances are required to optimize gene delivery and regulation of gene expression before gene therapy can be used widely. For instance, the genes for β-globin and insulin have been available for about a decade. We cannot attempt gene therapy for these disorders because we lack the ability to regulate gene expression properly. Once we have elucidated their genetic control mechanisms and have devised a method to deliver them efficiently, gene therapy may be attempted for a variety of hemoglobin disorders and diabetes mellitus. As the enthusiasm for the development of clinical gene therapy applications grows, there has been a parallel growth in the biotech industry. This new pharmaceutical industry will speed the development of new delivery methods and new curative therapies to patients and decrease personal and public health care expenditures. As a result, we are likely to witness dramatic changes in the pharmaceutical industry over the next decade as the use of genetically produced pharmaceuticals, diagnostics, and therapeutics becomes a standard aspect of our delivery of health care.

REFERENCES CITED IN TEXT

Haq, T.A., Mason, H.S., Clements, J.D. and Arntzen, C.J. (1995): Oral immunization with recombinant bacterial antigen produced in transgenic plants. Science 268:714–716.

Maga, E.A. and Murray, J.D. (1995): Mammory gland expression of transgenes and the potential for altering the properties of milk. Bio/technology. 13:1452–1457.

Valle, D. (1987): Genetic disease: An overview of current therapy. Hosp. Prac. July:167–182.

Van Ostade, X., Vandenabeele, P., Everaerdt, B., Loetscher, H., Gentz, R., Brockhaus, M., Lesslauer, W., Tavernier, J., Brouckaert, P., and Fiers, W. (1993): Human TNF mutants with selective activity on the p55 receptor. Nature (London) 361:266–269.

BIBLIOGRAPHY

Carson, E.A. (1991): Defining the gene: An evolving concept. Am. J. Hum. Genet. 49:475–487.

Cohn, S., Chang, A., Boyer, H., and Heiling, R. (1973): Construction of biologically functional bacterial plasmids in vitro. Proc. Natl. Acad. Sci. U.S.A. 69:3240–3244.

Crystal, R.G. (1995): Transfer of genes to humans: Early lessons and obstacles to success. Science 270:404–410.

Culotta, E. (1993): New startups move in as gene therapy goes commercial. Science 260:914–915.

Culver, K.W., Blaese, R.M., and Anderson, W.F. (1992): Gene therapy. In *The 1993 Yearbook of Science and the Future*, pp. 126–137, Encyclopedia Britannica, Chicago.

Culver, K.W. (1993): Splice of life. Genetic therapy comes of age. The Sciences 33:18–24.

Stein, C.A., and Cheng, Y.-C. (1993): Antisense oligonucleotides as therapeutic agents—is the bullet really magical? Science 261:11004–11012.

Wagner, R.W. (1995): The state of art in antisense research. Nature Med. 1:1116–1121.

Watson, J.D., Gilman, M., Witkowski, J., and Zoller, M. (1992): *Recombinant DNA*, 2d ed., Freeman and Co., New York.

Wolff, J.A. (1993): Gene therapy—a primer. Pediatr. Ann. 22:312–325.

2

IDENTIFICATION OF GENES IN THE HUMAN GENOME

The first requirement for the application of gene therapy is the identification and cloning of normal genes. Genes are usually isolated by first mapping the gene to a specific chromosome and then to a subchromosomal location. The specific location of a gene on a chromosome can be identified with a variety of techniques. Functional cloning predominated in the early years of gene cloning. Functional cloning requires working backward from a known protein sequence to the DNA sequence. A more recent and efficient technique, positional cloning, identifies an abnormal DNA sequence in an affected individual and maps that region in a normal person (see Fig. 2–1). This is an essential technique for disorders in which the abnormal protein has not been identified. Positional cloning has been utilized to identify a number of genes, including those responsible for cystic fibrosis, Huntington disease, polycystic kidney disease, and neurofibromatosis.

As scientists survey the human genome, they are accumulating genetic information with and without specific correlations to a specific disease entity. The result is an enormous amount of non-disease-associated information that is now stored in computers and available to the scientific community at large. These databases have substantially improved the efficiency of gene identification by converting positional cloning to a new technique termed positional candidate cloning (Collins, 1995). This process is advantageous because it combines traditional positional cloning, which narrows the gene location to a 0.5–5 megabase region (still a large distance), with matching to candidate genes in the computer databases. In other words, once a specific genetic abnormality has been identified by positional cloning in a patient, the computer databases are searched to see what candidate genes might already be identified in that area. The sequences of the candidate genes are used to examine the DNA from the patient. Obviously, if candidate genes match with the patient's gene, the tedious task of sequencing the entire DNA region identified by positional cloning is avoided. Examples of the successful use of positional candidate cloning include the identification of the fibrillin gene for Marfan syndrome and the RET protooncogene for Hirschsprung's disease.

There are an estimated 100,000 or more genes in the human genome. In an effort to unite researchers and resources in a worldwide effort to map and sequence the entire human genome, the Human Genome Organization (HUGO) was formed in October 1990. As of December 1995, about 6,000 human genes have been located to a specific chromosomal location. Genetic mutations asso-

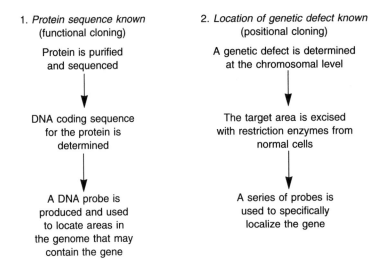

Fig. 2–1. Functional and positional cloning gene isolation techniques. The traditional method for gene isolation was to identify a protein, sequence the protein, and then search the genome for the DNA sequence that could produce such a protein sequence (1). This is a very labor-intensive and time consuming process. A recent advance in gene mapping has been the use of positional cloning (2). In this technique, the DNA of patients with known clinical abnormalities are compared to normals. Areas in which differences in the chromosomal maps occur are then sequenced to identify the normal and abnormal genes.

ciated with human disease are listed in Appendix D. The United States has been the leader in this effort through funding provided by the National Institutes of Health and the Department of Energy. It is estimated that $10–15 billion will be required to sequence the entire human genome over a decade. Obviously, this project will eventually provide the materials and the understanding required for the genetic treatment of the more than 4,000 known genetic disorders. The continued funding of this project as well as continuing international collaboration is vital for gene therapy to develop to its full potential.

Mapping and cloning of the normal genes and cross-referencing them with genes that are associated with disease are just the first step in the process of developing gene therapy. Identification of the gene sequence is not sufficient in and of itself for treatment. Characterization of the normal function of the gene product must be complete before a rational plan can be formulated for genetic correction. There are a variety of mechanisms whereby a defective gene may result in the production of a defective protein or result in dysregulation of normal gene expression (Table 2-1).

For gene therapy to become a practical therapeutic modality, the gene and its regulatory elements must be identified. Insulin, for instance, is a hormone that is under very tight physiologic regulation. Diabetes mellitus (DM) can result from direct alterations to the insulin gene, the genetic control regions that regulate insulin gene expression and the insulin receptor. Therefore, when one begins to consider gene therapy for disorders such as diabetes, there must be a thorough understanding of not only the insulin gene but also the associated control genes and physiologic pathways. Because all of the regulatory elements have not been precisely identified and characterized for insulin and for β-globin, both of which were cloned more than 10 years ago, clinical application of gene therapy for DM and hemoglobin-related disorders remains a dream. Therefore, the application of gene therapy as a treatment modality will require genetic correction of the regulatory elements or insertion of a normal copy of the gene with the proper regulatory elements for certain disorders. At this point in the historical development of gene therapy, the best candidates are hereditary diseases that involve relatively simple "housekeeping" genes that do not require tight regulation of gene expression to match physiologic needs and whose function is

Table 2–1. Examples of Ways in Which Genetic Abnormalities Cause Disease

1. *Alterations in a critical gene.* Certain genes encode for gene products that are required for cell survival (e.g., adenosine deaminase [ADA] in T lymphocytes). When defective, the resulting protein is either nonfunctional or poorly functional, depending upon where in the gene the actual defect has occurred. Damage to the ADA gene results in T-lymphocyte death and severe combined immunodeficiency.

2. *Abnormalities in regulatory genes.* Certain genes are responsible for the control of the production of a specific gene product (e.g., the locus control regions [LCR] that regulate the production of hemoglobin). When defective, a functional gene product is not produced in proper quantities. Damage to the LCR for β-globin results in thalassemia even though the β-globin gene is normal.

3. *Abnormalities in cell-surface proteins or their associated intracellular pathways.* Other genes are required for normal intracellular and extracellular signaling (e.g., the T-cell receptor). When defective, the cell does not respond appropriately to external stimuli. An abnormal T-cell receptor results in congenital immunodeficiency disease.

4. *Abnormalities in cellular growth control genes.* Certain genes are responsible for controlling the rate of cell growth (e.g., tumor suppressor genes or oncogenes). When either defective or over-expressed, the cells have an increased risk of becoming malignant.

5. *Abnormalities in the DNA repair process.* Our DNA is constantly repairing itself. Abnormalities in DNA repair mechanisms produce clinical disorders (e.g., Xeroderma pigmentosum, Bloom's syndrome, Fanconi's anemia, ataxia telangiectasia) because cells are unable to effectively repair damaged DNA. This also results in hypersensitivity to a variety of DNA-damaging agents and an elevated risk of malignancy.

6. *Abnormalities in intercellular communication.* Normal cellular homeostasis involves the intercellular transport of ions, nutrients and other small molecules via gap junctions. Abnormalities in connexin genes, which encode gap junction proteins, can result in disease such as the peripheral neuropathy associated with Charcot-Marie-Tooth disease.

not absolutely critical to the differentiation and development of the affected cell lineage.

SUMMARY

The international effort to map the entire 100,000 or more genes in our human genome is expected to be a 10- to 15-year effort. Fortunately, techniques for gene isolation and sequencing continue to improve, allowing the completion of the first phase of the genome project much sooner than estimated. The gene mapping process will certainly unveil new aspects of the molecular basis of disease. However, when the project is complete, there will still be much to be learned. First, the function and regulation of each of the genes alone and in combination will need to be determined. Second, to utilize the new genetic information fully, the variations in gene expression among the billions of people who inhabit the planet will need to be elucidated. As this revolution in human genetics progresses, there will be an astonishing increase in the number of opportunities for improved diagnosis and therapy.

BIBLIOGRAPHY

Bergoffen, J., Scherer, S.S., Wang, S., Scott, M.O., Bone, L.J., Paul, D.L. Chen, K., Lensch, M.W., Chance, P.F., and Fischbeck, K.H. (1993): Connexin mutations in X-linked Charcot-Marie-Tooth disease. Science 262:2039–2042.

Cohen, D., Chumakov, I., and Weissenbach, J. (1993): A first-generation physical map of the human genome. Nature (London) 366:698–701.

Collins, F., and Galas, D. (1993): A new five-year plan for the U.S. human genome project. Science 262:43–46.

Collins, F.S. (1995): Positional cloning moves from the perditional to traditional. Nature Genet. 9:347–350.

Cuticchia, A.J., Chipperfield, M.A., Porter, C.J., Kearns, W. and Pearson, P.L. (1993): Managing all those bytes: the human genome project. Science 262:47–48.

Hudson, T.J., Stein, L.D., Sebastain, S.S., et al. (1996): An STS-based map of the human genome. Science 270:1945-1954.

McKusick, V.A. (1993): Medical genetics. A 40-year perspective on the evolution of a medical specialty from a basic science. J. Am. Med. Assoc. 270:2351–2356.

Naldini, L., Blömer, U., Galley, P., Ory, D., Mulligan, R., Gage, F.H., Verma, I.M., and Trono, D. (1996): In vivo gene delivery and stable transduction of nondividing cells by a lentiviral vector. Science 272:263-267.

Olson, M.V. (1995): A time to sequence. Science 270:394-396.

3

METHODS FOR GENE TRANSFER AND REPAIR

GENERAL CONCEPTS

The discovery of efficient gene transfer methods is currently a major obstacle impeding the delivery of most genes that have been cloned. A number of methods have been developed for introducing genes into living cells; however, most of these methods are too inefficient for clinical use. Available gene transfer techniques include chemical, physical, and fusion methods, receptor-mediated endocytosis, and recombinant viral vectors. Each technique has its own advantages and disadvantages. All of the clinical methods discussed in this chapter may ultimately find a niche in the clinical application of gene therapy, but none are likely to be a dominant gene transfer system.

One discriminating feature among gene transfer methods is related to whether the transferred gene is integrated into the DNA of the target cell (Fig. 3–1). For example, if a corrective gene is to be inserted into the bone marrow stem cell, a process that will give highly efficient, stable integration of the inserted gene must be a major feature of the transfer system. Otherwise, as the stem cell proliferates and differentiates, the inserted gene will be progressively diluted out and eventually lost from, or unevenly distributed in, the mature erythroid, myeloid, and lymphoid lineages. By contrast, gene insertion into a terminally differentiated nonproliferative tissue such as skeletal muscle might not need integration as a feature of the gene transfer system. Currently, the application of gene transfer to humans has predominantly utilized murine retroviral vectors that integrate stably.

GENE TRANSFER *IN VITRO*

All of the methods listed in Table 3–1 can be used to transfer genes *in vitro*. The *in vitro* method has been used most widely in clinical trials because it has the advantage of eliminating the possibility of gene transfer into germ-line tissues and because *in vitro* gene transfer techniques are generally more efficient than *in vivo* gene transfer methods. However, *in vitro* methods are only suitable for those tissues that can be removed from the body, altered genetically, and returned to the patient, where they will engraft and survive for a long period of time (e.g., cells of the hematopoietic system). Unfortunately, for many tissues of the body (e.g., kidney, brain), individual cells cannot be grown in large num-

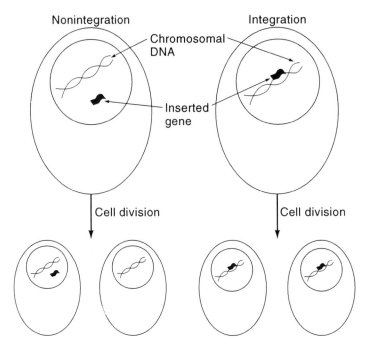

Fig. 3–1. Integration versus nonintegration. Not all gene delivery systems integrate their genes in the genome. If the vector is nonintegrating, the exogenous DNA will remain extrachromosomal in the nucleus and not be passed on to all of the daughter cells as the cells divide. In contrast, integrating vectors insert their genes into a chromosome and are expected to pass the integrated gene to all progeny.

bers for sufficient lengths of time in the laboratory to achieve efficient, stable gene transfer. In the case of other tissues (e.g., fibroblasts, hepatocytes), reimplantation of cells grown in culture does not generally result in long-term survival of a large proportion of the graft. Due to these limitations, *in vitro* gene transfer will be applied primarily to hematopoietic, endothelial, and tumor cells.

Methods to Improve Cell Survival **In Vivo**

One possible solution is to encapsulate genetically engineered, established cell lines within an immunoprotective capsule (microencapsulation) before injection into the body. The capsules are designed to protect allogeneic cells from destruction by the immune system allowing long-term secretion of the gene product by the encapsulated cells. One theoretical advantage of this delivery system is that one genetically altered cell line could be used to secrete the desired product (e.g., hemophilia factors VIII or IX, growth hormone) in all patients. Technologic advances in polymer design have resulted in capsules that can protect cells from rejection for long periods *in vivo* (Soon-Shiong et al., 1995). Problems remain with inadequate levels of gene expression and with a limited duration of cell survival.

Another approach is the implantation of "neo-organs" or "organoids." Cells, typically autologous fibroblasts, are genetically altered in culture, solidified on

Table 3–1. *In Vitro* Gene Transfer Methods

	Transduction efficiency	Integration efficiency
Chemical		
Calcium-phosphate transfection[a]	Low	Low
Physical		
Electroporation[a]	Low	Low
Microinjection	High	Low
Particle bombardment[a]	High	Low
Fusion		
Liposomes[a]	Low	Low
Receptor-mediated endocytosis		
DNA–protein complexes	High	Low
Viral envelope/capsid–DNA complexes	High	Low
Recombinant viruses		
Adenovirus[a]	High	Low
Adeno-associated virus (AAV)[a]	High	High
Herpes simplex	Low	Low
Human immunodeficiency virus (HIV)	High	High
Moloney murine leukemia virus (MoMLV)[a]	High	High

[a]Approved for clinical trial use.

a collagen or Gore-Tex matrix with angiogenic factors, and reinjected (Fig. 3–2). The angiogenic factors induce a network of capillaries, allowing survival of the graft and secretion of the gene product directly into the blood stream. Animal studies have demonstrated that fibroblasts in organoids can survive for 6 weeks, compared to less than 15 days when not delivered as an organoid (Descamps et al., 1995). These methods have potential clinical usefulness for the secretion of hormones (e.g., erythropoietin), clotting factors, antibodies or proteins (e.g., soluble CD4) to bind infectious agents, and/or the creation of an enzyme sink to detoxify metabolic byproducts (e.g., lysosomal enzymes). Further refinements to increase the level of gene expression and the duration of cell survival are needed for these methods to progress into clinical trials.

GENE TRANSFER FOR *IN VIVO* AND *IN VITRO* APPLICATIONS

Direct Injection of Recombinant DNA In Vivo

This method can be used in a number of fashions: (1) Direct injection of "naked" DNA (not coated or bound to antibody, protein, or lipid) directly with a syringe and needle into a specific tissue (e.g., muscle, thyroid), infused through a vascular bed (e.g., liver), or transferred through a catheter into endothelial cells. The transfer of either DNA or RNA has been shown to elicit a systemic immune response to the encoded surface protein. The direct injection of DNA

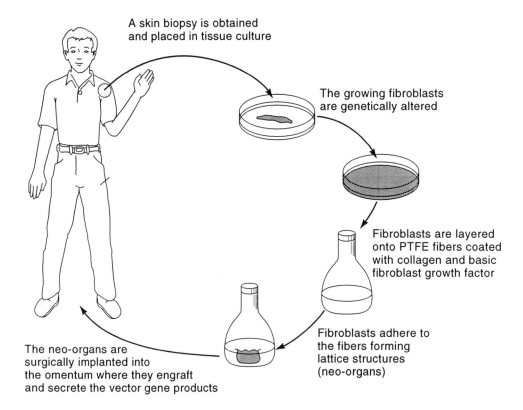

A skin biopsy is obtained
and placed in tissue culture

The growing fibroblasts
are genetically altered

Fibroblasts are layered
onto PTFE fibers coated
with collagen and basic
fibroblast growth factor

Fibroblasts adhere to
the fibers forming
lattice structures
(neo-organs)

The neo-organs are
surgically implanted into
the omentum where they engraft
and secrete the vector gene products

Fig. 3–2. Production of neo-organs. Fibroblasts derived from a skin biopsy are grown in tissue culture. Stable genetic alteration is achieved with either viral or nonviral vectors. When gene transfer and vector gene product expression is known to be adequate, the cells are layered on polytetrafluoroethylene (PTFE) fibers that have been coated with collagen and basic fibroblast growth factor. As the cells adhere and grow on the fibers, a lattice forms. These masses of tissue are then surgically inserted into the peritoneal cavity, typically into the omentum where they are able to establish a blood supply.

is currently approved for use in experimental trials for vascular disease and cancer (see Chapters 5 and 6). (2) Direct injection of DNA that is contained in artificially generated lipid vesicles, or liposomes. The lipid coating allows the DNA to survive *in vivo*, bind to cells, and be endocytosed into the cell. This method is being used in several human clinical trials for cancer, cystic fibrosis, and α_1-antitrypsin deficiency (see Chapters 5 and 6). (3) Direct injection of DNA conjugated to a targeting structure (e.g., antibodies to a specific cell-surface moiety or attachment to asialoglycoprotein to target the DNA to receptors in the liver). This method is called "receptor-mediated endocytosis" and is discussed in more detail later in this chapter. These techniques are in preclinical development for targeting tumor cells and for the genetic manipulation of the liver. (4) Direct injection by particle bombardment, where the DNA is coated onto gold particles and shot into the cells. Bombardment has been successfully used to inject DNA into liver, skin, pancreas, muscle, and spleen cells in animals (Yang et al., 1990). This approach is currently approved to transfer genes into T lymphocytes in the experimental study of gene transfer for HIV infection (see Chapter 5).

The advantage of these direct injection systems is their simplicity, as compared to the production of recombinant virus vectors, thus diminishing the potential risks and the expense of the procedure. The disadvantages of direct injection methods are poor gene transfer efficiency and a low level of stable integration of the injected DNA. Long-term expression of nonintegrating vectors will be a problem, especially in the proliferating cell types, and repeated injections may be required. However, in cell types that do not regularly proliferate (e.g., muscle), the injected DNA may continue to express its genes for months.

There are several circumstances in which the direct DNA gene transfer method may have a place in clinical gene therapy application. First, this form of gene transfer may be used effectively in cancer therapy in which transient expression in tumor cells may be sufficient to induce tumor cell destruction (e.g., insertion of cytokine or foreign HLA genes to enhance tumor immunogenicity). Second, it might be useful for repeated injection into nonproliferative target tissues if permanent expression is not absolutely required (e.g., hormone production). Third, the direct injection of DNA into cells of the skin might be a useful method for immunization. Animal studies have shown that the insertion of DNA into skin cells by direct DNA injection or with particle bombardment results in transient expression of the gene by the cell inducing a systemic immune response against the gene product.

Human Artificial Chromosomes

This novel gene delivery approach involves the use of human chromosomes that have been stripped down to contain only the essential components for replication and the genes desired for transfer. The primary theoretical advantages of this delivery system are the system's ability to carry very large pieces of the human genome (hundreds of kilobases) that include not only the entire normal gene but also all of its regulatory components and its ability to replicate, thus being heritable to all daughter cells. These are substantial advantages compared with many vector systems in development that do not allow the concurrent delivery of the native regulatory elements or stable inheritance. This advantage is balanced by major problems with delivering very large pieces of DNA and ensuring stable, long-term replication of the introduced chromosome. Recent laboratory advances have improved the likelihood that this system may be used clinically. Currently, there are no approved gene therapy or marking trials with human artificial chromosomes.

Receptor-Mediated Gene Transfer

An increasing number of investigators are working on the development of *in vivo* targeting of genes to specific cell-surface receptors such as liver-associated asialoglycoprotein receptors. In this system, DNA is linked to a targeting molecule that will bind to specific cell-surface receptors, inducing endocytosis and transfer of the DNA into mammalian cells. One such technique uses poly-L-ly-

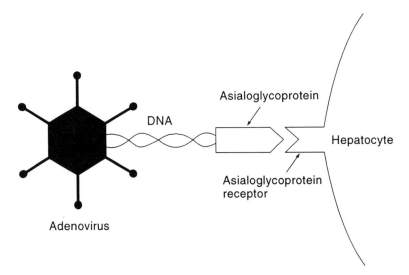

Fig. 3–3. Receptor-mediated gene transfer. This gene delivery method targets specific cell-surface proteins. In this example, DNA is coupled to asialogly-coprotein, which binds to liver-specific receptors, delivering the DNA into the cell. An adenovirus added to the complex disrupts the lysosome, allowing a marked increase in the survival of the transferred DNA.

sine to link asialoglycoprotein to DNA (Fig. 3–3). An adenovirus is also added to the complex to disrupt the lysosomes and thus allow the DNA to avoid degradation and move to the nucleus. Infusion of these particles intravenously has resulted in gene transfer into hepatocytes (Wu et al., 1991). The major advantages of this gene transfer system include specific *in vivo* targeting and a directly injectable delivery method. A major limitation at present is related to an inability to deliver genes stably into the DNA of the target tissues so that permanent genetic correction can be achieved.

There are several modifications of this receptor-mediated approach under development. First, there is the use of bacterial invasion proteins to induce the phagocytosis of the attached DNA or antibody attached to DNA. Second, this may be theoretically used to target unique cell-surface features on malignant cells, such as the overexpression of folate receptors, certain carbohydrates (e.g., glycocalyx), or tumor antigens. For instance, the intravenous injection of vectors that have been produced to target specific tumor antigens may be capable of eliminating microscopic deposits of metastatic cancer cells. Third, unique receptors are present in each normal tissue, allowing the potential for targeting any normal tissues for the preemptive correction of genetic abnormalities before a disease process has been initiated. This may be accomplished by coupling DNA to either a protein, a receptor, or an antibody. For example, antibodies or proteins that specifically bind to polymeric receptors on airway epithelium might be used to deliver tumor suppressor genes selectively into the airway in individuals at risk of cancer, for the prevention of bronchspasm in asthmatics, and/or the delivery of surfactant genes in children at risk of respiratory distress syndrome. No clinical trials using receptor-mediated endocytosis have been presented to the RAC. This approach to *in vivo* gene transfer holds great promise. As improvements in the specificity of *in vivo* targeting and integration efficiency are made, this approach will likely become a principal clinical gene transfer method.

RECOMBINANT VIRUS VECTORS

Moloney Murine Leukemia Virus (MoMLV) Vectors.   These vectors are the most commonly used gene delivery method in clinical gene transfer protocols because they infect and efficiently integrate their virions into a wide variety of cell types (Fig. 3–4). Sixty-eight therapy trials have been approved with these vectors including 43 for cancer, 15 for HIV infection, nine for genetic diseases, and one for arthritis. Major advantages and disadvantages are listed in Table 3–2.

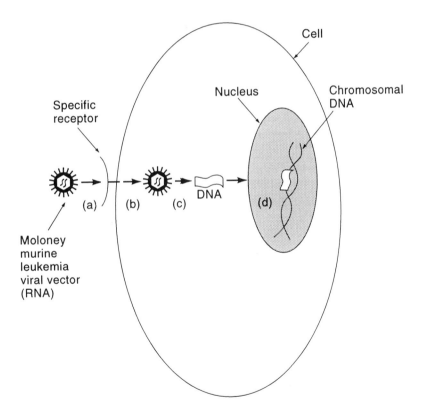

Fig. 3–4.   Moloney murine leukemia virus vectors. This viral-mediated gene delivery system takes advantage of the natural viral life cycle. These vectors bind to specific cell-surface receptors (a) and are internalized (b). Once inside the cell, the viral RNA is reverse-transcribed into DNA (c) and integrated into a host cell chromosome (d). This completes the cycle for replication-defective disabled vectors. The infectious, wild-type virus completes its life cycle by producing viral proteins and RNA, which assemble into virus particles and bud from the surface of the cell without inducing cell lysis.

Table 3–2. Features of MoMLV Retroviral Vectors

Advantages	Disadvantages
Broad host range	Low titer (10^{5-6})
Permanent transduction	Only transduces dividing cells
Established safety record	Risk of carcinogenesis

MoMLV vectors are produced by replacing the viral genes required for the production of replication-competent viruses with the genes desired for transfer, creating replication-defective or replication-incompetent viruses (Mann et al., 1983). This switch of genetic material renders the virus unable to produce a productive viral infection while maintaining its ability to bind to the cell surface (Fig. 3–5). Once the virus binds to the cell, it is internalized and the vector genes are integrated into the target cell chromosomes completing the process called transduction. This technique has the advantages of high-efficiency gene transfer, approaching 95% in some cell types *in vitro*, and stable integration into the target cell genome. Once the vector is integrated, the vector genes become a stable part of the inheritance of that cell, being passed along to all cell progeny during normal cell division. This feature is crucial for permanent cure of genetic diseases.

Another important feature of this vector system is that the target cell population must be proliferating to allow gene transfer (Miller et al., 1990). Totipotent bone marrow stem cells are not generally actively proliferating cells, but are usually in a resting state. Therefore, the use of retroviral vectors for effective stem-cell gene transfer requires *in vitro* culturing with growth factors such as interleukin-3 and -6 and stem-cell factor to induce stem-cell proliferation. Although this requirement has slowed the clinical application of gene transfer to bone marrow stem cells, it does allow some selective targeting of gene transfer into tumor cells because these cells generally have a much higher index of proliferation than the surrounding normal tissues.

One potential disadvantage of retroviral vectors is the fact that they integrate randomly into the host cell genome. In other words, these vectors insert into different locations within the chromosomes of each cell. This random nature of integration means that vector gene expression by each cell may vary, presumably due to differences in the local environment of the chromosome where neighboring genes influence the level of vector gene expression. For many genes, a very wide range of gene expression among cells will not be a problem. However, certain systems require tight regulation to maintain normal cellular metabolism (e.g., hemoglobin production).

Random integration also provides for the possibility that the integration event could occur within a gene that is absolutely required for normal cellular function or survival. In such a case, the transduced cell might be killed. With millions of cells being treated for human therapy, the loss of an occasional cell will be of little consequence. However, a more serious theoretical problem with ran-

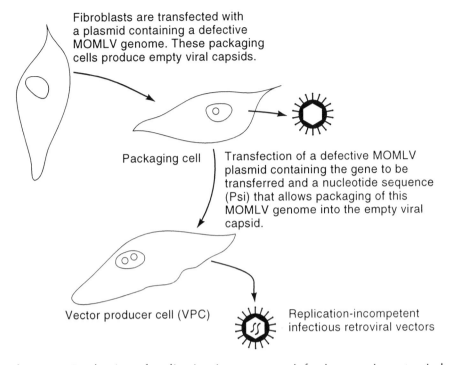

Fibroblasts are transfected with
a plasmid containing a defective
MOMLV genome. These packaging
cells produce empty viral capsids.

Packaging cell

Transfection of a defective MOMLV
plasmid containing the gene to be
transferred and a nucleotide sequence
(Psi) that allows packaging of this
MOMLV genome into the empty viral
capsid.

Vector producer cell (VPC)

Replication-incompetent
infectious retroviral vectors

Fig. 3–5. Production of replication-incompetent, infectious murine retroviral vectors. Murine fibroblasts, usually NIH 3T3 cells, are grown in tissue culture. The growing cells are transfected with a plasmid that contains a MoMLV genome that has been rendered defective by deletion of the Psi packaging sequence. After transformation with this packaging vector plasmid, the fibroblasts (packaging cells) produce empty virus particles. They are empty because deletion of the Psi sequence prevents incorporation of the viral genome. A second transfection is then performed with a plasmid containing a copy of the MoMLV genome that contains the Psi sequence, but is missing the viral genes responsible for building an infectious particle (gag, pol and env genes). This plasmid is termed the gene transfer plasmid. In cells that contain both plasmids, the vector particles produced are hybrids in that the viral particle is produced by the packaging vector and the encapsulated viral genome comes from the gene transfer plasmid. Because the gene transfer plasmid does not contain the gag, pol and env genes that are required to build an infectious virus, these hybrid vector particles are a one-time infectious vector system.

dom integration may result if vector insertion results in the activation of an oncogene or inactivates a tumor suppressor gene. Either of these events could potentially contribute to the eventual transformation of that cell to a malignant phenotype. Induction of oncogenesis by this method is termed "insertional mutagenesis." This currently remains a theoretical possibility because the use of replication-incompetent retroviral vectors has not been reported to result in malignant transformation in any *in vivo* system.

The use of recombinant DNA technology offers the potential to redesign these vectors to improve specificity, efficiency, and safety. To improve tissue specificity for *in vivo* application, scientists are engineering the viral envelope to contain proteins (e.g., erythropoietin) or antibodies (e.g., LDL receptor) that target hematopoietic stem cells (Kasahara et al., 1994) or hepatocytes (Somia et al., 1995), respectively. In other words, the modified envelopes on these viruses incorporate proteins or antibodies that redirect infectivity to specific cell populations as in receptor-mediated approaches. The production of hybrid viral vectors has enormous potential. For instance, gene transfer efficiency can be improved by combining envelope proteins from the vesicular stomatitis virus (VSV) with the MoMLV envelope proteins (Yee et al., 1994). The resulting chimeric virus combines the high-efficiency infection of the VSV proteins with the integration properties of the retroviral vector. Safety features may be enhanced by using viral elements from viruses that do not have a known life cycle in humans and, therefore, are thought to be innocuous. Until these hybrid vectors have been further developed, MoMLV vectors will likely continue to be a central feature of clinical efforts because of their high level of stable integration and excellent safety record in humans.

Adenovirus Vectors.   The adenovirus is a common DNA virus that produces infections of the upper respiratory tract. The viruses infect with high efficiency, but do not integrate their DNA into the host cell (Fig. 3–6). Adenovirus has a natural tropism for respiratory epithelium, the cornea, and the GI tract. Important features of the vector system are listed in Table 3–3. To improve their safety, adenovirus vectors are rendered replication-deficient by deletion of all or part of the E1A and E1B regulatory genes. However, one of the risks of the adenovirus gene transfer system is that wild-type adenoviruses may infect the same cell with their own E1A and E1B genes, thus allowing the production of infectious recombinant replication-*competent* vector particles.

This vector system was initially developed for transfer of the cystic fibrosis transmembrane conductance regulatory (CFTR) gene into airway cells as a treat-

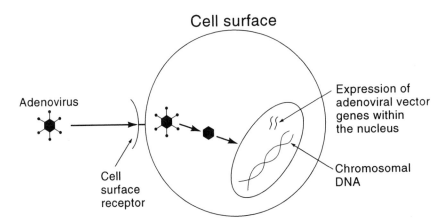

Fig. 3–6.   Adenovirus vectors. These viruses bind with high affinity to cell-surface receptors. They infect many cell types at high efficiency, expressing their genes in a nonintegrating fashion.

Table 3–3.   Features of Adenoviral Vectors

Advantages	Disadvantages
Efficient gene transfer	Lack of tissue specificity
High titer (10^{11-12})	Transient expression system
Independent of cell division	Risk of infectious recombination

ment for cystic fibrosis. Cystic fibrosis is an autosomal recessive disorder that results from defective transport of chloride ions through epithelial cells. The CFTR gene encodes a cyclic-AMP-regulated chloride channel. Insertion of a normal copy of the CFTR gene corrects the chloride transport defect *in vitro* (Rich et al., 1990). The injection of CFTR adenoviral vectors into the airways of animals results in highly efficient gene transfer into cells lining the airway (Rosenfeld et al., 1992). Nine clinical trials using adenoviral vectors to transfer the CFTR gene into the airway have been approved by the RAC. See Chapter 5 for more details.

Adenovirus vectors are also able to transfer genes into most tissues of the body (e.g., lung, brain, muscle, CNS, salivary gland, heart, liver, vascular endothelium, peritoneum). The primary advantages of this vector system are: (1) High-efficiency gene transfer and expression regardless of the proliferative state of the tissue. Whereas the retrovirus will insert its genes only into dividing cells, the adenovirus vector will transfer genes into dividing and nondividing cells. (2) Adenovirus vectors can be produced at very high titer—(10^{11-12} pfu/ml) versus retroviral vectors ($10^5–10^6$ cfu/ml). Therefore, the injection of 1 ml of adenovirus into the hepatic vein will transfer genes in a much larger proportion of the hepatic cells than 1 ml of murine retrovirus. (3) These viruses can be effectively delivered by an aerosol. (4) There is no concern about inducing malignancy. A live adenovirus vaccine has been used safely in more than 10 million military recruits.

As is true of all vector systems, there are several disadvantages. First, these vectors appear to be able to infect nearly all cells indiscriminately, expressing their genes in each infected cell. This lack of specificity could result in toxicity in normal surrounding cells. Tissue-specific promoters and enhancers may be required to overcome this problem (Table 3–4). One type of tissue-specific promoter is α-fetoprotein (AFP). Transfer of the AFP promoter coupled to the gene of interest into a variety of cell types will result in expression of the vector genes only within the cells that normally synthesize AFP (Huber et al., 1991). Since AFP is made almost exclusively by hepatocellular carcinoma cells, this suggests one potential approach to selective therapy for hepatoma. Second, the adenovirus vector does not integrate. Therefore, long-term expression without repeated administration of the vector is a problem, especially in the proliferating cell types. However, in cell types that do not regularly proliferate (e.g., muscle, hepatocytes), the adenovirus may continue to express its genes for months (Kay et al., 1994). Third, the *in vivo* administration of adenovirus vectors induces a specific antiviral immune response that can limit the survival of transduced cells

Table 3–4. Examples of Tissue-Specific Promoters and Enhancers

Promoter/enhancer	Tissue
α-Fetoprotein (AFP)	Hepatoma
Glial fibrillary acidic protein (GFAP)	Astrocytes
Muscle creatinine kinase (MCK)	Muscle fibers
Melanin	Melanoma
Surfactant protein B and C (SP-B/SP-C)	Respiratory epithelium

and the therapeutic effects of repeated administration. Immunologic studies have determined that both humoral and cellular immune responses occur in response to the first inoculation of the vector (Yang et al., 1995). Scientists are attempting to reengineer the vectors to minimize the immunologic reactivity (e.g., deletion of the E2A gene), and there has been some success to date (Engelhardt et al., 1994). However, the host immune response is directed at several viral components that are critical to efficient gene transfer and, therefore, may be indispensable. As a result, repeated *in vivo* administration of these vectors may require systemic immunosuppression.

While adenoviral vectors were initially targeted for the treatment of cystic fibrosis, their broad host range, high infectivity, and high level of gene expression have made them a candidate delivery system for many disorders. Of the RAC-approved trials with adenoviral vectors, nine are for cystic fibrosis, one for partial ornithine transcarbamylase deficiency and 14 are for cancer. As refinements in adenoviral vector design are made to facilitate integration in the host DNA, enhance tissue-specific expression, and minimize immunologic reactivity, the number and types of clinical uses of adenoviral vectors should increase dramatically.

Adeno-Associated Virus (AAV) Vectors. These recombinant vectors are based on a replication-defective human "dependent" parvovirus (Muzyczka, 1992). This virus is considered "dependent" because it requires coinfection with another virus such as adenovirus, vaccinia, or herpes virus to produce a productive infection (Fig. 3–7). The wild-type virus appears to integrate at a specific region (nonrandom) on chromosome 19, remaining latent until a coinfectious agent arrives (Kotin et al., 1990). Integration of AAV is not known to be associated with any alterations in cell growth. Table 3–5 lists some advantages and disadvantages of the gene transfer system.

The major advantages of AAV include an ability to transduce a variety of cell types, including tumor cells, respiratory epithelium, fibroblasts, hematopoietic stem cells, and cells of the CNS, at high efficiency. The AAV virus is not associated with any known disease and is not immunologically reactive like adenoviral vectors. A primary limitation in vector development is that the recombinant vectors may lose their nonrandom integration and that the frequency of integration in nondividing cells may be significantly lower than the wild-type virus.

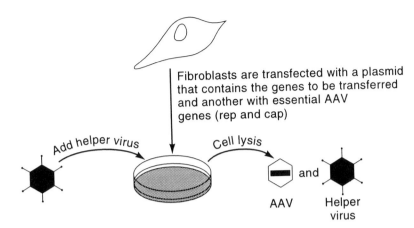

Fibroblasts are transfected with a plasmid that contains the genes to be transferred and another with essential AAV genes (rep and cap)

Add helper virus

Cell lysis

AAV   and   Helper virus

Fig. 3–7. The production of adeno-associated virus vectors. The production of infectious AAV vector particles is similar in concept to murine retroviral vectors, except that additional genes are required from a helper virus. Fibroblasts are grown in tissue culture. The growing cells are transfected with a plasmid comprising only the AAV rep and cap genes and a second plasmid that includes a copy of the AAV genome that is missing viral genes that are required for building an infectious particle (rep and cap genes). This plasmid is termed the gene transfer plasmid. The cells are then infected with wild-type adenovirus that provides proteins required for the virus to complete its life cycle. This triggers cell lysis and infectious AAV containing the gene transfer plasmid and wild-type adenovirus is recovered. The vector/viral preparation is heated to destroy the adenovirus (adenovirus is more heat labile than AAV) and the AAV particles are separated from the adenovirus by centrifugation.

Site-specific integration in chromosome 19 is a very attractive feature because it should eliminate the possibility of insertional mutagenesis.

Recent studies have shown that the vector may persist and express both in episomal and integrated forms for long periods. For example, the direct injection of recombinant AAV vectors into Parkinsonian rats revealed continued expression of the vector delivered tyrosine hydroxylase gene and behavioral improvement for 4 months (Kaplitt et al., 1994). Investigators have also used AAV vector DNA for transfection with liposomes into tumor cells in an effort to achieve prolonged vector cytokine gene expression in the target cells (Vieweg et al.,

Table 3–5. Features of Adeno-Associated Virus Vectors

Advantages	Disadvantages
Efficient gene transfer	Difficult to purify from coinfection agent
No known associated human disease	Small space for gene insertion
Wild-type integrates nonrandomly	Vectors lose nonrandom integration property

1995). Two trials using infectious AAV vector have been approved for human experimentation in patients with cystic fibrosis (see Chapter 5). Further technological advances in vector design and production methods, along with more extensive studies in animals and humans, will determine the true clinical utility of AAV vectors. AAV will likely find a niche in the clinical gene therapy arena, but the major clinical applications are not yet obvious.

Herpes Simplex Virus (HSV) Vectors. These lytic, nonintegrating DNA viruses have the unique advantage of being tropic for the central nervous system (CNS), and establishing life-long latent infections in neurons (Glorioso et al., 1992). Genetic attenuation of these viruses is required to produce nonlytic vectors for human use. See Table 3–6 for a list of the theoretical advantages and disadvantages. HSV vectors are in development for the treatment of neurologic diseases such as Parkinson's disease (tyrosine hydroxylase gene), Alzheimer's disease (e.g., nerve growth factor gene), and Lesch–Nyhan syndrome [hypoxanthine guanine phosphoribosyltransferase (HGPRT) gene]. Reengineering HSV to eliminate the lytic functions, facilitate the establishment of latency, and eliminate replication-competent virus is needed to fully develop HSV for clinical use. This is no small task because HSV is one of the most complex mammalian viruses, harboring more than 70 genes. Therefore, strategies to remove the lytic genes without compromising infection and vector gene expression during latency are very complicated. Researchers have deleted the thymidine kinase gene, the ribonuclease reductase gene, and/or a variety of early and late viral genes that are responsible for the production of infectious virions. These changes have resulted in a marked decrease in the HSV cytopathology (Boviatsis et al., 1994). For instance, attenuated HSV vectors containing the tyrosine hydroxylase gene were injected into the brain of Parkinsonian rats. Improved clinical and biochemical features were maintained for 12 months without significant toxicity (During et al., 1994). These results are encouraging, but further improvements in vector design that will result in latency and prolonged vector gene expression are needed to correct genetic disorders such as Lesch–Nyhan syndrome and Alzheimer disease.

HSV vectors may also be used for the selective destruction of CNS malignancies. There is a two-pronged approach for the treatment of CNS tumors with HSV: (1) The delivery of a gene to induce destruction of the tumor cells (e.g., "suicide" genes) and (2) the induction of an immunologic destruction of the tumor induced by HSV components. Investigators have noted an antitumor effect

Table 3–6. Features of Herpes Simplex Virus (HSV) Vectors

Advantages	Disadvantages
Neurotropic	Produces a lytic infection
High titer (10^{12})	Transient expression system
Can carry large genes	May reactivate latent herpes virus

with the direct injection of attenuated HSV-1 vectors into murine CNS tumors (Martuza et al., 1991). However, there was significant associated damage to the surrounding normal brain tissue, presumably due to the immune response to the experimental viral infection. Efficient *in vivo* gene transfer is a problem for all current gene delivery systems. While recombinant HSV vectors offer the theoretical possibility of establishing an infectious process that will spread selectively through tumor tissue. As new generations of vector design are produced, HSV may well become a primary vector for the treatment of CNS malignancies.

However, the potential use of recombinant HSV vectors goes well beyond the treatment of primary genetic and malignant diseases of the CNS. Acquired neurologic disorders such as pain and traumatic nerve injury may be treatable with transient HSV gene transfer of analgesic genes into sensory neurons or neurotrophic genes to induce nerve regeneration. Although HSV vectors are neurotropic, they will infect a number of histologic cell types, including non-CNS tumor cells and muscle cells (Huard et al., 1995). No trials using HSV have been submitted for review by the RAC. As advances are made in the development of safer HSV vectors, they will likely become a major method for the transfer of genes *in vivo* for both CNS and systemic disorders.

Poxvirus Vectors.   Vaccinia virus was first employed as the vaccination that resulted in the eradication of smallpox. Researchers are now using recombinant DNA techniques to convert poxviruses into gene transfer vectors. Poxvirus vectors are double-stranded DNA viruses that integrate at low frequency, while replicating in the cytoplasm. Their major advantages are that they can carry large genes (four to five times greater than murine retroviral vectors), they are heat stable, and they have a broad range of infectable cell types. In fact, the viruses can be delivered into the nasal mucosa and into the intestine with documented infection and expression of the vector genes. A primary concern has been safety. The adverse reaction rate was one in 50,000 vaccinia doses when used for smallpox vaccination; however, it is much greater in those with deficiencies in immune function. Using recombinant DNA techniques, the vaccinia genome has been altered to attenuate the virus, including deletion of the thymidine kinase gene (Moss, 1991).

The first use of recombinant vaccinia vaccines was for the prevention of rabies in animals using a vector expressing the rabies glycoprotein gene. Field studies demonstrated that a recombinant vaccinia vaccine was effective in protecting raccoons and foxes from rabies (Brochier et al., 1991). The first human use of recombinant vaccinia vaccines for human use has centered on human immunodeficiency virus (HIV) infection (Graham et al., 1993). A phase I trial involving 36 healthy individuals has demonstrated no significant side effects and an immune response to the HIV-1 envelope proteins expressed by the vector. However, none of the individuals developed neutralizing antibodies to the HIV antigen. A new vector that may generate a more vigorous immune response is now in clinical trials. Vaccinia vectors are currently limited to use in people who have not been previously vaccinated against smallpox.

Vaccinia virus is a potent inducer of immunity and is therefore an ideal virus to consider for developing gene therapy vaccine vectors. The concomitant expression of tumor antigens, or other foreign antigens, on the surface of the virus results in enhanced immunologic responses to the foreign gene product. The first group of gene therapy clinical trials using poxviruses was recently approved by the RAC. Investigators plan to inject a canarypox virus DNA plasmid that encodes the human carcinoembryonic antigen (CEA) into patients with colon cancer in an effort to induce antitumor immunity against tumor cells bearing CEA on their surface (Kawakita et al., 1995). The canarypox virus was chosen, in part, because there is a diminished risk of an adverse reaction against this avian virus compared to the standard vaccinia virus (see Chapter 6 for more details). Two other trials will use vaccinia that express either the prostate-specific antigen (PSA) or CEA.

Vaccinia may also have potential as an oral vaccine. Instillation of a recombinant vaccinia virus expressing influenza virus hemagglutinin antigen on the cell surface into the GI tract produced both specific humoral and cellular immune responses (Meitin et al., 1994). Clinical adverse side effects were minimal. The ability to use vaccinia or related poxviruses as vaccines has tremendous potential. The next 5–10 years of laboratory and clinical research should define the areas in which vaccinia vaccines will become a standard in the clinical care of our patients.

Human Immunodeficiency Virus (HIV) Vectors. Genetic alterations in HIV have been used to produce human retroviral gene transfer vectors in the laboratory. Researchers are interested in determining if a disabled HIV virus could be used to target genes selectively into HIV-containing cells as a means to destroy HIV-infected cells with "toxin" genes. This can be accomplished by attaching a toxin gene to a promoter that can only turn on expression of the toxin gene if the HIV virus resides in the cell (Harrison et al., 1991). For instance, the Tat and Rev genes are normally found only in HIV-infected cells. The use of Tat- and Rev-inducible promoters (the promoter will only turn on expression of the toxin gene if there are functional Tat and Rev genes within the cell) may be used to destroy HIV-containing cells selectively. For instance, investigators have shown in the laboratory that an HIV vector can transfer the diphtheria toxin A chain under control of the Tat and Rev genes into HIV-infected cells, resulting in a significant impairment of HIV virus production (Caruso and Klatzmann, 1992).

HIV vectors can be disabled to prevent the development of replication-competent vectors during production in tissue culture, using the same technologies as have been successful with murine retroviral vectors (Richardson et al., 1995). However, there is a substantial risk of genetic recombination in HIV-infected patients where recombinations between the infectious HIV virus and the HIV vector can take place. These recombinatorial events could lead to new infectious HIV viruses and this would render HIV vectors unsuitable for human use. Therefore, in contrast to murine retroviral vectors, HIV vectors will require that additional safeguards be added to minimize the risk of recombinations within a patient. One method would be to include a "suicide gene" in the HIV vector. Suicide genes confer a selective sensitivity to drugs, a property that allows the selective destruction of the vector-containing cells by administration of an otherwise nontoxic drug. One example is the herpes simplex thymidine kinase gene (HS-tk). This gene confers a selective toxicity to the antiherpes drugs acyclovir and ganciclovir, allowing destruction of HS-tk positive cells with IV administration (HS-tk is discussed in detail in Chapter 6). Incorporation of one or more "sensitivity" genes into the HIV vector could enhance the safety of the method and may provide an additional ability to kill the HIV-infected cells, because activation of the sensitivity gene would induce death of HIV-infected cells.

Initial clinical uses of HIV vectors will likely be in areas other than the treatment of HIV infection. For instance, because the HIV virus can integrate and express its genes in both dividing and nondividing cells, something murine retroviral vectors cannot achieve. They may be used to stably transfer genes into a variety of tissues *in vivo* such as fibroblasts, macrophages, and neurons (Naldini et al., 1996). The HIV genes responsible for this feature might be cloned into other vectors. Another possibility is to use the HIV envelope to target CD4-positive cells *in vivo* for the treatment of T-cell-mediated autoimmune disorders (e.g., multiple sclerosis) and cancer (e.g., leukemia, lymphoma). The creation of clinically acceptable HIV vectors and novel new vectors with HIV components is in the early stages of development. It is likely that these vectors will not enter clinical trials for several years.

Other Types of Viral Vectors.   Researchers around the world are investigating nearly every known virus as a possible vector for the treatment of human disease. Table 3–7 lists some of the viral vectors that have been constructed for laboratory studies. As the field of gene transfer grows, recombinant viruses will clearly be at the center of the development of many new therapeutics.

Table 3–7.   Examples of Other Viruses under Investigation as Gene Transfer Vectors

Foamy virus	Gibbon ape leukemia virus
Influenza virus	Cytomegalovirus
Papillomavirus	Epstein–Barr virus
Polio virus	Avian leukosis virus
Newcastle disease virus	Feline immunodeficiency virus
Sendai virus	Hepatitis delta virus
Lymphocytic choriomeningitis virus	Harvey murine sarcoma virus
Polyoma virus	Hemagglutinating virus of Japan
Reticuloendotheliosis virus	Spleen necrosis virus
Sindbis virus	Myeloproliferative sarcoma virus
Theiler's virus	Baculovirus

GENE REPLACEMENT AND REPAIR

All clinical gene transfer methods approved to date add DNA to the total DNA of the cell. Risks associated with integration of exogenous DNA include disruption of regulatory genes that might induce cellular dysfunction and the possibility of oncogene activation. The ideal genetic manipulation for treatment of a genetic disease would be the actual replacement of the defective gene with a normal copy of the gene. This would not only solve the problems related to integration noted above, but should also place the inserted gene in the proper location for regulation of expression by normal endogenous genetic sequences. This is essential for the reconstitution of metabolic functions that require physiologic regulation (e.g., hormone secretion).

Homologous recombination is the term used for switching out a section of DNA and replacing it with a new piece (Fig. 3–8). Using this technique, scientists can actually replace a defective gene or the defective portion of a gene with the normal gene or sequence. Unfortunately, the efficiency of this technique has been extremely poor, with only about 1 in about 100,000 cells making the proper genetic switch. This efficiency is much too low for somatic cell gene therapy where millions of cells need to be corrected. However, there are novel new possibilities to achieve gene repair or site-specific homologous recombination with higher efficiencies. One of those is the use of third-strand oligonucleotides that damage DNA at a specific site, inducing the normal DNA repair mechanisms to repair DNA abnormalities or to achieve homologous recombination (Fig. 3–9). Oligonucleotides are advantageous because they can be infused IV, they are taken up by cells by endocytosis, and they bind specifically to only a single DNA sequence. In this process, long-term binding by the oligonucleotide is not required. Once the damaging agent has induced damage at a specific site, the normal DNA repair machinery corrects the defect with the proper sequence in 1%–4% of cells (Wang et al., 1995). This process has potential utility for wide-

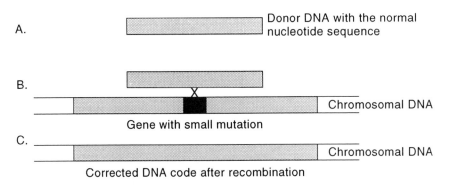

Fig. 3–8. Classical homologous recombination. A DNA-repair process by which a segment of DNA in a chromosome is exchanged for another with nearly identical nucleotide sequence homology. (A) A segment of donor DNA known to have the correct sequence is transferred into the cell. (B) The normal DNA segment binds the homologous area. Normal DNA repair and replication processes then exchange the two segments at low frequency in tissue culture. (C) The end result is correction of the nucleotide sequence within a chromosomal gene.

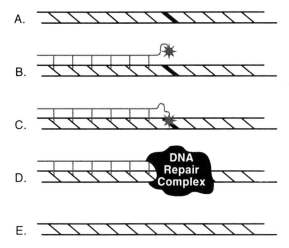

Fig. 3–9. Gene repair. (A) DNA sequencing reveals a disease-causing point mutation in the DNA code. (B) An oligonucleotide is prepared that will bind adjacent to the mutation. A DNA-damaging agent is added to the end of the oligonucleotide so that binding of the oligonucleotide will position the DNA-damaging agent at the point mutation. (C) The DNA-damaging agent damages the mutated nucleotide, activating the DNA-repair process to repair the lesion (D). In a limited proportion of the cells, the normal nucleotide sequence is restored (E).

spread application to genetic diseases in which most individuals share the same point mutation (e.g., sickle cell disease). This approach may also result in a much higher efficiency of homologous recombination. The development of these processes for clinical use is in the early stages for *ex vivo* gene repair of hematopoietic stem cells.

SUMMARY

Efficient gene delivery remains a substantial obstacle preventing widespread human clinical trials. Fortunately, there are a large number of gene delivery methods under investigation. These include both viral and nonviral methods. At this point, *in vitro* gene transfer methods predominate because *in vivo* methods are either inefficient or nonintegrating, thus limiting their applications. The initiation of human gene therapy clinical trials with *in vitro* gene transfer methods was very important, because this method allows the genetically altered cells to be safety tested prior to redemonstration to the patient. As the field evolves, *in vitro* gene transfer will become a standard therapy for tissues that can be removed easily and manipulated *ex vivo*, such as hematopoietic stem cells. However, for most organs of the body, especially those that cannot be cultured and easily reimplanted (e.g., lung, brain), the gene delivery must be accomplished *in situ*.

   Murine retroviral vectors have been used most extensively for both *ex vivo* and *in vivo* gene transfer in human clinical gene therapy trials. These vectors are popular because they are well characterized and stably integrate their genes into the genome of the target cell. Stable integration is clearly the ultimate goal for the treatment of genetic diseases, where stable gene expression may allow a permanent cure. Because retroviral vectors integrate randomly into the genome, they have the potential to induce a malignancy. Modifications in these vectors and the development of other integrating vector systems such as AAV are under intensive investigation for human application. A more ideal circumstance would be to replace a defective gene selectively with a normal gene or repair the defective sequence, allowing the gene to be controlled by the endogenous regulatory elements.

Despite all the efforts to achieve gene integration, stable insertion may not always be required. This may be particularly true in the development of gene therapy for cancer. The therapeutic gene(s) may no longer be needed once the malignancy has been eliminated. On the other hand, gene transfer systems that utilize targeting moieties (e.g., receptor-mediated endocytosis) may allow repeated injection with selective gene delivery to the CNS, liver, synovium, etc. as an interim therapeutic step until permanent genetic correction can be achieved. Therefore, each of the delivery systems discussed in this chapter will likely find a niche in which their inherent advantages and disadvantages serve the best interests of the patient. Further development of injectable viral and nonviral vectors that target specific cell types and integrate and express their genes appropriately in a specific tissue will create an opportunity for a significant improvement in our current medical therapies for many congenital and acquired disorders.

BIBLIOGRAPHY[1]

Gene Transfer in Vitro

Al-Hendy, A., Hortelano, G., Tannenbaum, G.S., and Chang, P.L. (1995): Correction of the growth defect in dwarf mice with non-autologous microencapsulated myoblasts—An alternative approach to somatic gene therapy. Hum. Gene Ther. 6:165–175.

Chang, P.L., Shen, N., and Westcott, A.J. (1993): Delivery of recombinant gene products with microencapsulated cells in vivo. Hum. Gene Ther. 4:433–440.

Descamps, V., Blumenfeld, N., Perricaudet, M., Beuzard, Y., and Kremer, E.J. (1995): Organoids direct systemic expression of erythropoietin in mice. Gene Ther. 2:411–417.

Heartlein, M.W., Roman, V.A., Jiang, J-L., Sellers, J.W., Zuliani, A.M., Treco, D.A., and Selden, R.F. (1994): Long-term production and delivery of human growth hormone in vivo. Proc. Natl. Acad. Sci. U.S.A. 91:10967–10971.

Hughes, M., Vassilakos, A., Andrews, D.W., Hortelano, G., Belmont, J.W., and Chang, P.L. (1994): Delivery of a secretable adenosine deaminase through microcapsules—A novel approach to somatic gene therapy. Hum. Gene Ther. 5:1445–1455.

Liu, H.W., Ofosu, F.A., and Chang, P.L. (1993): Expression of human factor IX microencapsulated recombinant fibroblasts. Hum. Gene Ther. 4:291–301.

Maysinger, D., Piccardo, P., Filipovic-Grcic, J., and Cuello, A.C. (1993): Microencapsulation of genetically engineered fibroblasts secreting nerve growth factor. Neurochem. Int. 23:123–129.

Moullier, P., Bohl, D., Cardoso, J., Heard, J.M., and Danos, O. (1995): Long-term delivery of a lysosomal enzyme by genetically modified fibroblasts in dogs. Nature Med. 1:353–357.

---

[1]Bibliography subsections refer to specific sections in the text, and are listed in the order that those sections appear.

Naffakh, N., Henri, A., Villeval, J.L., Rouyer-Fessard, P., Moullier, P., Blumenfeld, N., Danos, O., Vainchenker, W., Heard, J.M., and Beuzard, Y. (1995): Sustained delivery of erythropoietin in mice by genetically modified skin fibroblasts. Proc. Natl. Acad. Sci. U.S.A. 92:3194-3198.

Salvetti, A., Moullier, P., Cornet, V., Brooks, D., Hopwood, J.J., Danos, O., and Heard, J.M. (1995): In vivo delivery of human α-L-iduronidase in mice implanted with neo-organs. Hum. Gene Ther. 6:1153-1159.

Soon-Shiong, P., Heintz, R.E., Merideth, N., Yao, Q.X., Yao, Z., Zheng, T., Murphy, M., Moloney, M.K., Schmehl, M., Harris, M., Mendez, R., Mendez, R., and Sandford, P.S. (1994): Insulin independence in a type 1 diabetic patient after encapsulated islet cell transplantation. Lancet 343:950-951.

Valere, T., Bohl, D., Klatzmann, D., Danos, O., Sonigo, P., and Heard, J.M. (1995): Continuous secretion of human soluble CD4 in mice transplanted with genetically modified cells. Gene Ther. 2:197-202.

Direct Injection of Recombinant DNA in Vivo

Acsadi, G., Dickson, G., Love, D.R., Jani, A., Walsh, F.S., Gurusinghe, A., Wolff, J.A., and Davies, K.E. (1991): Human dystrophin expression in mdx mice after intramuscular injection of DNA constructs. Nature (London) 352:815-818.

Conry, R.M., LoBuglio, A.F., Wright, M., Sumerel, L., Pike, M.J., Johanning, F., Benjamin, R., Lu, D., and Curiel, D.T. (1995): Characterization of a messenger RNA polynucleotide vaccine vector. Cancer Res. 55:1398-1400.

Felgner, P.L., Gadek, T.R., Holm, M., Roman, R., Chan, H.W., Wenz, M., Northrop, J.P., Ringold, G.M., and Danielsen, M. (1987): Lipofection: A highly efficient, lipid-mediated DNA-transfection procedure. Proc. Natl. Acad. Sci. U.S.A. 84:7413-7417.

Hoffman, R.M., and Li, L. (1995): Model of selective gene therapy of hair growth: Liposome targeting of the active lacZ gene to hair follicles of histocultured skin. In Vitro. 31:11-13.

Hyde, S.C., Gill, D.R., Higgins, C.F., Trezise, A.E.O., MacVinish, L.J., Cuthbert, A.W., Ratcliff, R., Evans, M.J., and Colledge, W.H. (1993): Correction of the ion transport defect in cystic fibrosis transgenic mice by gene therapy. Nature (London) 362:250-255.

Lasic, D.D., and Papahadjopoulos, D. (1995): Liposomes revisited. Science 267:1275-1276.

Stewart, M.J., Plautz, G.E., Buono, L.D., Yang, Z.Y., Xu, L., Gao, X., Huang, L., Nabel, E.G., and Nabel, G.J. (1992): Gene transfer in vivo with DNA-liposome complexes: Safety and acute toxicity in mice. Hum. Gene Ther. 3:267-275.

Sun, W.H., Burkholder, J.K., Sun, J., Culp, J., Turner, J., Lu, X.G., Pugh, T.D., Ershler, W.B., and Yang, N-S. (1995): In vivo cytokine gene transfer by gene gun reduces tumor growth in mice. Proc. Natl. Acad. Sci. U.S.A. 92:2889-2893.

Tsukamoto, M., Ochiya, T., Yoshidama, S., Sugimura, T., and Terada, M. (1995): Gene transfer and expression in progeny after intravenous DNA injection into pregnant mice. Nat. Genet. 9:243-248.

Tang, D., DeVit, M., and Johnston, S.A. (1992): Genetic immunization is a simple method for eliciting an immune response. Nature (London) 356:152-154.

Yang, N.-S., Burkholder, J., Roberts, B., Martinelli, B., and McCabe, D. (1990): In vivo and in vitro gene transfer to mammalian cells by particle bombardment. Proc. Natl. Acad. Sci. U.S.A. 87:9568-9572.

Wolff, J.A., Malone, R.W., Williams, P., Chong, W., Ascardi, G., Jani, A., and Felgner, P. (1990): Direct gene transfer into mouse muscle in vivo. Science 247:1465-1468.

Zhu, N., Liggitt, D., and Debs, R. (1993): Systemic gene expression after intravenous DNA delivery into adult mice. Science 261:209-211.

Human Artificial Chromosomes

Hirst, M.C., and Porteous, D.J. (1991): Molecular cloning of a rearranged HRAS1 oncogene in chromosome mediated gene transfer associated with elevated tumorigenicity. Oncogene 6:153-157.

Huxley, C. (1994): Mammalian artificial chromosomes: A new tool for gene therapy. Gene Ther. 1:7-12.

Porteous, D.J., Dorin, J.R., Wilkinson, M.M., Fletcher, J.M., Emslie, E., and van Heyningen, V. (1990): SV40-mediated tumor selection and chromosome transfer to enrich for cystic fibrosis region. Somat. Cell Mol. Genet. 16:29-38.

Sun, T-Q., Fenstermacher, D.A., and Vos, J-M.H. (1994): Human artificial chromosomes for cloning large DNA fragments in human cells. Nature Genet. 8:33-41.

Receptor-Mediated Gene Transfer

Batra, R.K., Wang-Johanning, F., Wagner, E., Garver, R.I., and Curiel, D.T. (1994): Receptor-mediated gene delivery employing lectin-binding specificity. Gene Ther. 1:255-260.

Cotten, M., Längle-Rouault, F., Kirlappos, H., Wagner, E., Mechtler, K., Zenke, M., Beug, H., and Birnstiel, M.L. (1990): Transferrin-polycation-mediated introduction of DNA into human leukemic cells: Stimulation by agents that affect the survival of transfected DNA or modulate transferrin receptor levels. Proc. Natl. Acad. Sci. U.S.A. 87:4033–4037.

Cristiano, R.J., Smith, L.C., and Woo, S.L.C. (1993): Hepatic gene therapy: Adenovirus enhancement of receptor-mediated gene delivery and expression in primary hepatocytes. Proc. Natl. Acad. Sci. U.S.A. 90:2122–2126.

Ferkol, T., Perales, J.C., Eckman, E., Kaetzel, C.S., Hanson, R.W., and Davis, P.B. (1995): Gene transfer into the airway epithelium of animals by targeting the polymeric immunoglobulin receptor. J. Clin. Invest. 95:493–502.

Gao, L., Wagner, E., Cotten, M., Agarwal, S., Harris, C., Romer, M., Miller, L., Hu, P.-C., Curiel, D., and Rmer, M. (1993): Direct in vivo gene transfer to airway epithelium employing adenovirus-polylysine-DNA complexes. Hum. Gene Ther. 4:17–24.

Gottschalk, S., Cristiano, R.J., Smith, L.C., and Woo, S.L.C. (1994): Folate receptor-mediated DNA delivery into tumor cells: Potosomal disruption results in enhanced gene expression. Gene Ther. 1:185–191.

Michael, S.I., and Curiel, D.T. (1994): Strategies to achieve targeted gene delivery via the receptor-mediated endocytosis pathway. Gene Ther. 1:223–232.

Perales, J.C., Ferkol, T., Beegen, H., Ratnoff, O.D., and Hanson, R.W. (1994): Gene transfer in vivo: Sustained expression and regulation of genes introduced into the liver by receptor-targeted uptake. Proc. Natl. Acad. Sci. U.S.A. 91:4086–4090.

Remy, J.S., Kichler, A., Mordvinov, V., Schuber, F., and Behr, J.P. (1995): Targeted gene transfer into hepatoma cells with lipopolyamine-condensed DNA particles presenting galactose ligands: a stage toward artificial viruses. Proc. Natl. Acad. Sci. U.S.A. 92:1744–1748.

Wagner, E., Plank, C., Zatloukal, K., Cotten, M., and Birnstiel, M.L. (1992): Influenza virus hemagglutinin HA-2 N-terminal fusogenic peptides augment gene transfer by transferrin-polylysine-DNA complexes: Toward a synthetic virus-like gene-transfer vehicle. Proc. Natl. Acad. Sci. U.S.A. 89:7934–7938.

Wu, G.Y., and Wu, C.H. (1987): Receptor-mediated in vitro gene transformation by a soluble DNA carrier system. J. Biol. Chem. 262:4429–4432.

Wu, G.Y., and Wu, C.H. (1988): Evidence for targeted gene delivery to Hep G2 hepatoma cells in vitro. Biochemistry 27:887–892.

Wu, G.Y., Wilson, J.M., Shalaby, F., Grossman, M., Shafritz, D.A., and Wu, C.H. (1991): Receptor-mediated gene delivery in vivo. Partial correction of genetic analbuminemia in Nagase rats. J. Biol. Chem. 266:14338–14342.

Zenke, M., Steinlein, P., Wagner, E., Cotten, M., Beug, H., and Birnstiel, M.L. (1990): Receptor-mediated endocytosis of transferrin-polycation conjugates: An efficient way to introduce DNA into hematopoietic cells. Proc. Natl. Acad. Sci. U.S.A. 87:3655–3659.

Moloney Murine Leukemia Virus Vectors

Chu, T-H.T., and Dornburg, R. (1995): Retroviral vector particles displaying the antigen-binding site of an antibody enable cell-type specific gene transfer. J. Virol. 69:2659–2663.

Cornetta, K., Moen, R.C., Culver, K., Morgan, R.A., McLachlin, J.R., Sturm, S., Selegue, J., London, W., Blaese, R.M., and Anderson, W.F. (1990): Amphotropic murine leukemia virus is not an acute pathogen for primates. Hum. Gene Ther. 1:15–30.

Donahue, R.E., Kessler, S.W., Bodine, D., McDonagh, K., Dunbar, C., Goodman, S., Agricola, B., Byrne, E., Raffeld, M., Moen, R., Bacher, J., Zsebo, K.M., and Nienhuis, A.W. (1992): Helper virus induced T cell lymphoma in nonhuman primates after retroviral mediated gene transfer. J. Exp. Med. 176:1125–1135.

Eglitis, M.A., Kantoff, P., Gilboa, E., and Anderson, W.F. (1985): Gene expression in mice after high efficiency retroviral-mediated gene transfer. Science 230:1395–1398.

Kasahara, N., Dozy, A.M., and Kan, Y.W. (1994): Tissue-specific targeting of retroviral vectors through ligand-receptor interactions. Science 266:1373–1376.

Kavanaugh, M.P., Miller, D.G., Zhang, W., Low, W., Kozak, S.L., Kabat, D., and Miller, A.D. (1994): Cell-surface receptors for gibbon ape leukemia virus and amphotropic murine retrovirus are inductible sodium-dependent phosphate symporters. Proc. Natl. Acad. Sci. (USA). 91:7071–7075.

Mann, R., Mulligan, R.C., and Baltimore, D. (1983): Construction of a retrovirus packaging mutant and its use to produce helper-free defective retrovirus. Cell 33:153–159.

Markowitz, D., Goff, S., and Bank, A. (1988): Construction and use of a safe efficient amphotropic packaging cell line. Virology 167:400–406.

Miller, A.D. (1992): Retroviral vectors. Curr. Topics Microbiol. Immunol. 158:1–24.

Miller, D.G., Adam, M.A., and Miller, A.D. (1990): Gene transfer by retrovirus vectors occurs only in cells that are actively replicating at time of infection. Mol. Cell Biol. 10:4239–4242.

Salmons, B., and Gunzburg, W.H. (1993): Targeting of retroviral vectors for gene therapy. Hum. Gene Ther. 4:129–141.

Scherdin, U., Rhodes, K., and Breindl, M. (1990): Transcriptionally active genome regions are preferred targets for retrovirus integration. J. Virol. 64:907–912.

Somia, N.V., Zoppé, M., and Verma, I.M. (1995): Generation of targeted retroviral vectors by using single-chain variable fragment: An approach to in vivo gene delivery. Proc. Natl. Acad. Sci. U.S.A. 92:7570–7574.

Yee, J-K., Miyanohara, A., LaPorte, P., Bouic, K., Burns, J.C., and Friedmann, T. (1994): A general method for the generation of high-titer, pantropic retroviral vectors: Highly efficient infection of primary hepatocytes. Proc. Natl. Acad. Sci. U.S.A. 91:9564–9568.

Adenovirus Vectors

Draghia, R., Caillaud, C., Manicom, R., Pavirani, A., Kahn, A., and Poenaru, L. (1995): Gene delivery into the central nervous system by nasal instillation in rats. Gene Ther. 2:418–423.

Engelhardt, J.F., Ye, X., Doranz, B., and Wilson, J.M. (1994): Ablation of E2A in recombinant adenoviruses improves transgene persistence and decreases inflammatory response in mouse liver. Proc. Natl. Acad. Sci. U.S.A. 91:6196–6200.

Ferrari, G., Salvatori, G., Rossi, C., Cossu, G., and Mavilio, F. (1995): A retroviral vector containing a muscle-specific enhancer drives gene expression only in differentiated muscle fibers. Hum. Gene Ther. 6:733–742.

Huber, B.E., Richards, C.A., and Krenitsky, T.A. (1991): Retroviral-mediated gene therapy for the treatment of hepatocellular carcinoma: An innovative approach for cancer therapy. Proc. Natl. Acad. Sci. U.S.A. 88:8039–8043.

Kass-Eisler, A., Falck-Pederson, E., Alvira, M., Rivera, J., Buttrick, P.M., Wittenberg, B.A., Cipriani, L., and Leinwand, L.A. (1993): Quantitative determination of adenovirus-mediated gene delivery to rat cardiac myocytes in vitro and in vivo. Proc. Natl. Acad. Sci. U.S.A. 90:11498–11502.

Kay, M.A., Landen, C.M., Rothenberg, S.R., Taylor, L.A., Leland, F., Wiehle, S., Fang, B., Bellinger, D., Finegold, M., Thompson, A.R., Read, M., Brinkhous, K.M., and Woo, S.L.C. (1994): In vivo hepatic gene therapy: Complete albeit transient correction of factor IX deficiency in hemophilia B dogs. Proc. Natl. Acad. Sci. U.S.A. 91:2353–2357.

Le Gal La Salle, G., Robert, J.J., Ridoux, V., Stratford-Perricaudet, L.D., Perricaudet, M., and Mallet, J. (1993): An adenovirus vector for gene transfer into neurons and glia in the brain. Science 259:988–990.

Mastrangeli, A., Danel, C., Rosenfeld, M.A., Stratford-Perricaudet, K., Perricaudet, M., Pavirani, A., Lecocq, J.P., and Crystal, R.G. (1993): Diversity of airway epithelial cell targets for in vivo recombinant adenovirus-mediated gene transfer. J. Clin. Invest. 91:225–234.

Ragot, T., Vincent, N., Chafey, P., Vigne, E., Gilgenkrantz, H., Couton, D., Cartaud, J., Briand, P., Kaplan, J.-C., Perricaudet, M., and Kahn, A. (1993): Efficient adenovirus-mediated transfer of a human minidystrophin gene to skeletal muscle of mdx mice. Nature (London) 361:647–650.

Rich, D.P., Anderson, M.P., Gregory, R.J., Cheng, S.H., Paul, S., Jefferson, D.M., McCann, J.D., Klinger, K.W., Smith, A.E., and Welsh, M.J. (1990): Expression of cystic fibrosis transmembrane conductance regulator corrects defective chloride channel regulation in cystic fibrosis airway epithelial cells. Nature (London) 347:358–363.

Rosenfeld, M.A., Siegfried, W., Yoshimura, K., Yoneyama, K., Fukayama, M., Steir, L.E., Paakko, P.K., Gilardi, P., Stratford-Perricaudet, L.D., Perricaudet, M., Jallat, S., Pavirani, A., Lecocq, J-P., and Crystal, R.G. (1991): Adenovirus-mediated transfer of a recombinant α1-antitrypsin gene to the lung epithelium in vivo. Science 252:431–434.

Rosenfeld, M.A., Yoshimura, K., Trapnell, B.C., Yoneyama, K., Rosenthal, E.R., Dalemans, W., Fukayama, M., Bargon, J., Stier, L.E., Stratford-Perricaudet, L., Perricaudet, M., Guggino, W.B., Pavirani, A., Lecocq, J-P., and Crystal, R.G. (1992): In vivo transfer of the human cystic fibrosis transmembrane conductance regulator gene to the airway epithelium. Cell 68:143–155.

Venkatesh, L.K., Arens, M.Q., Subramanian, T., and Chinnaduari, G. (1990): Selective induction of toxicity to human cells expressing human immunodeficiency virus type 1 tat by a conditionally cytotoxic adenovirus vector. Proc. Natl. Acad. Sci. U.S.A. 87:8746–8750.

Vile, R.G., and Hart, I.R. (1993): In vitro and in vivo targeting of gene expression to melanoma cells. Cancer Res. 53:962–967.

Wikenheiser, K.A., Clark, J.C., Linnoila, R.I., Stahlman, M.T., and Whitsett, J.A. (1992): Simian virus large T antigen directed by transcriptional elements of the human surfactant protein in C gene produces pulmonary adenocarcinomas in transgenic mice. Cancer Res. 52:5342–5352.

Yang, Y., Li, Q., Ertl, H.C.J., and Wilson, J.M. (1995): Cellular and humoral immune responses to viral antigens create barriers to lung-directed gene therapy with recombinant adenoviruses. J. Virol. 69:2004–2015.

Adeno-Associated Virus Vectors

Alexander, I.E., Russell, D.W., and Miller, A.D. (1995): DNA-damaging agents greatly increase the transduction of nondividing cells by adeno-associated virus vectors. J. Virol. 68:8282-8287.

Einerhand, M.P.W., Antoniou, M., Zolotukhin, S., Muzyczka, N., Berns, K.I., Grosveld, F., and Valerio, D. (1995): Regulated high-level human beta-globin gene expression in erythroid cells following recombinant adeno-associated virus-mediated gene transfer. Gene Ther. 2:336-343.

Flotte, T.R., and Carter, B.J. (1995): Adeno-associated virus vectors for gene therapy. Gene Ther. 2:357-362.

Flotte, T.R., Barraza-Ortiz, X., Solow, R., Afione, S.A., Carter, B.J., and Guggino, W.B. (1995): An improved system for packaging recombinant adeno-associated virus vectors capable of in vivo transduction. Gene Ther. 2:29-37.

Halbert, C.L., Alexander, I.E., Wolgamot, G.M., and Miller, A.D. (1995): Adeno-associated virus vectors transduce primary cells much less efficiently than immortalized cells. J. Virol. 69:1473-1479.

Kaplitt, M.G., Leone, P., Samulski, R.J., Xiao, X., Pfaff, D.W., O'Malley, K.L., and During, M.J. (1994): Long-term gene expression and phenotypic correction using adeno-associated virus vectors in the mammalian brain. Nature Genet. 8:148-154.

Kotin, R.M., Siniscalco, M., Samulski, R.J., Zhu, X.D., Hunter, L., Laughlin, C.A., McLaughlin, S., Muzycka, N., Rocchi, M., and Berns, K.I. (1990): Site-specific integration by adeno-associated virus. Proc. Natl. Acad. Sci. U.S.A. 87:2211-2215.

Miller, J.L., Donahue, R.E., Sellers, S.E., Samulski, R.J., Young, N.S., and Nienhuis, A.W. (1994): Recombinant adeno-associated virus (rAAV)-mediated expression of a human gamma-globin gene in human progenitor-derived erythroid cells. Proc. Natl. Acad. Sci. U.S.A. 91:10183-10187.

Muzyczka, N. (1992): Use of adeno-associated virus as a general transduction vector for mammalian cells. Curr. Top. Microbiol. Immunol. 158:97-129.

Samulski, R.J., Zhu, X., Xiao, X., Brook, J.D., Housman, D.E., Epstein, N., and Hunter, L.A. (1991): Targeted integration of adeno-associated virus (AAV) into human chromosome 19. EMBO J. 10:3941-3950.

Shelling, A.N., and Smith, M.G. (1994): Targeted integration of transfected and infected adeno-associated virus vectors containing the neomycin resistance gene. Gene Ther. 1:165-169.

Thrasher, A.J., de Alwis, M., Casimir, C.M., Kinnon, C., Page, K., Lebkowski, J., Segal, A.W., and Levinsky, R.J. (1995): Functional reconstitution of the NADPH-oxidase by adeno-associated virus gene transfer. Blood. 86:761-765.

Vieweg, J., Boczkowski, D., Roberson, K.M., Edwards, D.W., Philip, M., Philip, R., Rudoll, T., Smith, C., Robertson, C., and Gilboa, E. (1995): Efficient gene transfer with adeno-associated virus-based plasmids complexed to cationic liposomes for gene therapy of human prostate cancer. Cancer Res. 55:2366-2372.

Walsh, C.E., Nienhuis, A.W., Samulski, R.J., Brown, M.G., Miller, J.L., and Young, N.S. (1995): Phenotypic correction of Fanconi anemia in human hematopoietic cells with a recombinant adeno-associated virus vector. J. Clin. Invest. 94:1440-1448.

Weitzman, M.D., Kyostiö, S.R.M., Kotin, R.M., and Owens, R.A. (1994): Adeno-associated virus (AAV) rep proteins mediate complex formation between AAV DNA and its integration site in human DNA. Proc. Natl. Acad. Sci. U.S.A. 91:5808-5812.

Zhou, S.Z., Cooper, S., Kang, L.Y., Ruggieri, L., Heimfeld, S., Srivastava, A., and Broxmeyer, H.E. (1994): Adeno-associated virus 2-mediated high efficiency gene transfer into immature and mature subsets of hematopoietic progenitor cells in human umbilical cord blood. J. Exp. Med. 179:1867-1875.

Herpes Simplex Virus (HSV) Vectors

Ali, M., Lemoine, N.R., and Ring, C.J.A. (1994): The use of DNA viruses as vectors for gene therapy. Gene Ther. 1:367-384.

Boviatsis, E.J., Park, J.S., Sena-Esteves, M., Kramm, C.M., Chase, M., Efird, J.T., Wei, M.X., Breakefield, X.O., and Chiocca, E.A. (1994): Long-term survival of rats harboring brain neoplasms treated with ganciclovir and a herpes simplex virus vector that retains an intact thymidine-kinase gene. Cancer Res. 54:5745-5751.

Chambers, R., Gillespie, G.Y., Soroceanu, L., Andreansky, S., Chatterjee, S., Chou, J., Roizman, B., and Whitley, R.J. (1995): Comparison of genetically engineered herpes simplex viruses for the treatment of brain tumors in a SCID mouse model of human malignant glioma. Proc. Natl. Acad. Sci. U.S.A. 92:1411-1415.

Chiocca, E.A., Choi, B.B., Cai, W., DeLuca, N.A., Schaffer, P.A., DiFiglia, M., Breakfield, X.O., and Martuza, R.L. (1990): Transfer and expression of the lacZ gene in rat brain neurons mediated by herpes simplex virus mutants. New Biol. 2:739-746.

During, M.J., Naegele, J.R., O'Malley, K.L., and Geller, A.I. (1994): Long-term behavioral recovery in parkinsonian rats by an HSV vector expressing tyrosine hydroxylase. Science 266:1399-1403.

Fink, D.J., Sternberg, L.R., Weber, P.C., Mata, M., Goins, W.F., and Glorioso, J.C. (1992): In vivo expression of β-galactosidase in hippocampal neurons by HSV-mediated gene transfer. Hum. Gene Ther. 3:11–19.

Geller, A.I., and Breakfield, X.O. (1988): Defective HSV-1 vector expresses *Escherichia coli* β-galactosidase in cultured peripheral neurons. Science 241:1667–1669.

Glorioso, J.C., Goins, W.F., and Fink, D.J. (1992): Herpes simplex virus-based vectors. Semin. Virol. 3:265–276.

Huard, J., Goins, W.F., and Glorioso, J.C. (1995): Herpes simplex virus type 1 vector mediated gene transfer to muscle. Gene Ther. 2:385–392.

Johnson, P., Miyanohara, A., Levine, F., Cahill, T., and Friedmann, T. (1992): Cytotoxicity of a replication-defective mutant of herpes simplex virus type 1. J. Virol. 66:2952–2965.

Martuza, R.L., Malick, A., Markert, J.M., Ruffner, K.L., and Coen, D.M. (1991): Experimental therapy of human glioma by means of a genetically engineered virus mutant. Science 252:854–856.

Smith, R.L., Geller, A.I., Escudero, K.W., and Wilcox, C.L. (1995): Long-term expression in sensory neurons in tissue culture from herpes simplex virus type 1 (HSV-1) promoters in an HSV-1-derived vector. J. Virol. 69:4593–4599.

Wood, M.J.A., Byrnes, A.P., Pfaff, D.W., Rabkin, S.D., and Charlton, H.M. (1994): Inflammatory effects of gene transfer into the CNS with defective HSV-1 vectors. Gene Ther. 1:283–291.

Vaccinia Vectors

Brochier, B., Kieny, M.P., Costy, F., Coppens, P., Bauduin, B., Lecocq, J-P., Languet, B., Chappuis, G., Des Mettres, P., Afindemanyo, K., Libois, R., and Pastoret, P-P. (1991): Large scale eradication of rabies using recombinant vaccinia-rabies vaccine. (London) Nature 354:520–522.

Elkins, K.L., Ennist, D.L., Winegar, R.K., and Weir, J.P. (1994): In vivo delivery of interleukin-4 by recombinant vaccinia virus prevents tumor development in mice. Human Gene Ther. 5:809–820.

Graham, B.S., Matthews, T.J., Belshe, R.B., Clements, M.L., Dolin, R., Wright, P.F., Gorse, G.J., Schwartz, D.H., Keefer, M.C., Bolognesi, D.P., Corey, L., Stablein, D.M., Esterlitz, J.R., Hu, S-L., Smith, G.E., Fust, P.E., and Koff, W.C. (1993): Augmentation of human immunodeficiency virus type 1 neutralizing antibody by priming with gp160 recombinant vaccinia and boosting with rgp160 in vaccinia-naive adults. J. Infect. Dis. 167:533–537.

Kawakita, M., Ritchey, J.K., Hudson, M.A., Ratcliff, T.L., Tartaglia, J., and Paoletti, E. (1995): Effect of canary-pox (ALVAC) virus-mediated cytokine gene expression on prostate tumor growth. J. Urol. 153(Suppl.):469A.

Kaslow, D.C., Isaacs, S.N., Quakyi, A., Gwadz, R.W., Moss, B., and Keister, D.B. (1991): Induction of plasmodium falciparum transmission-blocking antibodies by recombinant vaccinia virus. Science 1310–1313.

Lee, S.S., Eisenlohr, L.C., McCue, P.A., Mastrangelo, M.J., and Lattime, E.C. (1994): Intravesical gene therapy: In vivo gene transfer using recombinant vaccinia virus vectors. Cancer Res. 54:3325–3328.

McCabe, B.J., Irvine, K.R., Nishimura, M.I., Yang, J.C., Spiess, P.J., Shulman, E.P., Rosenberg, S.A., and Restifo, N.P. (1995): Minimal determinant expressed by a recombinant vaccinia virus elicits therapeutic antitumor cytolytic T-lymphocyte responses. Cancer Res. 55:1741–1747.

Meitin, C.A., Bender, B.S., and Small, P.A., Jr. (1994): Enteric immunization of mice against influenza with recombinant vaccinia. Proc. Natl. Acad. Sci. U.S.A. 91:11187–11191.

Moss, B. (1991): Vaccinia virus: A tool for research and vaccine development. Science 252:1662–1667.

Tanaka, N., Sivanandham, M., and Wallack, M.K. (1994): Immunotherapy of a vaccinia colon oncolysate prepared with interleukin-2 gene-encoded vaccinia virus and interferon-alpha increases the survival of mice bearing syngeneic colon adenocarcinoma. J. Immunother. 16:283–293.

Human Immunodeficiency Virus (HIV) Gene Transfer Vectors

Aguilar-Cordova E., Chinen, J., Donehower, L.A., Harper, J.W., Rice, A.P., Butel, J.S., and Belmont, J.W. (1995): Inhibition of HIV-1 by a double transdominant fusion genes. Gene Ther. 2:181–186.

Brodsky, R.A., Jane, S.M., Vanin, E.F., Mitsuya, H., Peters, T.R., Shimada, T., Medof, M.E., and Nienhuis, A.W. (1994): Purified GPI-anchored CD4DAF as a receptor for HIV-mediated gene transfer—GPI-anchored protein decay accelerating factor/CD4 extracellular domain hybrid gene transfer into HeLa; susceptibility to HIV virus vector-mediated gene therapy. Hum. Gene Ther. 5:1231–1239.

Caruso, M., and Klatzmann, D. (1992): Selective killing of CD4$^+$ cells harboring a human immunodeficiency virus-inducible suicide gene prevents viral spread in an infected population. Proc. Natl. Acad. Sci. U.S.A. 89:182–186.

Chelucci, C., Hassan, H.J., Locardi, C., Bulgarini, D., Pelosi, E., Mariani, G., Testa, U., Federico, M., Valtieri, M., and Peschle, C. (1995): In vitro human immunodeficiency virus-1 infection of purified hematopoietic progenitors in single-cell culture. Blood 85:1181–1187.

Garzino-Demo, A., Gallo, R.C., and Arya, S.K. (1995): Human immunodeficiency virus type-2 (HIV-2): Packaging signal and associated negative regulatory element. Hum. Gene Ther. 6:177–184.

Harrison, G.S., Maxwell, F., Long, C.J., Rosen, C.A., Glode, L.M., and Maxwell, I.H. (1991): Activation of a diphtheria toxin A gene by expression of human immunodeficiency virus-1 tat and rev proteins in transfected cells. Hum. Gene. Ther. 2:53–60.

Naldini, L., Blömer, U., Gallay, P., Ory, D., Mulligan, R., Gage, F.H., Verma, I.M., and Trono, D. (1996): In vivo gene delivery and stable transduction of nondividing cells by a lentiviral vector. Science 272:263–267.

Page, K.A., Landau, N.R., and Littman, D.R. (1990): Construction and use of a human immunodeficiency virus vector for analysis of virus infectivity. J. Virol. 64:5270–5276.

Parolin, C., and Sodroski, J. (1995): A defective HIV-1 vector for gene transfer into human lymphocytes. J. Mol. Med. 73:279–288.

Lu, S., Santoro, J.C., Fuller, D.H., Haynes, J.R., and Robinson, H.L. (1995): Use of DNAs expressing HIV-1 env and noninfectious HIV-1 particles to raise antibody responses in mice. Virology 209:147–154.

Richardson, J.H., Kaye, J.F., Child, L.A., and Lever, A.M.L. (1995): Helper virus-free transfer of human immunodeficiency virus type 1 vectors. J. Gen. Virol. 76:691–696.

Shimada, T., Fujii, H., Mitsuya, H., and Nienhuis, A.W. (1991): Targeted and highly efficient gene transfer into CD4+ cells by a recombinant human immunodeficiency virus retroviral vector. J. Clin. Invest. 88:1043–1047.

Other Types of Viral Vectors

Ansardi, D.C., Moldoveanu, Z., Porter, D.C., Walker, D.E., Conry, R.M., LoBuglio, A.F., McPherson, S., and Morrow, C.D. (1994): Characterization of poliovirus replicons encoding carcinoembryonic antigen. Cancer Res. 54:6359–6364.

Dornburg, R. (1955): Reticuloendotheliosis viruses and derived vectors. Gene Ther. 2:301–310.

Forstová, J., Krauzewicz, N., Sandig, V., Elliott, J., Palková, Strauss, M., and Griffin, B.E. (1995): Polyoma virus pseudocapsids as efficient carriers of heterologous DNA into mammalian cells. Human Gene Ther. 6:297–306.

García-Sastre, A. and Palese, P. (1995): Influenza virus vectors. Biologicals 23:171–178.

Girod, A., Cosset, F.L., Verdier, G., and Ronfort, C. (1995): Analysis of ALV-based packaging cell lines for production of contaminant defective viruses. Virology 209:671–675.

Johanning, F.W., Conry, R.M., LoBuglio, A.F., Wright, M., Sumerel, L.A., Pike, M.J., and Curiel, D.T. (1995): A sindbis virus mRNA polynucleotide vector achieves prolonged and high level heterologous gene expression in vivo. Nucleic Acids Res. 23:1495–1501.

Kato, K., Yoneda, Y., Okada, Y., Kiyama, H., and Shiosaka, S. (1994): Gene transfer and the expression of a foreign gene in vivo in post-mitotic neurons of the adult rat brain using the hemagglutinating virus of the Japan-liposome method. Mol. Brain. Res. 25:359–363.

Kempkes, B., Pich, D., Zeidler, R., and Hammerschmidt, W. (1995): Immortalization of human primary B-lymphocytes in vitro with DNA. Proc. Natl. Acad. Sci. U.S.A. 92:5875–5879.

Lewis, M.E.S., Forsythe, I.J., Marth, J.D., Brunzell, J.D., Hayden, M.R., and Humphries, R.K. (1995): Retroviral-mediated gene transfer and expression of human lipoprotein-lipase in somatic cells. Hum. Gene Ther. 6:853–863.

Martinez, I., and Dornburg, R. (1995): Improved retroviral packaging lines derived from spleen-necrosis virus. Virology 208:234–241.

Metz, M.Z., Best, D.M., and Kane, S.E. (1995): Harvey murine sarcoma virus/MDR1 retroviral vectors: Efficient virus production and foreign gene transduction using MDR1 as a selectable marker. Virology 208:634–643.

Ohe, Y., Zhao, D., Saijo, N., and Podack, E.R. (1995): Construction of a novel papillomavirus vector without detectable transforming activity suitable for gene transfer. Hum. Gene Ther. 6:325–333.

Plaksin, D., Porgador, A., Vadai, E., Feldman, M., Schirrmacher, V., and Eisenbach, L. (1994): Effective anti-metastatic melanoma vaccination with tumor cells transfected with MHC genes and/or infected with Newcastle disease virus (NDV). Int. J. Cancer 59:796–801.

Polo, J.M., Lim, B., Govindarajan, S., and Lai, M.M.C. (1995): Replication of hepatitis delta virus RNA in mice after intramuscular injection of plasmid DNA. J. Virol. 69:5203–5207.

Schmidt, M., and Rethwilm, A. (1995): Replicating foamy virus-based vectors directing high level expression of foreign genes. Virology 210:167–178.

Simpson, A.M., Tuch, B.E., Swan, M.A., Tu, J., and Marshall, G.M. (1995): Functional expression of the human insulin gene in a human hepatoma cell line (HepG2). Gene Ther. 2:223–231.

von der Leyen, H.E., Gibbons, G.H., Morishita, R., Lewis, N.P., Zhang, L., Nakajima, M., Kaneda, Y., Cooke, J.P., and Dzau, V.J. (1995): Gene therapy inhibiting neointimal vascular lesion: In vivo transfer of endothelial cell nitric-oxide-synthase gene. Proc. Natl. Acad. Sci. U.S.A. 92:1137–1141.

Wang, R.F., and Mullins, J.I. (1995): Mammalian cell/vaccinia virus expression vectors with increased stability of retroviral sequences in Escherichia coli: Production of feline immunodeficiency virus envelope protein. Gene 153:197–202.

Zarozinski, C.C., Fynan, E.F., Selin, L.K., Robinson, H.L., and Welsh, R.M. (1995): Protective CTL-dependent immunity and enhanced immunopathology in mice immunized by particle bombardment with DNA encoding an internal virion protein. J. Immunol. 154:4010–4017.

Zhang, L., Sato, S., Kim, J.I., and Roos, R.P. (1995): Theiler's virus as a vector for foreign gene delivery. J. Virol. 69:3171–3175.

Zhou, X., Berglund, P., Zhao, H., Liljestrom, P., and Jondal, M. (1995): Generation of cytotoxic and humoral immune responses by nonreplicative recombinant Semliki forest virus. Proc. Natl. Acad. Sci. U.S.A. 92:3009–3013.

Gene Replacement and Repair

Brookes, A.J., Stevenson, B.J., Porteous, D.J., and Dorin, J.R. (1993): A series of vectors that simplify mammalian gene targeting. Transgenic Res. 2:238–244.

Camerini-Otero, R.D., and Hsieh, P. (1993): Parallel DNA triplexes, homologous recombination, and other homology-dependent DNA interactions. Cell 73:217–223.

Capecchi, M.R. (1989): Altering the genome by homologous recombination. Science 244:1288–1292.

Capecchi, M. (1990): How efficient can we get? Nature (London) 348:109.

Chauhan, S.S., and Gottesman, M.M. (1992): Construction of a new universal vector for insertional mutagenesis by homologous recombination. Gene 120:281–285.

Dickson, P., Kimber, W.L., Kilanowski, F.M., Stevenson, B.J., Porteous, D.J., and Dorin, J.R. (1993): High frequency gene targeting using insertional vectors. Hum. Mol. Genet. 2:1299–1302.

Dorin, J.R., Inglis, J.D., and Porteous, D.J. (1989): Selection for precise chromosomal targeting of a dominant marker by homologous recombination. Science 243:1357–1360.

Haber, J.E. (1992): Exploring the pathways of homologous recombination. Curr. Opin. Cell Biol. 4:401–412.

Lukacsovich, T., Yang, D., and Waldman, A.S. (1994): Repair of a specific double-strand break generated within a mammalian chromosome by yeast endonuclease I-SceI. Nucleic Acids Res. 22:5649–5657.

Sullenger, B.A., and Cech, T.R. (1994): Ribozyme-mediated repair of defective mRNA by targeted trans-splicing. Nature (London) 371(6498):619–622.

van Deursen, J., Fornerod, M., van Rees, B., and Grosveld, G. (1995): Cre-mediated site-specific translocation between nonhomologous mouse chromosomes. Proc. Natl. Acad. Sci. U.S.A. 92:7376–7380.

Waldmann, A.S. (1992): Targeted homologous recombination in mammalian cells. Crit. Rev. Oncol. Hematol. 12:49–64.

Wang, G., Levy, D.D., Seidman, M.M., and Glazer, P.M. (1995): Targeted mutagenesis in mammalian cells mediated by intracellular triple helix formation. Mol. Cell. Biol. 15:1759–1768.

Williams, S.R., Ousley, F.C., Vitez, L.J., and DuBridge, R.B. (1994): Rapid detection of homologous recombinants in nontransformed human cells. Proc. Natl. Acad. Sci. U.S.A. 91:11943–11947.

THE FIRST HUMAN GENE THERAPY EXPERIMENT

The first approved human gene therapy experiment in the United States began on September 14, 1990, for the treatment of a rare, congenital immunodeficiency disorder called adenosine deaminase (ADA) deficiency. This genetic disease was chosen as the first test of clinical gene therapy for the following reasons: (1) The gene had been cloned in 1983, and, subsequently, a large body of knowledge had accumulated about the gene and its function. ADA is considered a "housekeeping" gene because it does not require tight regulation and produces its gene product (ADA enzyme) continually within the cell. (2) Screening studies revealed that ADA enzyme activity levels range between 10% of normal level to 50 times normal in humans and are consistent with normal immune functioning without significant adverse effects. This variation in activity provides a 500-fold safety margin for vector gene expression to be effective without producing adverse effects, a property not shared by many genes. (3) Murine retroviral vectors can efficiently and stably insert functional copies of the human ADA (hADA) gene into cultured ADA-deficient [ADA(−)] lymphocytes. Although the goal continues to be the development of a gene transfer method for the genetic correction of hematopoietic stem cells, engraftment of T lymphocytes alone by allogeneic bone marrow transplantation can be curative and, therefore, the genetic correction of T lymphocytes may be beneficial. (4) Insertion of a normal hADA gene into ADA(−) T lymphocytes restored normal biochemical cellular functioning. In fact, genetically corrected T lymphocytes acquired the ability for normal growth *in vitro* compared to noncorrected duplicate cultures. (5) The group of children to be enrolled had not experienced complete immunologic reconstitution by any other form of therapy and were therefore at risk of opportunistic infection and malignancy. The results of this initial trial highlight the potential safety and healing power of gene therapy.

THE GENETICS OF ADA DEFICIENCY

ADA deficiency is an autosomal recessive disorder. Children develop ADA deficiency when they inherit two defective ADA genes, one from each parent. Every person carries two adenosine deaminase genes, one on each chromosome 20. These ADA genes produce an enzyme that participates in normal cellular metabolism and is essential for the complete development and functioning of the immune system; therefore, the ADA enzyme is normally produced inside every cell. If the child inherits one normal gene and one defective gene, this individual is a carrier of one defective gene and has the potential for passing that defective gene to his or her offspring. Carriers maintain 50% of normal ADA levels in their cells and have an immune system capable of normal development and function. The incidence of complete ADA deficiency in the general population is estimated to be less than one in 100,000 live births or about 10 affected children born per year in North America.

Children afflicted with complete ADA deficiency (two defective genes) will have a significant deficit in immune function. They do not produce normal antibody responses to immunization with standard childhood vaccines (e.g., tetanus, diphtheria). Skin testing reveals anergy to multiple antigens. As a result, these children are unable to resolve completely viral infections such as common respiratory and gastrointestinal infections. This category of congenital immunodeficiency is called severe combined immunodeficiency (SCID). For most of the children, one single point mutation (a specific abnormality in one nucleotide out of the more than 30,000 in each copy of the gene) results in the production of an inactive ADA enzyme leading to failure of the immune system to protect against persistent viral and fungal infections, repeated bacterial infections, and early cancer.

CURRENT CLINICAL TREATMENTS FOR ADA DEFICIENCY

The treatment of choice for children with ADA deficiency is an HLA-matched sibling bone marrow transplant. Matched sibling bone marrow transplants will cure most of the children (70%–90%). Unfortunately, only about 15%–25% of patients have a matched sibling donor. Bone marrow transplantation with partially matched ($\geq$50%) marrow from parents is less successful in ADA deficiency, with only about 40% achieving successful engraftment (O'Reilly et al., 1989).

ADA($-$) children without an identically matched marrow donor usually receive ADA enzyme replacement therapy. The use of ADA enzyme replacement therapy has been considered because the substrate that ADA normally metabolizes (deoxyadenosine), can freely diffuse across cell membranes (Fig. 4–1). Therefore, systemic injection of the enzyme may produce an osmotic gradient to remove and degrade the toxic metabolic products from the cell (Polmar et al., 1976). The current form of enzyme replacement in use is Adagen, which is a bovine (cow) ADA enzyme that has been conjugated to polyethylene glycol (PEG) to allow survival and function of the cow ADA enzyme in the body for days (Hershfield et al., 1987). Without the PEG, the ADA enzyme is degraded in minutes after injection (Davis et al., 1981). The weekly intramuscular injection of Adagen has been generally helpful to many of the more than 30 children treated, as evidenced by fewer infections and improved growth (Hershfield, 1995). However, enzyme replacement does not provide full immune reconstitution and life expectancy is expected to be shortened without a curative bone marrow transplant or curative gene therapy.

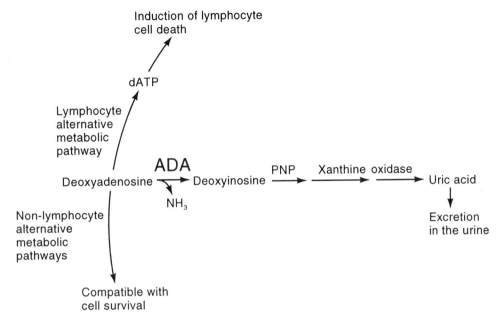

Fig. 4–1. The biochemical pathway of adenosine deaminase. ADA is an intracellular enzyme that functions in the purine salvage pathway of nucleic acid degradation. A lack of ADA activity results in the build-up of deoxyadenosine and other toxic products that leads to T-lymphocyte cell death. Other cell types have alternative metabolic pathways to degrade deoxyadenosine that are not cytopathic.

THE DEVELOPMENT OF GENE THERAPY FOR ADA DEFICIENCY

Ideally, the genetic correction of ADA($-$)SCID would involve insertion of a human ADA gene into totipotent hematopoietic stem cells. The insertion of a normal ADA gene into primitive bone marrow stem cells would theoretically correct the ADA($-$) immunodeficiency, resulting in normal immunity and a lifetime cure. Unfortunately, isolation of totipotent stem cells has proven very difficult. In addition, the ability to correct stem cells stably with retroviral vectors in monkeys and humans has been very inefficient (1%–5%) (Bodine et al., 1993). Recent advances in clinical methods for enrichment for totipotent marrow stem cells (separation from more mature, short-lived progenitor cells) and techniques to induce proliferation of the stem cell to allow effective gene transfer have made it possible to initiate the first attempts at stem cell genetic correction of ADA deficiency (Hoogerbrugge et al., 1992; Bordignon et al., 1993; Blaese et al., 1993). Thus, for ADA deficiency, the isolation of the gene has not been the primary obstacle to curative hematopoietic stem cell gene therapy, but rather the development of an efficient gene delivery system has limited its application.

Because hematopoietic stem cells could not be used for the gene therapy in 1990, the possibility of genetically correcting the mature T lymphocyte was considered. T lymphocytes are easy to grow from the blood and are currently much easier to alter genetically in the laboratory than bone marrow stem cells. The genetic correction of ADA(−) T lymphocytes was thought to be potentially useful because transplantation of identical bone marrow will completely cure ADA deficiency if only the T lymphocytes engraft (Keever et al., 1988). Engraftment of the other types of donor bone marrow stem cells is not necessary. Animal experiments proved that the insertion of vectors into mature T lymphocytes did not harm the cells and that the genetically altered T lymphocytes could survive *in vivo* for months (Culver et al., 1991a and 1991b). Experiments with ADA(−) human cells in the laboratory demonstrated that the insertion of a normal hADA gene into an ADA(−) cell corrected the ADA deficiency and resulted in the production of normal amounts of functional ADA enzyme (Culver et al., 1991c). In addition, the now ADA(+) T lymphocytes grew like normal ADA(+) T lymphocytes when compared to noncorrected ADA(−) T lymphocytes. Together, these laboratory findings suggested that the periodic infusion of autologous, genetically corrected ADA(−) T lymphocytes might result in an improvement of overall immune system functioning.

THE FIRST GENE THERAPY TRIAL

This experimental therapy began with the treatment of a 4-year-old girl suffering from ADA deficiency on September 14, 1990 (Fig. 4–2). A second child, a 9-year-old girl, was enrolled in the protocol on January 31, 1991 (Fig. 4–2). Our team attempted to enroll a third patient, but due to her worsening chronic lung disease and despite PEG-ADA enzyme replacement therapy, she was clinically too unstable to undergo apheresis. Each of the two children treated received infusions of their own ADA gene-corrected cells every 1–2 months over the first year with no significant adverse effects. During the second year, the interval was increased to every 3–6 months. Once it was determined that there were no significant adverse effects from this therapy, this protocol became an outpatient procedure, allowing the children to return home several hours after the administration of the genetically corrected T lymphocytes. This course of treatment highlights one of the promises of gene therapy: this new therapeutic modality will not have significant toxicity requiring expensive inpatient treatment, such as with bone marrow transplantation.

Results of this trial have been published (Blaese et al., 1995). As predicted by preclinical laboratory experiments, the ADA gene-corrected T lymphocytes appear to survive much longer in the human body than the non-gene-corrected T lymphocytes. This conclusion is based upon increasing numbers of T lymphocytes in the blood and the persistence of vector-containing cells for months without additional infusions of ADA(+) T lymphocytes. Persistently normal numbers of T lymphocytes were achieved in both children with regular infusions of genetically corrected cells. This is important because one of the key aspects in mounting an effective immune response against invading microorganisms and in preventing cancer is sufficient numbers of T lymphocytes.

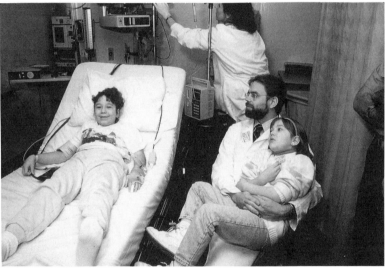

Fig. 4–2. Ashanthi V. DeSilva (*top*), 4 years old, was the first recipient of human gene therapy on September 14, 1990. Others present for the event were her parents, Raj and Van (left), and doctors Melvin Berger (back), W. French Anderson (front), Kenneth W. Culver (back center), and R. Michael Blaese (back right). Cynthia M. Cutshall (*bottom*) was the second recipient of human gene therapy. She received her first treatment on January 31, 1991. Others pictured are Dr. Kenneth W. Culver and Cynthia's sister, Laura.

Both children have developed clear evidence of improved immune function (Table 4–1). The first laboratory evidence of improved immune function was the spontaneous production of antibodies called isohemagglutinins. Normal individuals spontaneously produce isohemagglutinins, which are antibodies to blood types different from their own. For example, a person with type A blood will

Table 4–1. Changes in Measures of Humoral and Cellular Immunity

Characteristic	Normal values	Patient 1 (Pre-gene therapy)	Patient 1 (After 1 yr. of gene therapy)	Patient 2 (Pre-gene therapy)	Patient 2 (After 1 yr. of gene therapy)
Total CD3+ (per μl of blood)	≥1,000	571	2,034	800	1551
Serum Isohemagglutinins	≥1:16	≤1:16	1:32	<1:16	1:128
Serum IgG (mg/dl)	540–1500	606	769	622	1090
Serum IgA (mg/dl)	48–336	25	52	70	131
Tonsils	Present	Absent	Present	Absent	Present
No. of positive DTH skin tests*	7 of 8	0 of 8	5 of 8	0 of 8	5 of 8

*Skin tests were performed more than 12 months (455 and 501 days, respectively) after initiating the protocol in patients 1 and 2.

spontaneously make antibodies to type B blood due to cross-reacting glycoproteins on the surface of *E. coli* in the gut. Children with ADA deficiency do not make these antibodies. Following the initiation of infusion of autologous gene-corrected T lymphocytes, both children made persistently normal quantities of the appropriate type of isohemagglutinin.

Additionally, both children have now developed an ability to mount normal antibody responses to immunization (e.g., HIB, influenza). These findings were accompanied by the development of normal amounts of tonsillar tissue in both children and the presence of palpable lymph nodes in one child. Since tonsils and lymph nodes contain T and B lymphocytes, this suggests that genetically corrected T cells can migrate to these areas and provide the T-helper cell function required to mount normal antibody responses *in vivo*. T-cell function has also improved based upon the development of delayed-type hypersensitivity (DTH) immune responses to multiple antigens (e.g., tetanus toxoid, diphtheria toxoid, *Candida* species). The growth of tonsillar tissues and the ability of T lymphocytes to leave the blood to mount normal immune responses in the skin suggests that the increased number of T cells measured in the blood may not accurately reflect the total number of surviving and functioning ADA(+) T cells in the bodies of these two patients. Therefore, there has been persistent and significant recovery in both humoral and cellular immune functions associated with the infusion of ADA gene-corrected T cells in both of these two children.

There has also been evidence of clinical improvement in each child. The youngest child had a dramatic decrease in her number of infections and days on antibiotics compared to her pregene therapy condition on Adagen alone for 2 years. This prompted the family to decrease their self-imposed homebound isolation, a common restriction used to help minimize the number of infections. Over these past 4 years, she has fully participated in public school and is now in the fourth grade (Figure 4–3). She does occasionally become ill, but she usually recovers in the same fashion as her siblings, a significantly different clinical response compared to her life before gene therapy. The older child found relief from her chronic sinusitis and headaches as well as a decrease in the number of days she was ill compared to the number she had experienced during the 5-year period of PEG-ADA therapy alone. She is now in 9th grade at a public high school (Figure 4–3). These clinical findings correlate well with the new immune functions acquired with gene therapy treatments in these children.

THE NEXT STEPS IN THE GENETIC TREATMENT OF ADA DEFICIENCY

The ideal method for the treatment of ADA deficiency would be the insertion of a normal ADA gene into totipotent hematopoietic stem cells. Human clinical trials for the genetic correction of totipotent stem cells have been initiated in Italy, France, Britain, and the United States. The results of these protocols are discussed in Chapter 5.

SUMMARY

The continuous immunologic improvement seen in each of the two ADA(−) children treated suggests that the genetic correction of ADA(−) T lymphocytes can provide additional immunologic improvement beyond injections of the missing enzyme. While the use of genetically altered T lymphocytes is not a one-

Fig. 4–3.   School photographs for 1995-1996. Ashi DeSilva (left), 9 years old and in 4th grade. Cindy Cutshall (right), 14 years old and in 9th grade.

shot cure for ADA deficiency, it seems to provide continued improved overall health and immune system reconstitution in combination with PEG-ADA. It is hoped that once efficient transfer of the ADA gene into hematopoietic stem cells becomes a reality, ADA(−) children can be cured with a single gene therapy treatment, negating the need for enzyme replacement and repeated infusions of ADA(+) T lymphocytes.

This initial human gene therapy protocol has provided additional insight. First, the use of *in vitro* murine retroviral-mediated gene transfer has shown no evidence of adverse side effects resulting from 23 infusions of T lymphocytes during the more than 5 years of observation in each of these two immunodeficient children. Although a longer observation period is required, these vulnerable patients have tolerated the procedure well. Second, these findings suggest that there is an advantage to genetic correction as opposed to infusion of the missing gene product. Third, these findings have set the stage for the genetic correction of T lymphocytes in other disorders such as human immunodeficiency virus (HIV)-infected patients, cancer, and other primary immunodeficiency disease. And finally, this successful experiment has provided a foundation for the new era of molecular medicine and gene therapy, demonstrating that gene transfer can provide beneficial effects in patients.

BIBLIOGRAPHY

Blaese, R.M. (1993): Development of gene therapy for immunodeficiency: Adenosine deaminase deficiency. Pediatr. Res. 33(Suppl):S49–S55.

Blaese, R.M., Culver, K.W., and Anderson, W.F. (1990): The ADA human gene therapy clinical protocol. Hum. Gene Ther. 1:331–362.

Blaese, R.M., Culver, K.W., Anderson, W.F., Nienhuis, A., Dunbar, C., Chang, L., Mullen, C., Carter, C., and Leitman, S. (1993): Treatment of severe combined immunodeficiency disease (SCID) due to adenosine deaminase deficiency with CD34+ selected autologous peripheral blood cells transduced with a human ADA gene. Hum. Gene Ther. 4:521–527.

Blaese, R.M., Culver, K.W., Miller, A.D., Carter, C.S., Fleisher, T., Clerici, M., Shearer, G., Chang, L., Chiang, Y., Tolstoshev, P., Greenblatt, J.J., Rosenberg, S.A., Klein, H., Berger, M., Mullen, C.A., Ramsey, W.J., Muul, L., Morgan, R.A., and Anderson, W.F. (1995): T lymphocyte-directed gene therapy for ADA-SCID: Initial trial results after 4 years. Science 270:475–480.

Bodine, D.M., Moritz, T., Donahue, R.E. Luskey, B.D., Kessler, S.W. and Martin, D.I.K. (1993): Long-term in vivo expression of a murine adenosine-deaminase gene in rhesus monkey hemopoietic cells of mutiple lineages after retroviral mediated gene transfer into CD34+ bone marrow cells. Blood 82:1975–1980.

Bordignon, C., Mavilio, F., Ferrari, G., Servida, P., Ugazio, A.G., Notarangelo, L.D., and Gilboa, E. (1993): Transfer of the ADA gene into bone marrow cells and peripheral blood lymphocytes for the treatment of patients affected by ADA-deficient SCID. Hum. Gene Ther. 4:513–520.

Culver, K.W., Anderson, W.F., and Blaese, R.M. (1991): Lymphocyte gene therapy. Hum. Gene Ther. 2:107–109.

Culver, K.W., Berger, M., Miller, A.D., Anderson, W.F., and Blaese, R.M. (1992): Lymphocyte gene therapy for adenosine deaminase deficiency. Pediatr. Res. 31:149A.

Culver, K.W., and Blaese, R.M. (1994): Gene therapy for adenosine deaminase deficiency and malignant solid tumors. In *Gene Therapeutics*, Wolff, J.A. (ed). Birkhauser, Boston, pp. 256–273.

Culver, K., Cornetta, K., Morgan, R., Morecki, S., Aebersold, P., Kasid, A., Lotze, M., Rosenberg, S.A., Anderson, W.F., and Blaese, R.M. (1991): Lymphocytes as cellular vehicles for gene therapy in mouse and man. Proc. Natl. Acad. Sci. U.S.A. 88:3155–3159.

Culver, K.W., Morgan, R.A., Osborne, W.R.A., Lee, R.T., Lenschow, D., Able, C., Cornetta, K., Anderson, W.F., and Blaese, R.M. (1991): In vivo expression and survival of gene-modified Rhesus T lymphocytes. Hum. Gene Ther. 3:399–410.

Culver, K.W., Osborne, W.R.A., Miller, A.D., Fleisher, T.A., Berger, M., Anderson, W.F., and Blaese, R.M. (1991): Correction of ADA deficiency in human T-lymphocytes using retroviral-mediated gene transfer. Transpl. Proc. 23:170–171.

Davis, S., Abuchowski, A., Park, Y.K., and Davis, F.F. (1981): Alteration of the circulating life and antigenic properties of bovine adenosine deaminase in mice by attachment of polyethylene glycol. Clin. Exp. Immunol. 46:649–652.

Hershfield, M.S. (1995): PEG-ADA: An alternative to haploidentical bone marrow transplantation and an adjunct to gene therapy for adenosine deaminase deficiency. Hum. Mut. 5:107–112.

Hershfield, M.S., Buckley, R.H., Greenberg, M.L., Melton, A.L., Schiff, R., Hatem, C., Kurtzberg, J., Markert, M.L., Kobayashi, R.H., Kobayashi, A.L., and Abuchowski, A. (1987): Treatment of adenosine deaminase deficiency with polyethylene glycol-modified adenosine deaminase. N. Engl. J. Med. 16:589–596.

Hirschhorn, R. (1983): Genetic deficiencies of adenosine deaminase and purine nucleoside phosphorylase: Overview, genetic heterogeneity and therapy. Birth Defect 19:73–81.

Hoogerbrugge, P.M., Vossen, J.M.J.J., van Beusechem, V.W., and Valerio, D. (1992): Treatment of patients with severe combined immunodeficiency due to adenosine deaminase (ADA) deficiency by autologous transplantation of genetically modified bone marrow cells. Hum. Gene Ther. 3:553–558.

Kantoff, P.W., Kohn, D.B., Mitsuya, H., Armentano, D., Sieberg, M., Zwiebel, J.A., Eglitis, M.A., McLachlin, J.R., Wigindon, D.A., Hutton, J.J., Horowitz, S.D., Gilbon, E., Blaese, R.M., and Anderson, W.F. (1986): Correction of adenosine deaminase deficiency in cultured human T and B cells by retrovirus-mediated gene transfer. Proc. Natl. Acad. Sci. U.S.A. 83:6563–6567.

Keever, C.A., Flomenberg, N., Brochstein, J., Sullivan, M., Collins, N.H., Burns, J., Dupont, B., and O'Reilly, R.J. (1988): Tolerance of engrafted donor T cells following bone marrow transplantation for severe combined immunodeficiency. Clin. Immunol. Immunopath. 48:261–276.

Nienhuis, A.W., McDonagh, K.T., and Bodine, D.M. (1991): Gene transfer into hematopoietic stem cells. Cancer 67(suppl.):2700–2704.

O'Reilly, R.J., Keever, C.A., Small, T.N., and Brochstein, J. (1989): The use of HLA-non-identical T-cell-depleted marrow transplants for the correction of severe combined immunodeficiency disease. Immunodeficiency Rev. 1:273–309.

Polmar, S.H., Stern, R.C., Schwartz, A.L., Wetzler, E.M., Chase, P.A., and Hirschhorn, R. (1976). Enzyme replacement therapy for adenosine deaminase deficiency and severe combined immunodeficiency. N. Engl. J. Med. 295:1337–1343.

Thompson, L. (1993): The first kids with new genes. Time 141:50–53.

APPLICATIONS OF GENE THERAPY TO NONNEOPLASTIC DISORDERS

Albert Einstein said, "Imagination is more important than knowledge." Dr. Einstein's comment is especially pertinent since creative ways are needed to fully develop gene therapy to cure human disease. As technology continues to advance, many current ideas will be subsequently considered quite primitive; but at this point, they are novel and serve to generate new information that will stimulate a variety of successful creative research endeavors. To this point in the development of clinical gene therapy, efforts have been primarily directed at establishing safety. Success in this area will allow a greater emphasis on efficacy. Authorized clinical trials encompass primary genetic diseases, HIV infection, vascular disease, and arthritis (Fig. 5-1). Approved trials and principal investigators are listed in Appendix B.

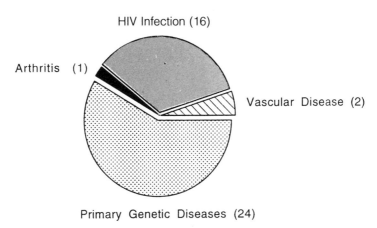

Fig. 5–1. RAC approved gene therapy trials for non-neoplastic diseases. There are forty-three trials in four categories.

DISORDERS OF HEMATOPOIETIC CELLS

Immunologic Disorders (Lymphocytes and Granulocytes)

As previously discussed, the immunodeficiency disorder adenosine deaminase (ADA) deficiency was the first clinical disorder treated with gene therapy (see Chapter 4). In March 1992, the first attempted use of genetically corrected hematopoietic stem cells for the treatment of ADA deficiency occurred in Italy (Bordignon et al., 1993). In March 1993, researchers in Britain and France, in cooperation with scientists in The Netherlands, initiated similar gene therapy experiments for ADA deficiency using bone marrow stem cells (Hoogerbrugge et al., 1992). These initial bone marrow gene therapy experiments utilized *ex vivo* gene transfer with murine retroviral vectors. Results from both studies have been recently published (Table 5–1). The Italian study demonstrated persistence of ADA-positive cells in the peripheral blood, recovery of immune functions, and clinical benefit without evidence of toxicity (Bordignon et al., 1995). These exciting results are comparable to those in the first ADA trial at NIH. The ADA trial based in the Netherlands found only transient presence of the ADA gene in peripheral blood cells and no evidence of immunologic or clinical benefit (Hoogerbrugge et al., 1996). The differences between these studies is most likely secondary to the use of different components to produce retroviral vectors, different stem cell isolation mechanisms, and different conditions for transduction of the ADA gene. As is typical of the gene transfer

Table 5–1. Human Clinical Results from the First Four Gene Therapy Trials for ADA Deficiency

Parameter	Blaese et al.	Bordignon et al.	Hoogerbrugge et al.	Kohn et al.
Vector system	MRV	MRV	MRV	MRV
Ex vivo gene transfer	+	+	+	+
Cells administered	T-cells alone	T-cells and BM cells	CD34+ cells	CD34+ cells
Gene transfer efficiency in tissue culture	T-cells: 1%—10%	T-cells: 1%—40% BM progenitors: 30%—40%	BM progenitors: 5%—12%	CD34: 1% BM progenitors: 30%—40%
No. of patients treated	2	2	3	3
Percentage of genetically-corrected cells in patients	T-cells: 1%—100%	T-cells: 2%—5%	T-cells: None identified	T-cells: 1 in 10,000
Concomitant PEG-ADA treatment	+ (decreased dose by ~50% during trial)	+ (decreased dose by ~50% during trial)	+ (Two patients received PEG-ADA from the beginning of the trial and one started 6 months after receiving genetically altered cells)	+ (Twice the usual dose)
Toxicities	−	−	−	−
Clinical benefit	+	+	−	?

ADA=adenosine deaminase; BM=bone marrow.

field in general, each group of investigators is using different gene delivery systems and model systems making direct comparisons of their results difficult.

Another unique approach is to use cord blood hematopoietic stem cells. In 1993, three newborn infants with ADA deficiency were treated in the United States. At the time of birth, umbilical cord and placental blood was collected. Using an antibody to a cell-surface glycoprotein (CD34) that is present on earlier lineages of stem cells, hematopoietic stem cells were purified and placed in culture. The LASN retroviral vector, the same one used in the initial T lymphocyte gene therapy trial at NIH, was used to transfer the ADA gene into the CD34-positive cells. The treated cells were returned by intravenous (IV) infusion several days later. The results of this initial cord blood gene therapy trial were recently published (Kohn et al., 1995). They demonstrated that about 1% of bone marrow hematopoietic stem cells were successfully corrected and have continued to produce ADA normal granulocytes and T lymphocytes for 2 years (Table 5–1). This is a very exciting beginning and a proof of principle that cord blood stem cells are suitable vehicles for successful transduction with retroviral vectors and engraftment in humans. Clinical benefit is difficult to assess at this time because the children continue on full dose ADA enzyme replacement therapy. Investigators are in the process of reducing the dose of enzyme replacement. This procedure will allow them to confirm whether the genetically corrected cells have a selective growth advantage *in vivo* and whether these genetically corrected cells are able to reconstitute a broad range of immunologic functions.

In summary, published reports are now available of the results of gene therapy in 10 children with ADA deficiency—about 20% of all children in the world known to have the disease. Another clinical trial has recently been initiated in Japan. While none of these children are known to have been completely cured of their disease, clear immunologic and clinical benefit is apparent in several of them, with none of the children manifesting complications related to gene transfer. The success of these initial studies has laid a foundation for the refinement of gene transfer procedures and stem cell manipulation that will lead to genetic cures for ADA deficiency and other immunologic disorders.

The experimental use of gene therapy for the treatment of congenital immunodeficiency disorders has also moved into clinical trials for the T-lymphocyte disorder purine nucleoside phosphorylase (PNP) deficiency (Nelson et al., 1995) and the granulocyte disorder chronic granulomatous disease (CGD) (Cobbs et al., 1992). Both trials use retroviral vectors to transfer the gene into T lymphocytes or bone-marrow-derived hematopoietic stem cells, respectively (see Table 1–1). Both of these trials are in early stages of experimentation and no published clinical results are available at this time. A number of other genes for congenital immunodeficiency disorders have been cloned [e.g., leukocyte adhesion defect (LAD), agammaglobulinemia, hyper-IgM syndrome]. As a deeper understanding of the molecular basis of these disorders is developed, they may become treatable with gene transfer into autologous hematopoietic stem cells.

Lysosomal Storage Disorders (Macrophages)

There are a number of monocyte/macrophage disorders that potentially could be cured by the insertion of the normal gene into hematopoietic stem cells. These include the glycogen and lipid storage diseases that result from a specific molecular defect in genes that are responsible for the metabolism of sugars and lipids. Deficiencies in one of these enzymes results in the accumulation of sugar or lipid leading to organ dysfunction. The most common glycogen storage diseases are Hunter and Hurler syndromes, with the most common lipid storage disease being Gaucher disease.

Alone, these disorders do not represent large numbers numbers, but taken together, storage diseases are the tenth most common genetic abnormality and they can be very expensive to treat (see Table 1–4). *In vitro* and *in vivo* animal experimentation has shown that metabolic defects can be corrected with gene insertion into marrow stem cells (e.g., Gaucher disease, adrenoleukodystrophy, Sly's syndrome, Hunter syndrome) (Braun et al., 1993; Cartier et al., 1995; Wolfe et al., 1992; Xu et al., 1995).

Clinical trials using retroviral vectors to transfer the glucocerebrosidase gene into hematopoietic stem cells from patients with Gaucher disease have recently been initiated (Dunbar et al., 1996). One trial for Hunter syndrome has been approved using retroviral vectors to transfer the iduronidase-2-sulfatase gene into T lymphocytes; this trial is expected to begin enrolling patients this year (Whitley et al., 1996).

As the efficiency of gene transfer into hematopoietic stem cells improves, storage disorders should become amenable to correction with gene therapy. One factor that may slow the clinical application of gene therapy to many of the storage disorders is that, with the exception of Gaucher disease, there are very few patients with any one disease, and it is difficult for researchers to find corporate sponsorship to pay for these trials.

Hematologic System (Erythrocytes and Platelets)

The application of gene therapy to hematologic disorders has been the focus of years of research. As discussed previously, the efficient delivery of genes stably into hematopoietic stem cells has been difficult, and has slowed the development of gene therapy for hematologic disorders. The application of gene therapy to hemoglobinopathies is further complicated by a need to control hemoglobin synthesis tightly. The genetic correction of β-thalassemia major requires insertion of a normal β-globin gene. If the vector gene is to correct the anemia, the new β-globin gene must produce an amount of β-globin equal to the amount of α-globin produced within the cell. If the inserted gene does not make an amount of β-globin that exactly matches the amount of α-globin in the cell, the patient will remain anemic. Gene therapy researchers are currently focusing on the insertion of the locus control region into viral vectors because these regions appear to be responsible for regulating the β-globin/α-globin quantity in the cell (Plavec et al., 1993). When the gene can be transferred with the proper regulatory regions, the ability to cure thalassemia may be within our grasp. This will likely be accomplished with retroviral or AAV vectors, mammalian artificial chromosomes, and/or the use of gene repair to permanently correct the anemia.

The genetic correction of sickle cell anemia (SCA) has obstacles similar to those encountered in developing gene therapy for thalassemia. Both SCA and thalassemia require a regulated, functional β-globin gene. The use of gene therapy for the treatment of SCA may also require the development of a method to "turn off" the hemoglobin S gene to eliminate the possibility of further sickle crises (McCune et al., 1994). At this point in our technological development, we do not have the scientific capability to selectively "turn off" genes in cells *in vivo*. Gene repair, an emerging technology, may circumvent these problems thereby enabling the development of genetic treatments for thalassemia and SCA. Gene repair is a process whereby a genetic mutation is corrected allowing the gene to once again function under the intrinsic regulatory elements (see Chapter 3). This approach will avoid the problems related to control of expression associated with the transfer of complete genes. One to two more years of research are probably required before gene repair will move into clinical trials for any disorder.

Gene therapy for Fanconi's anemia type C has been approved for human clinical trials. This protocol will utilize retroviral vectors to insert the Fanconi anemia C-complementing (FACC) gene into peripheral blood hematopoietic progenitor cells. *In vitro* studies have shown that the insertion of this gene into cells from patients with a FACC defect (about 15% of Fanconi patients) results in increased progenitor cell growth *in vitro* (Walsh et al., 1994). Because patients who cannot find a suitable bone marrow donor commonly die from marrow aplasia or acute leukemia, the engraftment of genetically normal hematopoietic stem cells may have a significant beneficial effect on long-term survival. No published clinical results are available about this clinical trial.

Another approach to the treatment of congenital and acquired anemias is the transfer of the erythropoietin (EPO) gene. Investigators have used retroviral vectors (Osborne et al., 1995), adenoviral vectors (Tripathy et al., 1994), naked DNA, and transfer of *ex vivo* transfected cell lines (e.g., fibroblasts, muscle) to deliver therapeutically effective concentrations in rodents (Hamamori et al., 1995). Using a mouse model of β-thalassemia, investigators were able to demonstrate that the transfer of hematopoietic cells transduced with an EPO-containing retroviral vector was able to correct the erythrocyte phenotype (Villeval et al., 1994). Further safety and efficacy studies are needed to determine if this approach will be safe and effective for both acute and chronic anemias.

In an effort to learn more about gene transfer into human hematopoietic stem cells, several investigators initiated stem cell "gene marking" experiments in humans. These studies were initiated in 1992 to address three important issues. The first issue is the ability of murine retroviral vectors to insert genes into human totipotent bone marrow stem cells. Totipotent stem cells are the most primitive stem cells found in the bone marrow and are responsible for the production of all of the cellular elements of the blood. Unfortunately, there are no adequate *in vitro* rodent model assays with which to determine the actual efficiency of gene transfer into human totipotent stem cells. The second issue is to mark the stem cells so that the fate of the gene altered cells *in vivo* can be determined. And the third is to compare the actual gene transfer efficiency into bone marrow stem cells (BMSC), with that in peripheral blood stem cells (PBSC). The first published clinical trial comparing engraftment of BMSC and PBSC demonstrated the persistent survival of both marked cell populations (Dunbar et al., 1995). The marker gene was found in multiple lineages for over 18 months in three of nine patients. While no definitive conclusions can be drawn from this initial study, their results suggest that the PBSC may have provided better long-term marking.

Therapeutics for thrombocytopenia are also being investigated. One example is the adenovirus-mediated transfer of the HST-1 (fibroblast growth factor-4) gene into mice. This process doubled the peripheral blood platelet count for 20–30 days longer than injecting the HST-1 protein alone (Sakamoto et al., 1994). In a set of follow-up experiments in mice with chemotherapy-induced thrombocytopenia, the adenoviral vector-delivered HST-1 gene increased megakaryocytes in the marrow and induced recovery of platelet counts (Konishi et al., 1995). With further investigation, this approach may be a valuable adjunct for treating acute thrombocytopenia that uses the advantages of the adenoviral vector system without a need for permanent genetic correction.

HUMAN IMMUNODEFICIENCY VIRUS (HIV) INFECTION

The alteration of T lymphocyte and macrophage functions as a consequence of HIV infection is a potential target for the genetic treatment or prevention of the acquired immunodeficiency syndrome (AIDS). The genetic correction of T lymphocytes in the first gene therapy experiment with ADA deficiency has shown that "sick" T lymphocytes can be made "healthy." Because the immunodeficiency results when the human immunodeficiency virus (HIV) makes T lymphocytes "sick," genetically altering HIV-infected T lymphocytes may be a useful therapy. Scientists are working on genetic methods for the modification of body tissues that might prevent HIV infection and prevent the spread of HIV by genetically disabling HIV growth at various stages of its life cycle (Fig. 5-2) or by preventing the HIV-induced immunodeficiency.

Sixteen gene therapy trials for the experimental treatment of HIV infection have been approved since 1992 (Table 5–2). Two protocols do not actually use the transferred genes for therapy, but rather insert the herpes simplex-thymidine kinase (HS-*tk*) "suicide" gene into CD8-positive anti-HIV activated T cell clones. The HS-tk gene would be used in the event that the activated T lymphocytes begin to harm the patient. HS-tk confers a sensitivity to the antiherpes drug ganciclovir, allowing the selective destruction of the HS-tk-containing cells *in vivo* (see Chapter 6 for more details about HS-tk). In this experiment, T lymphocyte

Table 5–2.   Approved Human Gene Therapy Experiments for HIV in the United States

Tissue	Gene(s)
T cells	CD8$^+$ HIV-specific T cells with HS-*tk*
Muscle	HIV-1 IIIB *env/rev* genes[a]
T cells	Transdominant negative *rev*
T cells	Anti-HIV-1 ribozyme
HSC	Anti-HIV-1 ribozyme
T cells	Antisense TAR and transdominant negative *rev*
T cells	Anti-*env* intracellular antibody
T cells	Anti-rev intracellular antibody
T cells	CD4-zeta HIV targeting gene
T cells	PolyTAR decoy or RRE-polyTAR decoy
HSC	RRE decoy

[a]*In vivo* gene transfer protocol; HSC = hematopoietic stem cells.

clones specifically reactive against HIV-infected cells are grown from the blood of HIV-infected patients with lymphoma (Riddell et al., 1992). The cells are genetically altered in tissue culture, and reinfused intravenously into patients following cytoablation and bone marrow transplantation in an attempt to eradicate the lymphoma and the hematopoietic cellular pool of HIV-infected cells. Their particular vector is unique in that the HS-tk gene is fused to a hygromycin (Hy) gene. The addition of Hy to the culture medium will kill all cells except those that contain a functional Hy gene (positive selectable marker). Unfortunately, their clinical results demonstrate that all six of the patients developed potent immunologic responses to the HS-tk/Hy gene resulting in elimination of the genetically-altered cells within a few weeks (Riddell et al., 1996). A second clinical trial has been approved to evaluate another positive selectable marker (NeoR) in their system.

Five gene therapy trials have been approved involving the direct injection of retroviral vectors into muscle (Galpin et al., 1994; Haubrich and McCutchan, 1995a). The vectors encode for the HIV envelope (*env*) and *rev* genes. Investigators hope to induce an immunizing cytotoxic T lymphocyte immune response in the recipient in response to the expression of HIV IIIB env/rev proteins on muscle cells.

Injection of these retroviral vectors into rodents and nonhuman primates has demonstrated specific anti-HIV humoral and cellular immune responses (Irwin et al., 1994; Laube et al., 1994). Several hundred human subjects have reportedly been injected with the vector. Investigators first treated symptomatic HIV-infected individuals in a phase I study. Now they are treating asymptomatic HIV-infected persons with CD4$^+$ cells/100 μl in a multicenter phase II trial. A published report suggests that either new and/or potentiated anti-HIV immune responses can be induced in some of the HIV-infected patients as a result of the retroviral-mediated gene transfer (Haubrich et al., 1995b).

Other protocols focus on the genetic alteration of T lymphocytes and hematopoietic stem cells. In one, T lymphocytes are altered by the insertion of a "dominant negative" gene called *rev* M10. In this experiment, a mutant *rev* gene (M10) produces an RNA that binds the functional HIV *rev* RNA inactivating it (Nabel et al., 1994). Rev is a very important HIV regulatory protein that is involved in the transport of HIV RNA from the nucleus to the cytoplasm where it is packaged into an infectious virus particle. Analysis of the first three patients treated in this study suggests that the *rev* M10 transfected cells had a 4–5-fold selective survival advantage over control cells marked with a defective *rev* M10 gene plasmid (Woffendin et al., 1996). A second trial will use an RRE decoy (mutant) vector in an attempt to block HIV production in stem cells. In two trials,

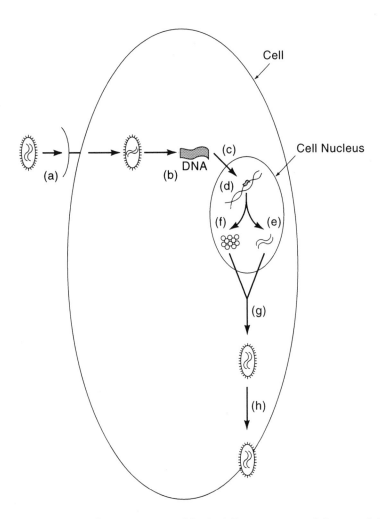

Fig. 5–2. Gene transfer strategies to block different stages of the HIV life cycle. These include blocking attachment to the cell-surface receptor (a), uncoating and reverse transcription (b), DNA migration to the nucleus (c), integration (d), viral transcription and movement of RNA from the nucleus to the cytoplasm (e), protein synthesis (f), virion assembly (g), and budding (h).

an HIV ribozyme gene is being inserted into T lymphocytes. A ribozyme is an RNA molecule that cleaves other RNAs. In this trial, the inserted gene will produce a ribozyme that is expected to cleave HIV RNA specifically, preventing translation and production of infectious HIV virions. (Yu et al., 1995).

Four more of these protocols will attempt to block the production of HIV in T lymphocytes. The first combines a transdominant negative *rev* gene with antisense Tar (trans-activation response element). Tar is a critical element in the activation of viral gene expression. Therefore, this approach attempts to block virus production at two different steps, selectively inhibiting viral gene expression and the movement of HIV RNA from the nucleus (Vandendriessche et al., 1995). Another will compare a polyTAR decoy with an RRE-polyTAR decoy in T lymphocytes. Two other trials will use intracellular antibodies to target different steps in the HIV life cycle. In these experiments, investigators will insert a gene that produces an antienvelope (*env*) antibody within the cell. *In vitro* experiments have shown that the antibody will selectively bind HIV *env* within the cells and block the reproduction of infectious HIV virions (Chen et al., 1994). A number of these clinical trials are being conducted with two different populations of transduced cells to determine if the anti-HIV vectors improve survival of the infused T lymphocytes versus cells with only a *NeoR* gene marker. A second study will use an anti-Rev intracellular antibody in an attempt to protect T lymphocytes. No published data on any of these HIV trials are currently available.

The final protocol is altogether different from the others. In this case, the investigators are attempting to redirect the immune system to target HIV-infected cells. To accomplish this, they have engineered a murine retroviral vector containing a chimeric CD4 receptor gene (CD4-zeta chain chimera). When this novel receptor recognizes the HIV envelope (gp120), a signal for antigen binding is sent via the zeta chain to the nucleus. As a result, when cytotoxic CD8$^+$ T cells are transduced with this novel vector, they become highly cytolytic for HIV-infected cells (Roberts et al., 1994). HLA-identical seronegative twins of HIV-positive siblings will serve as donors for multiple infusions of these cells (Walker et al., 1996).

As described above, a variety of techniques have produced a significant decrease in HIV virus production. However, the results with fresh isolates have not been as significant as strains adapted to tissue culture and the dose of virus used *in vitro* has significant effects on the results. Therefore, at this time, it appears that no one system will completely and permanently shut down HIV expression. Until a combination of synergistic approaches can be developed, the outlook for a therapeutic HIV gene therapy trial is uncertain. Hopefully these early gene therapy clinical trials will provide critical information that will be effective in the treatment of HIV infection.

RECOMBINANT VACCINES

Scientists are attempting to produce vaccines against a variety of antigens using direct DNA injection, the genetic alteration of microorganisms, and *in vivo* gene transfer of DNA using recombinant viral vectors.

Direct DNA Injection

The direct injection of *Influenza* virus DNA (that is conserved among several different strains) into muscle has been effectively used to induce a potent antibody response against *Influenza* in mice (Ulmer et al., 1993). The prior injection of DNA even afforded protection from a challenge with several species of live *Influenza* virus. Further investigations have shown that the influenza DNA can be delivered not only by direct intramuscular injection, but also by the intravenous route, drops into the nares or trachea, and particle bombardment into the epidermis (Fynan et al., 1993). Therefore, the use of DNA vaccines for influenza may not only provide an inexpensive, safe method for vaccination, but also might preclude the need to produce a new *Influenza* vaccine each year. Other investigators have been developing direct DNA gene transfer as a method for vaccination against other infectious organisms. Immune responses have been generated following the direct injection of DNA from hepatitis B (Michel et al., 1995), hepatitis C (Major et al., 1995), malaria (Sedegah et al., 1994), leshmaniasis (Xu and Liew, 1995), and *Mycobacterium tuberculosis* (Lowrie et al., 1994). If further studies prove that these vaccines are protective and/or can modify chronically infected individuals, a new avenue of therapeutics will be available to more than 200 million people worldwide who suffer from these five infections alone.

Genetically Engineered Microorganisms

The genetic modification of microorganisms may take two forms: (1) the genetic disabling of an organism by removing genes required for pathogenesis or survival or (2) the insertion of an exogenous gene that will be expressed in bacteria or parasites. One example is the genetic attenuation of *Salmonella typhi*. Selective deletion of genes required for survival will induce immunity without pathogenicity following the oral administration of these organisms (Bloom, 1989). These genetically altered *Salmonella* might also be used as vectors for immunization against other microorganisms following the insertion of exogenous genes from the organisms that cause cholera or shigella (Sizemore et al., 1995).

There are exciting preliminary results with the use of Bacille Calmette–Guerin (BCG) as a vehicle for immunization (Aldovini and Young, 1991). BCG was chosen because it has been safely administered to more than 2 billion people and is known to be inherently immunostimulatory. BCG can be engineered to contain a variety of antigens from viruses (e.g., HIV), parasites (e.g., *Plasmodium falciparum, Schistosoma*), and tumor antigens. Insertion of a gene from *Schistosoma* into BCG has shown efficacy in preventing infection in animal models. The value in the development of a vaccine for schistosomiasis is enormous, with about 200 million sufferers worldwide.

Genetically engineered BCG and *Escherichia coli* have also been used in an attempt to develop a vaccine for Lyme disease (*Borrelia burgdorferi* infection). The *OspA* (outer surface membrane protein) gene from *B. burgdorferi* was transfected into BCG (Langerman et al., 1994) or *E. coli* (Fikrig et al., 1990). These genetically engineered microorganisms were then injected intranasally (BCG) or intraperitoneally (*E. coli*) into mice. A subsequent challenge with *B. burgdorferi* demonstrated that animals in both groups had developed systemic immunity and were protected from the challenge. These vaccines are in preclinical development.

Vaccination with Viral Vectors

A third approach is the direct transfer of genes with viral vectors *in vivo*. A recent trial attempted to vaccinate animals in the wild with a recombinant vaccinia virus expressing a rabies antigen. This study proved successful in protecting wild raccoons and foxes from rabies infection (Brochier et al., 1991). A variety of antigens (e.g., *Plasmodium* antigens) have been expressed in vaccinia, but human studies are lagging behind until vaccinia can be genetically engineered to decrease the frequency of adverse reactions. Other viruses, including the polio and yellow fever viruses, are under investigation as carriers for recombinant vaccines. Chapter 6 includes a discussion of viral vectors as cancer vaccines.

Conclusions

The production of recombinant vaccines has several very valuable advantages. First, these vectors can theoretically be engineered to contain multiple antigens (multivalent), thus decreasing the number of different immunizations that would need to be administered. Second, recombinant organisms can be used to carry genes for not only infectious agents, but also for tumors and, theoretically, autoantigens. Third, the undesirable toxicities and virulence factors associated with the wild-type organism can be removed genetically to minimize risks and side effects. Fourth, these vectors are capable of inducing potent systemic immunity with oral or intranasal administration, maximizing ease of use and minimizing cost. Finally, a variety of different organisms can be used to maximize the gene delivery, duration of immunization, and ease of delivery to large numbers of people. Overall, the use of recombinant vaccines will likely become the most prevalent application of molecular medicine and gene therapy in humans over the next decade.

HEPATIC SYSTEM

Application of techniques of gene transfer to the liver is another primary area of preclinical gene therapy research. There are a variety of genetic diseases of the liver that may be amenable to gene therapy in the near future. These include hypercholesterolemia, phenylketonuria, α_1-antitrypsin deficiency, and deficiencies of clotting factors VIII and IX. Hemophilias are discussed in the blood-clotting system section of this chapter. Each of these genes has been expressed in a variety of cell types *in vitro* and *in vivo*. The primary problem thwarting clinical application is the lack of an *in vivo* gene delivery method that will provide long-lasting, high-level gene transfer and expression in the liver.

The first human experiment to genetically modify human hepatocytes involved the transfer of the low-density lipoprotein receptor (LDLr) gene into hepatocytes from patients with familial hypercholesterolemia (FH). Because the clinical focus of this experiment is on the vascular complications, the protocol is described in some detail in the cardiovascular section of this chapter. The FH gene therapy trial uses an *ex vivo* gene delivery approach employing murine retroviral vectors to transfer the LDLr gene into cultured hepatocytes (Chowdhury et al., 1991). Once the LDLr gene has been transferred into the proliferating hepatocytes *in vitro*, the genetically altered cells are infused back into the liver through the hepatic blood vessels. This approach to the genetic modification of hepatocytes is thought to be a one-time surgical procedure. *In vivo* gene transfer into the liver without the need for surgery would be the preferred route.

The direct injection of murine retroviral vectors into liver or into the hepatic vasculature of mice results in very little gene transfer (1%–5%) into hepatocytes because the majority of the liver cells are not actively proliferating (Cardoso et al., 1993). In contrast, adenovirus vectors can transfer genes into a large number of hepatocytes *in vitro* and *in vivo*, but lack the ability to insert their genes stably into the chromosomes (Kozarsky et al., 1993). Therefore, adenoviral vector gene transfer would probably require repeated administration for sustained expression. Improved *in vivo* gene delivery such as the induction of liver cell proliferation to increase the gene transfer rate with murine retroviruses (Kaleko et al., 1991), the use of hepatitis virus vectors (Chiang et al., 1990), chimeric retrovirus-vesicular stomatitis virus (VSV) vectors (Miyanohara et al., 1995), receptor-mediated endocytosis to specifically target hepatocytes (Cristiano et al., 1993a/b), or a redesign of adenovirus vectors to result in integration may allow an advance in clinical gene delivery applications to the liver.

For α_1-antitrypsin deficiency and hemophilia, clinical improvement can theoretically be obtained through the insertion of the genes into other cell types. α_1-antitrypsin is a major plasma protease inhibitor that is produced in the liver and diffuses into the lung, where it inhibits excessive neutrophil elastase. T lymphocytes, which are readily available from the blood and circulate through both the liver and the lung, may be useful for the treatment of α_1-antitrypsin deficiency, providing enzyme function in the necessary organs. On the other hand, gene transfer into skin, endothelial cells, muscle, or lung may be suitable cellular vehicles that can function as *in vivo* factories secreting α_1-antitrypsin or clotting factors directly into the blood stream (see the section on the Pulmonary System in this chapter).

Another metabolic disease that could be potentially treated with gene therapy is phenylketonuria (PKU). PKU results from a deficiency in phenylalanine hydroxylase (PAH). A deficiency of PAH can result in severe mental retardation if a diet deficient in phenylalanine is not initiated at birth and maintained though adolescence and, in adult females, during subsequent pregnancies. Insertion of the PAH gene with adenovirus vectors into PAH-deficient cells in mice completely corrected the hyperphenylalaninemic phenotype (Fang et al., 1994). Therefore, the development of efficient, stably integrating gene transfer systems could, theoretically, restore PAH function in humans and eliminate the need for the expensive PKU diet.

The genetic alteration of liver is the aim for the genetic correction of hundreds of intrinsic diseases of the liver, an attractive tissue for the genetic treatment of nonhepatic disorders (e.g., restoration of hormone production), and the target of cancer therapeutics (e.g., cancers that are within the liver, alteration of chemotherapy drug metabolism). However, the problems of efficient gene transfer and expression have limited clinical application to one genetic disorder. Recently a clinical trial was approved to treat a urea cycle disorder, partial ornithine transcarbamylase (OTC) deficiency. The investigators plan an intra-arterial injection of adenoviral vectors containing the OTC gene into the right lobe of the liver. They plan to assess toxicity, the immune response against the vector, and the metabolic effects on plasma ammonium and urea cycle components. Hopefully, these clinical studies will produce critical information about gene delivery, vector gene expression, and safety that will enable the development of additional hepatic gene therapy protocols.

BLOOD-CLOTTING SYSTEM

Gene therapy for clotting factor deficiency is a well recognized target that could involve the genetic alteration of a variety of tissues. The genes for hemophilia A and B were isolated more than 10 years ago and were successfully expressed in mammalian cells over 10 years ago (Anson et al., 1985). However, when cultured fibroblasts expressing factor IX were transplanted into mice, the expression was only transient (St. Louis and Verma, 1988). The inability to find a cell type (e.g., hepatocytes, muscle, fibroblasts) that can be genetically altered *ex vivo* and survive in sufficient numbers *in vivo* long-term has delayed the initiation of clinical trials in the United States. A second problem that had been slowing the initiation of human clinical trials is the need to identify promoters that would produce high quantities of clotting factor *in vivo* over long periods. Promoters for "housekeeping" genes have been identified that result in sustained gene expression *in vivo* in fibroblasts, hepatocytes, and muscle (Scharfmann et al., 1991).

As the *in vivo* vector delivery efficiency and duration of vector gene expression have improved in rodent models, scientists have begun to attempt the correction of factor IX deficiency in dogs with hemophilia B. The first attempt was made by infusing retroviral vectors containing the canine factor IX gene into the portal vasculature following partial hepatectomy. This resulted in the production of low levels of factor IX (0.01% of normal levels) for more than 5 months (Kay et al., 1993). A second attempt involved the infusion of recombinant adenoviral vectors into the portal vasculature with partial hepatectomy. This approach resulted in a much greater production of factor IX (up to 300% of normal levels), but the concentration started to decline in a few days and was back to baseline in 1–2 months (Kay et al., 1994). These two experiments nicely highlight the advantages and disadvantages with retroviral and adenoviral gene delivery *in vivo*. Further modifications in both vectors systems that will allow them to infect and express at high levels with persistent expression *in vivo* should make hemophilia treatable with gene transfer.

In 1992, a group of Chinese scientists in Shanghai, China, treated two boys with factor IX deficiency (Hsueh et al., 1992). They used murine retroviral vectors to insert the human factor IX gene into autologous skin fibroblasts that they had grown from skin biopsies. Escalating numbers of these genetically altered cells were injected subcutaneously into the skin on their backs. Preliminary results suggested that there was an initial increase in the factor IX activity in the blood of both of the boys (Lu et al., 1993). No published follow-up data are available.

PULMONARY SYSTEM

There are no methods to culture lung cells routinely in the laboratory, allowing their transplantation back into the patient. As a result, gene transfer must occur in the body. The application of gene transfer to diseases of the lung is therefore limited by the development of gene transfer methods that will efficiently deliver the gene *in situ* into the correct cell types. The primary focus of pulmonary gene transfer research has been on the development of gene therapy for the treatment of cystic fibrosis (CF).

Cystic Fibrosis

CF is an autosomal recessive genetic disorder affecting as many as 1 in 2,500 births in families of central European background. The inheritance of two defective genes results in severe lung disease and poor growth due to chronic lung infections and an inability to absorb nutrients normally from the digestive tract. The defective gene responsible for the CF phenotype, the cystic fibrosis transmembrane conductance regulator (CFTR), has been isolated; insertion of the normal CFTR gene into defective cells in the laboratory has corrected the genetic defect (Rich et al., 1990). Transfer of the CFTR gene into CFTR-deficient rodent cells *in vivo* using recombinant adenoviral vectors or liposomes as gene transfer vehicles has corrected the biochemical abnormality without significant toxicity (Rosenfeld et al., 1992; Hyde et al., 1993). Based upon these preclinical data, there are nine approved human clinical trials using adenoviral vectors for the treatment of CF (see Appendix B). The first protocol began enrolling patients in April 1993. Two are approved using AAV and two with liposomes as the delivery method.

Preliminary data are available from several trials providing valuable data that will guide future clinical efforts. First, scientists have confirmed gene transfer into respiratory epithelium *in vivo* (Zabner et al., 1993; Crystal et al., 1994a; Caplen et al., 1995; Knowles et al., 1995). Second, very little is known about the efficiency and efficacy of this gene delivery system into the lung since most of the published studies have used nasal epithelium. There is also a concern about safety. Upon reaching the dose of 2×10^9 particles/treatment, one of the patients (the first at this dose) experienced transient pulmonary infiltrates and alterations in vital signs. The patient recovered uneventfully. There was no evidence of direct damage to the lungs, significant immune response to the recombinant viral vector, or evidence of recombination with E1A or E1B to create new replication-competent adenviruses. A comprehensive evaluation demonstrated that the injection of adenoviral vectors (in 20 ml of fluid) into the lung induced secretion of significant amounts of interleukin-6 (IL-6), an inflammatory cytokine (McElvaney and Crystal, 1995). Modifications in the protocol that decreased the volume of fluid alone have prevented similar side effects in the treatment of 6 subsequent patients at the same or higher dose. The approved trials are using very similar adenoviral vectors, with differing schedules and methods of administration (i.e., through a bronchoscope, into the nasal cavity, or into the sinuses). Fourth, the current generation of adenoviral vectors are also inducing significant immune reponses that pose problems for achieving clinical efficacy with repeated administration of the vectors and may be hazardous to patients. Several preclinical research efforts are in progress in an attempt to overcome this problem. Approaches include generalized immunosuppression, administration of cytokines that prevent blocking antibody formation, and the redesign of the adenoviral vectors. These types of immunologic concerns are not expected to be a problem with liposome-mediated gene transfer.

Investigators in the U.K. and the U.S. are attempting to deliver CFTR into the lung with liposomes. The group in the UK has completed a double-blind placebo-controlled trial (Caplen et al., 1995). There were no detectable adverse clinical effects from the administration of the placebo (liposomes with no gene) or the liposomes carrying the CFTR gene into the nose. The gene transfer was estimated to be very low because there was only transient, low-level correction of CFTR function. These investigators plan to work on methods to improve gene transfer efficiency by evaluating different liposome formulations and they intend to test the use of liposome delivery in the lung.

Two trials that will use AAV vectors to transfer the CFTR gene have been approved for human application. These trials will target nasal epithelium, the airways in a single lobe of the lung, or the maxillary sinuses. It is too early to know if the spectrum of toxicities, immunologic responses, and gene transfer efficiency will be significantly different from the adenoviral and liposomal delivery systems.

Perhaps the greatest disappointment in these trials has been the poor gene transfer efficiency ($\leq1\%$) of both systems in humans. This primarily related to the fact that the target cells are basal cells that differentiate into the columnar epithelial cells lining the respiratory tract (Grubb et al., 1994). The basal cells are not only covered by mucus, but also by the columnar cells. Modification of the airway to expose basal cells to vectors, development of strategies to target basal cells via the pulmonary vasculature, new liposome preparations, and/or new viral vector designs are needed to improve gene delivery to basal cells and decrease immunogenicity. Success in these areas will allow the successful clinical application of gene therapy to CF patients.

Other Pulmonary Disorders

Surfactant deficiency is a major complication related to premature birth and adult respiratory distress syndrome (ARDS). Several surfactant genes have been isolated and cloned. Surfactant genes *SP-A* and *SP-B* have been expressed in the respiratory epithelium of mice without evidence of adverse effect (Korst et al., 1995). This suggests that the delivery of the *SP-B* gene into the lungs of premature infants with respiratory distress syndrome (RDS) may have potential for the prevention of the atelectasis, cyanosis, and respiratory failure associated with surfactant deficiency.

One trial for the treatment of the pulmonary complications of α_1-antitrypsin deficiency has been approved. Researchers are using liposomes to transfer the α_1-antitrypsin gene into the nasal mucosa. No published information is available on the progress of this trial at this time.

CARDIOVASCULAR SYSTEM (CVS)

Preventive gene therapy for congenital cardiovascular malformations faces several obstacles. The congenital heart diseases are thought to be complex genetic abnormalities, not single-gene disorders. Once their genetic basis is understood, genetic correction may require germ-line modification prior to formation of the heart structures. For those who have a predisposing genetic condition such as familial hypercholesterolemia (FH), gene therapy may be an alternative.

Hypercholesterolemia, Hyperlipidemia, and Atherosclerosis

FH is a rare autosomal recessive disorder that is caused by a lack of low-density lipoprotein receptor (LDLr) expression. The incidence of this disorder is about one in 1 million live births. These individuals have serum cholesterol levels ranging to 1,000 mg/dl, with a mean of 600–700 mg/dl, resulting in the development of coronary heart disease in childhood. An initial attempt at the genetic correction of LDLr deficiency was initiated in 1992 at the University of Michigan (Wilson et al., 1992). In this study, a piece of liver (about 200–300 g) was resected; hepatocytes were grown in the laboratory and genetically altered with a murine retroviral vector containing LDLr, and then the cells were reinfused through the hepatic artery into the remaining liver. Published results have demonstrated persistent survival of the genetically altered hepatocytes, a 20%–40% decrease in the serum cholesterol levels, and a heightened response to cholesterol-lowering medications (Grossman et al., 1994). No toxicity related to the transfer of the gene has been identified in the five patients treated to date (Grossman et al., 1995). These results suggest that gene therapy for CVS and hepatic disorders may be practical in the near future as further improvements in gene delivery and expression are made.

A deficiency in apolipoprotein E (apoE) results in hyperlipidemia and atherosclerosis due to inefficient lipoprotein transport. Animal studies have shown that the IV injection of adenoviral vectors containing the apoE gene into apoE-deficient mice will normalize apoE levels and lead to a marked reduction in atherosclerosis for 4 weeks (Kashyap et al., 1995). It has also been shown that the expression of a normal apoE gene in hematopoietic stem cells will normalize plasma lipid profiles and provide nearly complete protection from atherosclerosis (Linton et al., 1995). Therefore, the expression of genes involved in lipid metabolism in one of several tissues may provide significant protection against coronary vascular disease.

Marfan Syndrome

Marfan syndrome is a collagen disorder that has significant cardiovascular complications. One group of investigators is developing the use of ribozymes against the fibrillin gene found on chromosome 15. The hope is that the ribozyme will specifically block the production of fibrillin, allowing normal collagen formation in the aorta and other treated organs.

Vascular Occlusive Disease

Gene therapy for the treatment of occlusive diseases of the CVS have entered clinical trials. Two trials attack different aspects of vascular disease with the vascular endothelial growth factor (VEGF) gene using direct DNA delivery through a vascular catheter. The first trial attempts to induce angiogenesis in ischemic vessels in patients with pain at rest or ischemic leg ulcers. Several patients have been treated with a low dose of DNA without toxicity, but there are no published results available at this time. The second approach also uses the same gene and delivery system, but attempts to facilitate reendothelialization after balloon angioplasty in patients with stenotic or occluded superficial femoral or popliteal arteries and limit restenosis. This is reasonable because VEGF is known to not only induce the formation of new blood vessels, but also accelerate healing after angioplasty, potentially limiting restenosis.

Other investigators have also been working on the preclinical development of procedures to prevent restenosis following angioplasty and insertion of vascular grafts. Their efforts have focused primarily on the prevention of smooth muscle proliferation. Transfer of the retinoblastoma tumor suppressor gene (Chang et al., 1995), inhibition of the ras gene (Indolfi et al., 1995), transfer of the nitric oxide synthetase gene (von der Leyen et al., 1995), or expression of the herpes simplex thymidine kinase (Ohno et al., 1994) has significantly inhibited smooth muscle proliferation and restenosis in animal models. Since the reported incidence of clotting within the some 300,000 vascular grafts performed each year in the United States is 30%, I expect that a number of clinical gene therapy strategies to prevent restenosis will enter clinical trials in the next several years.

Another approach to the prevention of ischemia is to transfer genes that will secrete anticlotting factors (e.g., tissue plasminogen activator). This might be performed at the time of the angioplasty or by covering the vascular graft with genetically altered cells. Whether or not the engrafted cells will survive the shearing forces of blood flow and prevent clotting long term *in vivo* in animals is under investigation.

Hypertension

The treatment of hypertension (HTN) may also be amenable to intervention with gene transfer. While the causes of HTN are many and complex, the results of initial studies in animals suggest that a knowledge of some of the physiologic pathways may lead to an ability to decrease vascular tone with gene transfer. For instance, the intramuscular or intravenous transfer of naked DNA containing the kallikrein gene resulted in a significant reduction in blood pressure in hypertensive rats for 6 weeks (Wang et al., 1995; Xiong et al., 1995). Kallikrein is a peptidase that is involved in kinin production—a potent vasodilator. Intravenous transfer of naked DNA containing the human atrial natriuretic factor (ANF) gene has demonstrated similar results for 7 weeks (Lin et al., 1995). As our understanding of the etiologies of HTN grow, it is very possible that periodic injections of DNA may be used to control blood pressure in lieu of long-term oral medication.

Cardiac Gene Transfer

Several investigators have shown that the direct injection of DNA into the myocardium will result in expression of the injected genes (Lin et al., 1990). This approach is theoretically useful for the revascularization of cardiac muscle fibers postmyocardial infarction. Laboratory experiments regarding gene delivery and revascularization effects are in the early stages of investigation. Another approach involves the development of a treatment for chronic heart failure. Because the inotropic responsiveness of these patients is decreased due to a reduction in the number of myocardial β-adrenergic receptors, scientists have studied the transfer of β-adrenergic receptors. Insertion of the receptor genes in mice results in enhanced myocardial function (Milano et al., 1994). Finally, transfer of ion channel genes may provide a strategy for preventing arrhythmias (Johns et al., 1995). Cardiovascular disease is a significant health problem, and I look forward to the transfer of creative gene transfer approaches to the prevention and treatment of cardiac disease into human clinical trials in the next several years.

MUSCLE

The genetic alteration of skeletal muscle may have substantial utility beyond the treatment of primary muscle disorders such as Duchenne's muscular dystrophy (DMD). This includes the transient expression of cell-surface antigens following gene transfer, which will result in protective immunization against viral infections (e.g., influenza antigens) and the insertion of secretory genes into muscle cells to result in the direct secretion of gene product into the blood stream (e.g., clotting factors, hormones). The easy accessibility of skeletal muscle for repeated treatments and the large cell mass provide an ideal tissue for gene transfer manipulations. The primary limitations are the need to develop efficient *in vivo* gene transfer methods, controllable gene expression mechanisms, and the identification of promoters that will provide long-term expression.

Muscular Dystrophy

Scientists have demonstrated that the insertion of a normal dystrophin gene into the germ line of DMD mice cures the animals (Cox et al., 1993). Early somatic cell gene transfer experiments in animals have suggested that the gene transfer efficiency of directly injected DNA remains too low for clinical use (Acsadi et al., 1991). However, adenoviral vectors can be used to transfer genes transiently into a large number of muscle fibers (Vincent et al., 1993). As discussed previously, adenoviral vectors do not stably insert into the DNA of the muscle fibers, and repeated treatments may be required since it is not known how long the vector will persist in nonreplicating cells. Direct injection of vectors into muscle must provide equal distribution of muscle function to allow symmetrical function of muscle groups. Other investigators are evaluating the use of transplanted normal myoblasts or genetically corrected myoblasts as an interim therapeutic approach while ideal gene transfer systems are under development (Mendell et al., 1995). Unless large numbers of autologous nonfibrotic cells are corrected, none of these approaches are unlikely to give the desired result (Webster and Blau, 1990). These technical limitations have prevented gene transfer for the treatment of muscular dystrophy in humans. Hopefully, they will be solved in the next 5 years.

Other Potential Applications

Several groups of researchers have demonstrated that the direct injection of DNA into muscle will lead to transient vector gene expression in muscle tissue (Wolff et al., 1990). One of the most exciting results is the effective immunization and protection of mice from viral infection with several strains of influenza (see recombinant vaccines section in this chapter). In addition, this type of immunization method—the transient expression of gene products on the surface of muscle cells—may also be useful for the prevention and treatment of other infectious diseases, autoimmune disorders, or cancer. Clinical trials involving the direct injection of DNA encoding tumor antigens (e.g., carcinoembryonic antigen) or HIV genes are already approved (see Chapter 6 or the HIV section in this chapter, respectively).

In other experiments, scientists have shown that muscle will secrete gene products. For instance, the direct injection of DNA encoding a secretory human growth hormone gene into muscle resulted in systemic production of the hormone in mice (Dhawan et al., 1991). Once the proper control elements that will regulate gene expression tightly have been identified, the direct injection of DNA into skeletal or vascular smooth muscle may have direct application for hormone deficiencies such as insulin and growth hormone. It is also possible that both muscle types could be developed into *in vivo* factories for substances such as clotting factors VIII and IX to correct blood clotting abnormalities (Dai et al., 1995), α_1-antitrypsin to prevent lung and liver disease, or granulocyte colony-stimulating factor (G-CSF) to prevent cyclic neutropenia. Muscle-specific promoters have been identified (Dahler et al., 1994), but obstacles in gene delivery and persistent expression currently limit application to clinical trials. This is likely to change during the next several years.

SKIN, BONE, AND JOINTS

Fibroblasts and Keratinocytes

The genetic modification of skin cells could have many applications (Table 5–3). If vectors could be stably inserted into epidermal stem cells, life-long correction could be potentially achieved. Currently, the stable introduction of genes into this tissue requires the induction of cellular proliferation to use retroviral vectors. Because skin cells do not regularly proliferate *in vivo*, most researchers

Table 5–3. Advantages and Potential Uses of Skin for Gene Therapy

Advantages	
Very accessible for therapy and monitoring	
Excisable, can be cultured, and is transplantable	
Stem cells provide continuous renewal of the epidermis	

Disease states	*Examples of treatment approaches*
Genetic disorders (e.g., epidermolytic hyperkeratosis)	• Transfer of the normal gene • Gene repair by homolgous recombination
Acquired hyperproliferative diseases (e.g., psoriasis)	• Targeted destruction of autoreactive T cells
(e.g.,	• Inhibitors of keratinocyte growth TGF-β)
Protection against disease (e.g., infections, cancer, and autoimmunity)	• Direct injection of DNA to produce a protective immune response
Treatment of infectious diseases	• Transfer of immune enhancing genes (e.g., IL-8) or genes that produce microbiocidal or static substances
Wounds (partial and full-thickness skin loss)	• Genes that promote faster healing (e.g., EGF, hGH) or prevent scarring
Replacement of secreted gene products (e.g., clotting factors, hormones)	• Hemophilia factor, insulin, growth hormone, etc.
Function as a metabolic waste unit (e.g., ADA deficiency)	• Overexpression of the ADA gene to metabolize 2'-deoxyadenosine
Prevention of malignancy (e.g., melanoma, squamous cell carcinoma)	• Insertion of gene that will block damage by UV light or reconstitute normal tumor suppressor gene function
Treatment of skin tumors	• Secretion of interferons

are using *ex vivo* gene insertion into proliferating cell cultures (keratinocytes and fibroblasts). The genetically altered skin could then be grafted back onto the patient, where the new skin would continuously secrete the needed factor into the bloodstream. This has not yet been attempted in humans in the United States since *in vivo* animal experiments have not resulted in the production of sufficient amounts of the gene product (such as blood clotting factors) to make this a feasible clinical approach. Adenoviral vectors and the direct injection of DNA into skin do not result in stable integration of the genes. However, vector gene expression may persist for weeks to a few months in skin cells. This approach may be suitable for the transient expression of genes in skin for the treatment of skin disorders (e.g., wound healing) or for immunization. For instance, the transfer of the human epithelial growth factor (hEGF) gene by particle bombardment or the transfer of keratinocytes containing the human growth hormone gene directly into an area of partial thickness skin loss induced faster healing (Andree et al., 1994; Vogt et al., 1994).

Use in Bone Disease

Efforts are being made to transfer genes into osteoclasts and osteoblasts to modulate bone formation (Roessler et al., 1994). Difficulties in postnatal delivery may be overcome with improved methods for receptor-mediated gene transfer. Gene transfer has important implications for the treatment of both congenital (e.g., osteopetrosis) and acquired disorders (e.g., osteoporosis).

Treatment of Arthritis

Arthritis is one of the most common chronic diseases in our poplulation. More than 20 million people in the Unites States alone suffer with rheumatoid arthritis (RA). Scientists have injected DNA, retroviral vectors, and adenoviral vectors into the joint space in animals, demonstrating that the DNA or vector is taken up by cells lining the joint (Chen et al., 1995; Makarov et al., 1995; Yovandich et al., 1995). One human clinical trial has been approved for patients with RA. Researchers will be attempting to block the inflammatory cytokine effect in the joint space. In this phase I trial, synoviocytes will be removed from a rheumatoid joint at the time of joint replacement and placed in tissue culture. The cells will then be engineered to produce the interleukin-1 (IL-1) receptor antagonist protein (IRAP) by retroviral vectors. The cells will then be reinjected into the joint space 7 days before a planned joint replacement to assess engraftment, vector gene expression, and the biological effects of IRAP at the time of joint replacement. A number of other genes may also function as antiinflammatory agents. These include anticytokines (e.g., anti-TNF-α), antiadhesion molecules (e.g., anti-ICAM-1), and free radical antagonists (e.g., superoxide dismutase). The ability to genetically modify the synovial lining to prevent disease, treat inflammation, or to improve the healing of injured joints would be very beneficial. This work is currently in the early stages of investigation and there are no published clinical results available at this time.

ENDOCRINE SYSTEM

There is also a great potential for the use of gene therapy to treat endocrinologic disorders, because much is known about the functional operation of the hormonal system and many of the genes have been cloned. However, endocrinologic disorders are an exception to my contention that gene delivery systems are the primary limiting factor for gene therapy application. In the case of hormone production and regulation, we are limited by an inability to control regulation to precisely meet the physiologic needs of the host.

Diabetes Mellitus

Diabetes mellitus (DM) continues to be associated with significant morbidity and mortality. Both cellular and gene therapy are being investigated as potentially more effective ways to treat diabetic patients. Microencapsulation devices to protect human islet cells have been successfully used to decrease the insulin need in several patients (see Chapter 3). However, the supply of normal islet cells is severely limited. In type I insulin-dependent diabetes mellitus (IDDM), diabetic patients no longer have islet cells that can be engineered. Therefore, in IDDM, the development of a successful gene therapy approach must not only find an efficient way to deliver controllable genes, but also must find a cell that will process and regulate insulin secretion appropriately.

The prospects of gene therapy are improving as more is learned about the intrinsic regulation of insulin, cellular processing, and gene transfer (Newgard, 1994). An ideal cell for engineering would mimic islet cell function in response to rising glucose concentrations. Alternatively, if a normal tissue could be stably altered to provide a baseline low level of insulin secretion, this may be sufficient to prevent the longer-term complications of DM (Vitullo et al., 1994). Once the regulatory genes have been identified and we have learned to insert the genes efficiently with their regulatory elements, we will then be able to move ahead with gene therapy for DM. These insights are likely to allow the development of novel replacement strategies for deficiencies in other hormones as well (e.g., growth hormone, thyroxine, erythropoietin, ADH). No clinical gene therapy trials for endocrinologic disorders have been proposed.

GASTROINTESTINAL (GI) TRACT

The identification of and ability to genetically alter human intestinal stem cells that reside in the crypts of the intestine will offer the potential for the long-term genetic correction of intestinal epithelium. *In vitro* and *in vivo* experiments in animals have suggested that these stem cells can be transduced with murine retroviral vectors (Lau et al., 1995). Primary diseases such as celiac disease would require stable gene transfer into intestinal stem cells to achieve a cure whereas infectious, autoimmune, and malignant processes may theoretically be successfully treated with transient gene expression. Investigators are currently focused primarily on the development of gene therapy for GI malignancies, the GI complications of CF, and autoimmune disease. No gene transfer clinical trials have been proposed.

URINARY SYSTEM

Currently, there are no clinical efforts to genetically alter tissues of the urinary tract for the treatment of primary diseases such as polycystic kidney disease. Although the gene for polycystic kidney disease has been isolated, further characterization is required before a gene therapy strategy can be developed.

Investigators have successfully transferred genes into rat glomeruli (Kitamura et al., 1994). They used electroporation to transfect a marker gene into mesangial cells. These genetically altered cells were then injected in the renal artery. Staining for the marker gene showed that about 50% of the glomeruli contained an expressing vector. These preliminary studies are encouraging. However, a substantial number of additional studies are needed to determine the optimal methods for gene delivery for the treatment of congenital and acquired disorders of the kidney and urinary tract.

NERVOUS SYSTEM AND THE EYE

The genetic alteration of cells that cannot be grown in the laboratory (i.e., cells of the CNS) requires an *in vivo* gene delivery system that will integrate and stably express genes in the appropriate location in the brain. Whereas retroviral vectors work reasonably well with T lymphocytes, liver cells, and skin cells, this method will not work with cells that are not growing, such as spinal cord and brain cells, unless one can induce the target cell population to divide *in vivo*. To treat a wide variety of neurologic disorders such as Parkinson's disease, Alzheimer's disease, and neurofibromatosis, new forms of *in vivo* gene transfer methods must be developed.

One possibility is the use of neurotropic viral vectors such as Herpes Simplex virus (HSV). The transfer of the tyrosine hydroxylase (TH) gene with HSV into parkinsonian rats resulted in biochemical and clinical recovery that was maintained for more than 1 year (During et al., 1994). TH converts tyrosine to L-DOPA and intracellular decarboxylase enzymes convert L-DOPA to dopamine. These findings suggest that the HSV vector is able to establish latency and continue expressing the vector genes for months. Other genes may also be useful for treating Parkinson's disease. For example, one research group has used the transfer of neurons from transgenic mice that overexpress the Cu/Zn superoxide dismutase (SOD) gene. The transplanted neurons prolonged survival in Parkinsonian rats, suggesting that if HSV could be used to transfer the Cu/Zn SOD gene into patients, it might halt disease progression (Nakao et al., 1995). Finally, AAV vectors (non-neurotropic) have been used to transfer the TH gene into Parkinsonian rats. These vectors demonstrated significant clinical benefit for 4 months (Kaplitt et al., 1994b). Together, these results are encouraging for the treatment of Parkinson's disease. However, significant issues of gene transfer efficiency and persistent gene expression remain. The HSV vector had the longest expression, but 10% of the rats died because of the wild-type HSV in the gene transfer inoculum. Further modifications are needed in HSV vectors to decrease virulence and improve transfer efficiencies while prolonged vector gene expression is needed for AAV vectors.

Hopefully, novel viral vectors can be produced that will selectively infect and express genes in the appropriate cell type in the brain after systemic injection. The possibility for such *in vivo* manipulation lies at least 5–10 years in the future. Nonetheless, the possibilities for gene transfer application in the nervous system are diverse and significant (Table 5–4).

Another gene transfer approach is the direct implantation of genetically altered cells to reconstitute normal biochemical processes. Researchers have published the results of animal experiments that demonstrate that the transplantation of TH gene-altered muscle cells into the brain results in a significant decease in neurologic symptoms (Jiao et al., 1993). Interestingly, the cultured myoblasts were shown to survive and express TH for 6 months after implantation. Other groups have injected nerve growth factor (NGF) gene-altered cells to study nerve

Table 5–4. Examples of Potential Uses of Gene Transfer in the CNS

Disease states	Examples of treatment approaches
Genetic disorders (e.g., Huntington disease)	Repair of the abnormal gene
Prevention and/or treatment of acquired disorders (e.g., Alzheimer, Parkinson)	Transfer of the normal gene Gene repair with homologous recombination Transfer of genes that prevent neurodegeneration
Autoimmune disorders (e.g., multiple sclerosis)	Targeted destruction of autoreactive T cells Tissue-specific, controlled expression of anti-inflammatory genes
Treatment of pain	Transfer of genes that abolish produce analgesia (e.g., β-endorphin)
Prevention and/or treatment of seizure	Transfer of genes that abolish epileptic foci disorders
Protection and/or treatment of the nervous system against traumatic and hypoxic injuries (e.g., stroke)	Transfer of the superoxide dismutase gene Transfer of genes to induce nerve healing (e.g., NGF)

Table 5–4. (continued)

Disease states	Examples of treatment approaches
Reconstitution of normal biochemical processes (e.g., hormones, dopamine)	Transfer of hormone genes for pituitary dysfunction Insertion of neurotransmitter genes
Prevention of blindness	Transfer of the genes for retinitis pigmentosa or other genes that prevent retinal degeneration Transfer of genes to regulate aqueous humor production for glaucoma
Prevention and treatment of mental illness	Transfer or repair of genes involved in these complex cellular and biochemical pathways

regeneration (Gage et al., 1991). It might be possible to induce healing of neurologic tissue by inserting the NGF gene into damaged areas of the brain, since NGF appears to protect neurons and improves survival after injury. Until genes can be safely and efficiently inserted *in vivo* into the CNS, cellular transplantation of genetically modified cells may be a useful intermediate therapeutic step.

Gene therapy may also have an application in the prevention and treatment of epilepsy and multiple sclerosis (MS). Theoretically, genetically altered cells or the direct gene transfer of genes that produce inhibitory enzymes could be injected into the seizure focus to prevent seizure activity. Gene transfer into oligodendrocytes to alter gene expression or to secrete anti-inflammatory products locally may be valuable in the treatment of MS. Other approaches to MS gene therapy may include the direct manipulation of T lymphocytes to block autoimmune reactivity, the insertion of genes such as transforming growth factor-β (TGF-β) into neural tissues to suppress the immune-mediated neuron destruction or the genetic alteration of CNS tissues to produce interferon-β (IFN-β) locally in the brain, since IFN-β has shown efficacy in diminishing the severity of this disease.

SUMMARY

This chapter has discussed some of the ever increasing number of potential applications of gene therapy to nonmalignant disorders. As this exciting, new clinical discipline evolves over the next several years, gene therapy trials will become commonplace in each medical specialty. The rate of development of human gene therapy applications for any given organ system is dependent upon the timing of gene isolation and sequencing, the availability of a suitable gene transfer method, the need for specific regulation of gene expression, and the priorities of the investigators. As our technologic ability for gene delivery and control of gene expression improves, clinical testing of these new therapeutic tools will dramatically increase. Then we will have an opportunity to offer preventative and potentially curative therapies, whereas now we have primarily symptomatic therapies at our disposal.

REFERENCES

Disorders of Hematopoietic Cells

Immunologic Disorders

Blaese, R.M., and Culver, K.W. (1992): Gene therapy for primary immunodeficiency disease. Immunodef. Rev. 3:329–349.

Blaese, R.M., Culver, K.W., Miller, A.D., Carter, C.S., Fleisher, T., Clerici, M., Shearer, G., Chang, L., Chiang, Y., Tolstoshev, P., Greenblatt, J.J., Rosenberg, S.A., Klein, H., Berger, M., Mullen, C.A., Ramsey, W.J., Muul, L., Morgan, R.A., and Anderson, W.F. (1995): T-lymphocyte-directed gene therapy for ADA-SCID: Initial trial results after 4 years. Science 270:475–480.

Bordignon, C., Mavilio, F., Ferrari, G., Servida, P., Ugazio, A.G., Notarangelo, L.D., and Gilboa, E. (1993): Transfer of the ADA gene into bone marrow cells and peripheral blood lymphocytes for the treatment of patients affected by ADA-deficient SCID. Hum. Gene Ther. 4:513–520.

Bordignon, C., Notarangelo, L.D., Nobili, N., Ferrari, G., Casorati, G., Panina, P., Mazzolari, E., Maggioni, D., Rossi, C., Servida, P., Ugazio, A.G., and Mavilio, F. (1995): Gene therapy in peripheral blood lymphocytes and bone marrow for ADA-immunodeficient patients. Science 270:470–475.

Cobbs, C.S., Malech, H.L., Leto, T.L., Freeman, S.M., Blaese, R.M., Gallin, J.I., and Lomax, K.J. (1992): Retroviral expression of recombinant p47phox protein by Epstein-Barr virus-transformed B lymphocytes from a patient with autosomal chronic granulomatous disease. Blood 79:1829–1835.

Ferrari, G., Rossini, S., Giavazzi, R., Maggioni, D., Nobili, N., Soldati, M., Ungers, G., Mavilio, F., Gilboa, E., and Bordignon, C. (1991): An in vivo model of somatic cell gene therapy for human severe combined immunodeficiency. Science 251:1363–1366.

Ferrari, G., Rossini, S., Nobili, N., Maggioni, D., Garofalo, A., Giavazzi, R., Mavilio, F., and Bordignon, C. (1992): Transfer of the ADA gene into human ADA-deficient T lymphocytes reconstitutes specific immune functions. Blood 80:1120–1124.

Foresman, M.D., Nelson, D.M., and McIvor, R.S. (1992): Correction of purine nucleoside phosphorylase deficiency by retroviral-mediated gene transfer in mouse S49 T cell lymphoma: A model for gene therapy of T cell immunodeficiency, Hum. Gene Ther. 3:625–631.

Hoogerbrugge, P.M., van Beusechem, V.W., Fischer, A., Debree, M., le Diest, F., Perignon, J.L., Morgan, G., Gaspar, B., Fairbanks, L.D., Skeoch, C.H., Moseley, A., Harvey, M., Levinsky, R.J., and Valerio, D. (1996): Bone marrow gene transfer in three patients with adenosine deaminase deficiency. Gene Ther. 3:179–183.

Hoogerbrugge, P.M., Vossen, J.M.J.J., Beusechem, V.W.v., and Valerio, D. (1992): Treatment of patients with severe combined immunodeficiency due to adenosine deaminase (ADA) deficiency by autologous transplantation of genetically modified bone marrow cells. Hum. Gene Ther. 3:553–558.

Kohn, D.B., Weinberg, K.I., Nolta, J.A., Heiss, L.N., Lenarsky, C., Crooks, G.M., Hanley, M.E., Annett, G., Brooks, J.S., El-Khoureiy, A., Lawrence, K., Wells, S., Moen, R.C., Bastian, J., Williams-Herman, D.E., Elder, M., Wara, D., Bowen, T., Hershfield, M.S., Mullen, C.A., Blaese, R.M., and Parkman, R. (1995): Engraftment of gene-modified umbilical cord blood cells in neonates with adenosine deaminase deficiency. Nature Med. 1:1017–1023.

Krauss, J.C., Ping, A.J., Mayo-Bond, L., and Wilson, J.M. (1990): Expression of retroviral transduced human CD18 in murine cells: an in vitro model of gene therapy for leukocyte adhesion deficiency. Hum. Gene Ther. 2:221–228.

Kume, A., and Dinauer, M.C. (1994): Retrovirus-mediated reconstitution of respiratory burst activity in X-linked chronic granulomatous disease cells. Blood 84:3311–3316.

Mitani, K., Wakamiya, M., and Caskey, C.T. (1993): Long-term expression of retroviral-transduced adenosine deaminase in human primitive hematopoietic progenitors. Hum. Gene Ther. 4:9–16.

Nelson, D.M., Butters, K.A., Markert, M.L., Reinsmoen, N.L., and McIvor, R.S. (1995): Correction of proliferative responses in purine-nucleoside-phosphorylase (PNP)-deficient T-lymphocytes by retroviral-mediated PNP gene transfer and expression. J. Immunol. 154:3003–3014.

Thrasher, A., Chetty, M., Casimir, C., and Segal, A.W. (1992): Restoration of superoxide generation to a chronic granulomatous disease-derived B-cell line by retrovirus mediated gene transfer. Blood 80:1125–1129.

Wilson, J.M., Ping, A.J., Krauss, J.C., Mayo-Bond, L., Rogers, C.E., Anderson, D.C., and Todd II, R.F. (1990): Correction of CD18 deficient lymphocytes by retrovirus mediated gene transfer. Science 248:1413–1416.

Wilson, R.W., Yorifuji, T., Lorenzo, I., Smith, W., Anderson, D.C., Belmont, J.W., and Beaudet, A.L. (1993): Expression of human CD18 in murine granulocytes and improved efficiency for infection of deficient human fibroblasts. Hum. Gene Ther. 4:25–34.

Lysosomal Storage Disorders

Anson, D.S., Bielicki, J., and Hopwood, J.J. (1992): Correction of mucopolysaccharide type I fibroblasts by retroviral-mediated transfer of the human α-L-iduronidase gene. Hum. Gene Ther. 3:371–379.

Bahnson, A.B., Nimgaonkar, M., Fei, Y., Boggs, S.S., Robbins, P.D., and Barranger, J.A. (1994): Transduction of CD34-enriched cord blood and Gaucher bone marrow cells by a retroviral vector carrying the glucocerebrosidase gene. Gene Ther. 1:176–184.

Baqué, S., Newgard, C.B., Gerard, R.D., Guinovart, J.J., and Gómez-Foix, A.M. (1994): Adenovirus-mediated delivery into myocytes of muscle glycogen phosphorylase, the enzyme deficient in patients with glycogen-storage disease type V. Biochem. J. 304:1009–1014.

Beutler, E. (1992): Gaucher disease: New molecular approaches to diagnosis and treatment. Science 256:794–799.

Braun, S.E., Aronovich, E.L., Anderson, R.A., Crotty, P.L., McIvor, R.S., and Whitley, C.B. (1993): Metabolic correction and cross-correction of mucopolysaccharidosis type II (Hunter syndrome) by retroviral-mediated gene transfer and expression of human iduronidate-2-sulfatase. Proc. Natl. Acad. Sci. U.S.A. 90:11830–11834.

Cartier, N., Lopez, J., Moullier, P., Rocchiccioli, F., Rolland, M-O., Jorge, P., Mosser, J., Mandel, J-L., Bougnères, P-F., Danos, O., and Aubourg, P. (1995): Retroviral-mediated gene transfer corrects very-long-chain fatty acid metabolism in adrenoleukodystrophy fibroblasts. Proc. Natl. Acad. Sci. U.S.A. 92:1674–1678.

Correll, P.H., Fink, J.K., Brady, R.O., Perry, L.K., and Karlsson, S. (1989): Production of human glucocerebrosidase in mice after retroviral gene transfer into multipotential hematopoietic progenitor cells. Proc. Natl. Acad. Sci. U.S.A. 86:8912–8916.

Dunbar, C., Kohn, D., Karlsson, S., Barton, N., Brady, R., Cottler-Fox, M., Crooks, G., Emmons, R., Esplin, J., Leitman, S., Lenarsky, C., Nolta, J., Parkman, R., Pensiero, M., Schifmann, R., Tolstoshev, P., and Weinberg, K. (1996): Retroviral mediated transfer of the cDNA for human glucocerebrosidase into hematopoietic stem cells of patients with Gaucher disease. A phase I study. Hum. Gene Ther. 7:231–253.

Enomaa, N., Danos, O., Peltonen, L., and Jalanko, A. (1995): Correction of deficient enzyme activity in a lysosomal storage disease, aspartylglucosaminia, by enzyme replacement and retroviral gene transfer. Hum. Gene Ther. 6:723–731.

Krall, W.J., Challita, P.M., Perlmutter, L.S., Skelton, D.C., and Kohn, D.B. (1994): Cells expressing human glucocerebrosidase from a retroviral vector repopulate macrophages and central nervous system microglia after murine bone marrow transplantation. Blood 83:2737–2748.

Moullier, P., Bohl, D., Heard, J-M., and Danos, O. (1993): Correction of lysosomal storage in the liver and spleen of MPS VII mice by implantation of genetically modified skin fibroblasts. Nature Genet. 4:154–159.

Moullier, P., Bohl, D., Cardoso, J., Heard, J.M., and Danos, O. (1995): Long-term delivery of a lysosomal enzyme by genetically modified fibroblasts in dogs. Nat. Med. 1:353–357.

Nolta, J.A., Sender, L.S., Barranger, J.A., and Kohn, D. (1990): Expression of human glucocerebrosidase in murine long-term bone marrow cultures after retroviral vector mediated transfer. Blood 75:787–791.

Snyder, E.Y., Taylor, R.M., and Wolfe, J.H. (1995): Neural progenitor cell engraftment corrects lysosomal storage throughout the MPS VII mouse brain. Nature (London) 374:367–370.

Whitley, C.B, McIvor, R.S., Aronovich, E.L., Berry, S.A., Blazar, B.R., Burger, S.R., Kersey, J.H., King, R.A., Faras, A.J., Latchaw, R.E., McCullough, J., Pan, D., Ramsay, N.K.C., and Stroncek, D.F. (1996): Retroviral-mediated transfer of the iduronidase-2-sulfatase gene into lymphocytes for treatment of mild Hunter syndrome (mucopolysaccharidosis type II). Hum. Gene Ther. 7:537–549.

Wolfe, J.H., Sands, M.S., Barker, J.E., Gwynn, B., Rowe, L.B., Vogler, C.A., and Birkenmeier, E.H. (1992): Reversal of pathology in murine mucopolysaccharidosis type VII by somatic cell gene transfer. Nature (London) 360:749–753.

Wolfe, J.H., Kyle, J.W., Sands, M.S., Sly, W.S., Markowitz, D.G., and Parente, M.K. (1995): High level expression and export of beta-glucuronidase from murine mucopolysaccharidosis VII cells corrected by a double-copy retrovirus vector. Gene Ther. 2:70–78.

Xu, L.C., Karlsson, S., Byrne, E.R., Kluepfel-Stahl, S., Kessler, S.W., Agricola, B.A., Sellers, S., Kirby, M., Dunbar, C.E., Brady, R.D., Nienhuis, A.W., and Donahue, R.E. (1995): Long-term in vivo expression of the human glucocerebrosidase gene in nonhuman primates after CD34+ hematopoietic cell transduction with cell-free retroviral preparations. Proc. Natl. Acad. Sci. U.S.A. 92:4372–4376.

Hematologic System

Dunbar, C.E., Cottler-Fox, M., O'Shaughnessy, J.A., Doren, S., Carter, C., Berenson, R., Brown, S., Moen, R.C., Greenblatt, J., Stewart, F.M., Leitman, S.F., Wilson, W.H., Cowan, K., Young, N.S., and Nienhuis, A.W. (1995): Retrovirally marked CD34-enriched peripheral blood and bone marrow cells contribute to long-term engraftment after autologous transplantation. Blood 85:3048–3057.

Einerhand, M.P.W., Antoniou, M., Zolotukhin, S., Muzyczka, N., Berns, K.I., Grosveld, F., and Valerio, D. (1995): Regulated high-level human beta-globin gene expression in erythroid cells following recombinant adeno-associated virus-mediated gene transfer. Gene Ther. 2:336–343.

Hamamori, Y., Samal, B., Tian, J., and Kedes, L. (1994): Persistent erythropoiesis by moblast transfer of erythropoietin cDNA. Hum. Gene Ther. 5:1349–1356.

Konishi, H., Ochiya, T., Sakamoto, H., Tsukamoto, M., Saito, I., Muto, T., Sugimura, T., and Terada, M. (1995): Effective prevention of thrombocytopenia in mice using adenovirus-mediated transfer of HST-1 (FGF-4) gene. J. Clin. Invest. 96:1125–1130.

Larochelle, A., Vormoor, J., Lapidot, T., Sher, G., Furukawa, T., Li, Q., Shultz, L.D., Olivieri, N.F., Stamatoyannopoulos, G., and Dick, J.E. (1995): Engraftment of immune-deficient mice with primitive hematopoietic cells from beta-thalassemia and sickle cell anemia patients: Implications for evaluating human gene therapy protocols. Hum. Mol. Genet. 4:163–172.

Leboulch, P., Huang, G.M.S., Humphries, R.K., Oh, Y.H., Eaves, C.J., and Tuan, D.Y.H. (1994): Mutagenesis of retroviral vectors transducing human beta-globin gene and beta-globin locus control region derivatives results in stable transmission of an active transcriptional structure. EMBO J. 13:3065–3076.

Liu, J.M., Buchwald, M., Walsh, C.E., and Young, N.S. (1994): Fanconi anemia and novel strategies for therapy. Blood 84:3995–4007.

McCune, S.L., Reilly, M.P., Chomo, M.J., Asakura, T., and Townes, T.M. (1994): Recombinant human hemoglobins designed for gene therapy of sickle cell disease. Proc. Natl. Acad. Sci. U.S.A. 92:9852–9856.

Miller, J.L., Donahue, R.E., Sellers, S.E., Samulski, R.J., Young, N.S., and Nienhuis, A.W. (1994): Recombinant adeno-associated virus (rAAV)-mediated expression of a human gamma-globin gene in human progenitor-derived erythroid cells. Proc. Natl. Acad. Sci. U.S.A. 91:10183–10187.

Novak, U., Harris, E.A., Forrester, W., Groudine, M., and Gelinas, R. (1990): High-level beta-globin expression after retroviral transfer of locus activation region-containing human beta-globin gene derivatives into murine erythroleukemia cells. Proc. Natl. Acad. Sci. U.S.A. 87:3386–3390.

Osborne, W.R.A., Ramesh, N., Lau, S., Clowes, M.M., Dale, D.C., and Clowes, A.W. (1995): Gene therapy for long-term expression of erythropoietin in rats. Proc. Natl. Acad. Sci. U.S.A. 92:8055–8058.

Plavec, I., Papayannopoulou, T., Maury, C., and Meyer, F. (1993): A human beta-globin gene fused to the human beta-globin locus control region is expressed at high levels on erythroid cells of mice engrafted with retrovirus-transduced hematopoietic stem cells. Blood 81:1384–1392.

Sadelain, M., Wang, C.H., Antoniou, M., Grosveld, F., and Mulligan, R.C. (1995): Generation of a high-titer retroviral vector capable of expressing high levels of the human beta-globin gene. Proc. Natl. Acad. Sci. U.S.A. 92:6728–6732.

Sakamoto, H., Ochiya, T., Sato, Y., Tsukamoto, M., Konishi, H., Saito, I., Sugimura, T., and Terada, M. (1994): Adenovirus-mediated transfer of the HST-1 (FGF4) gene induces increased levels of platelet count in vivo. Proc. Natl. Acad. Sci. U.S.A. 91:12368–12372.

Takekoshi, K.J., Oh, Y.H., Westerman, K.W., London, I.M., and Leboulch, P. (1995): Retroviral transfer of a human beta-globin/delta-globin hybrid gene linked to beta-locus control region hypersensitive site-2 aimed at the gene therapy of sickle cell disease. Proc. Natl. Acad. Sci. U.S.A. 92:3014–3018.

Tripathy, S.K., Goldwasser, E., Lu, M.M., Barr, E., and Leiden, J.M. (1994): Stable delivery of physiologic levels of recombinant erythropoietin to the systemic circulation by intramuscular injection of replication-defective adenovirus. Proc. Natl. Acad. Sci. U.S.A. 91:11557–11561.

Villeval, J.L., Rouyer-Fessard, P., Blumenfeld, N., Henri, A., Vainchenker, W., and Beuzard, Y. (1994): Retrovirus-mediated transfer of the erythropoietin gene in hematopoietic cells improves the erythrocyte phenotype in murine beta-thalassemia. Blood 84:928–933.

Walsh, C.E., Nienhuis, A.W., Samulski, R.J., Brown, M.G., Miller, J.L., and Young, N.S. (1994): Phenotypic correction of Fanconi anemia in human hematopoietic cells with a recombinant adeno-associated virus vector. J. Clin. Invest. 94:1440–1448.

Human Immunodeficiency Virus (HIV) Infection

Buchschacher, G.L., Freed, E.O. and Panganiban, A.T. (1992): Cells induced to express a human immunodeficiency virus type 1 envelope gene mutant inhibit the spread of wild-type virus. Hum. Gene Ther. 3:391–397.

Chatterjee, S., Johnson, P.R., and Wong, K.K., Jr. (1992): Dual-target inhibition of HIV-1 in vitro by means of an adeno-associated virus and antisense vector. Science 258:1485–1488.

Chen, S-Y., Khouri, Y., Bagley, J., and Marasco, W.A. (1994): Combined intra- and extracellular immunization against human immunodeficiency virus type 1 infection with a human anti-gp120 antibody. Proc. Natl. Acad. Sci. U.S.A. 91:5932–5936.

Duan, L., Bagasra, O., Laughlin, M.A., Oakes, J.W., and Pomerantz, R.J. (1994a): Potent inhibition of human immunodeficiency virus-1 replication by an intracellular anti-rev single-chain antibody. Proc. Natl. Acad. Sci. U.S.A. 91:5075–5079.

Duan, L., Zhang, H., Oakes, J.W., Bagasra, O., and Pomerantz, R.J. (1994b): Molecular and virological effects of intracellular anti-rev single-chain variable fragments on the expression of various human immunodeficiency virus type 1 strains. Hum. Gene Ther. 5:1315–1324.

Galpin, J.E., Casciato, D.A., and Richards, S.B. (1994): A phase I clinical trial to evaluate the safety and biological activity HIV-IT (TAF) (HIV-1(IIIB) env-transduced, autologous fibroblasts) in asymptomatic HIV-1-infected subjects. Hum. Gene Ther. 5:997–1017.

Graham, B.S., Matthews, T.J., Belshe, R.B., Clements, M.L., Dolin, R., Wright, P.F., Gorse, G.J., Schwartz, D.H., Keefer, M.C., Bolognesi, D.P., Corey, L., Stablein, D.M., Esterlitz, J.R., Hu, S-L., Smith, G.E., Fast, P.E., and Koff, W.C. (1993): Augmentation of human immunodeficiency virus type 1 neutralizing antibody by priming with gp160 recombinant vaccinia and boosting with rgp160 in vaccinia-naive adults. J. Infect Dis. 167:533–537.

Harrison, G.S., Long, C.J., Curiel, T.J., Maxwell, F., and Maxwell, I.H. (1992): Inhibition of human immunodeficiency virus-1 production resulting from transduction with a retrovirus containing an HIV-regulated diphtheria toxin A chain gene. Hum. Gene Ther. 3:461–469.

Haubrich, R. and McCutchan, J.A. (1995a): An open label, phase-I/II clinical trial to evaluate the safety and biological activity of HIV-IT (V) (HIV-1IIIB env/rev retroviral vector) in HIV-1-infected individuals. Hum. Gene Ther. 6:941–955.

Haubrich, R., Warner, J., Anderson, C.G., Merritt, J., Jacobsen, C., McCutchan, J.A. and the California Collaborative Treatment Group (CCTG). (1995b): Cytotoxic T lymphocyte augmentation using an HIV-1 env/rev encoding retroviral vector (HIV-IT(V)) as therapy for HIV. Gene Ther. 2:599–600.

Hope, T.J., Klein, N.P., Elder, M.E., and Parslow, T.G. (1992): Transdominant inhibition of human immunodeficiency virus type 1 rev occurs through formation of inactive protein complexes. J. Virol. 66:1849–1855.

Irwin, M.J., Laube, L.S., Lee, V., Austin, M., Chada, S., Anderson, C-G., Townsend, K., Jolly, D., and Warner, J.F. (1994): Direct injection of a recombinant retroviral vector induces human immunodeficiency virus-specific immune responses in mice and non-human primates. J. Virol. 68:5036–5044.

Laube, L.S., Burrascano, M., Dejesus, C.E., Howard, B.D., Johnson, M.A., Lee, W.T.L., Lynn, A.E., Peters, G., Ronlov, G.S., Townsend, K.S., Eason, R.L., Jolly, D.J., Merchant, B., and Warner, J.F. (1994): Cytotoxic T lymphocyte and antibody responses generated in rhesus monkeys immunized with retroviral vector-transduced fibroblasts expressing human immunodeficiency virus type-1 IIIB env/rev proteins. Hum. Gene Ther. 5:853–862.

Lisziewicz, J., Sun, D., Klotman, M., Agrawal, S., Zamecnik, P., and Gallo, R. (1992): Specific inhibition of human immunodeficiency virus type 1 replication by antisense oligonucleotides: an in vitro model for treatment. Proc. Natl. Acad. Sci. U.S.A. 89:11209–11213.

Malim, M.H., and Cullen, B.R. (1991): HIV-1 structural gene expression requires the binding of multiple Rev monomers to the viral RRE—implications for HIV-1 latency. Cell 65:241–248.

Malim, M.H., Freimuth, W.W., Liu, J., Boyle, T.J., Lyerly, H.K., Cullen, B.R., and Nabel, G.J. (1992): Stable expression of transdominant rev protein in human T cell inhibits human immunodeficiency virus replication. J. Exp. Med. 176:1197–1201.

Mouscadet, J-F., Carteau, S., Goulaouic, H., Subra, F., and Auclair, C. (1994): Triplex-mediated inhibition of HIV DNA integration in vitro. J. Biol. Chem. 269:21635–21638.

Nabel, G.J., Fox, B.A., Post, L., Thompson, C.B., and Woffendin, C. (1994): A molecular genetic intervention for AIDS—Effects of a transdominant negative form of rev. Hum. Gene Ther. 5:79–82.

Riddell, S.R., Elliott, M., Lewinsohn, D.A., Gilbert, M.J., Wilson, L., Manley. S.A., Lupton, S.D., Overell, R.W., Reynolds, T.C., Corey, L., and Greenberg, P.D. (1996): T-cell mediated rejection of gene-modified HIV-specific cytotoxic T lymphocytes in HIV-infected patients. Nature Med. 2:216–223.

Riddell, S.R., Greenberg, P.D., Overell, R.W., Loughran, T.P., Gilbert, M.J., Lupton, S.D., Agosti, J., Scheeler, S., Coombs, R.W., and Corey, L. (1992): Phase 1 study of cellular adoptive immunotherapy using genetically modified CD8+ HIV-specific T cells for HIV seropositive patients undergoing allogeneic bone marrow transplant. Hum. Gene Ther. 3:319–338.

Roberts, M.R., Qin, L., Zhang, D., Smith, D.H., Tran, A-C., Dull, T.J., Groopman, J.E., Capon, D.J., Byrn, R.A., and Finer, M.H. (1994): Targeting of human immunodeficiency virus-infected cells by CD8+ T lymphocytes armed with universal T-cell receptors. Blood 84:2878–2889.

Sozakiel, G., and Pawlita, M. (1991): Inhibition of human immunodeficiency virus type 1 replication in human T cells stably expressing antisense RNA. J. Virol. 65:468–472.

Sullenger, B.A., Gallardo, H.F., Ungers, G.E., and Gilboa, E. (1991): Analysis of transacting response decoy RNA-mediated inhibition of human immunodeficiency virus type 1 transactivation. J. Virol. 65:6811–6816.

Sun, J.Q., Pyati, J., Smythe, J., Wang, L., MacPherson, J., Gerlach, W., and Symonds, G. (1995): Resistance to human immunodeficiency virus type 1 infection conferred by transduction of human peripheral blood lymphocytes with ribozyme, antisense, or polymeric trans-activation response element constructs. Proc. Natl. Acad. Sci. U.S.A. 92:7272–7276.

Vandendriessche, T., Chuah, M.K.L., Chiang, L., Chang, H-K., Ensoli, B., and Morgan, R.A. (1995): Inhibition of clinical human immunodeficiency virus (HIV) type 1 isolates in primary CD4+ T lymphocytes by retroviral vectors expressing anti-HIV genes. J. Virol. 69:4045–4052.

Walker, R.E., Blaese, R.M., Davey, R.T., Falloon, R.T., Mullen, C., and Polis, M.A. (1996): A phase I/II pilot study of the safety of the adoptive transfer of syngeneic gene-modified cytotoxic T lymphocytes in HIV-infected identical twins. Hum. Gene Ther. 7:367–400.

Woffendin, C., Ranga, U., Yang, Z.-Y., Xu, L., and Nabel, G.J. (1996): Expression of a protective gene prolongs survival of T cells in human immunodeficiency virus-infected patients. Proc. Natl. Acad. Sci. U.S.A. 93:2889–2894.

Yu, M., Leavitt, M.C., Maruyama, M., Yamada, O., Young, D., Ho, A.D., and Wong-Staal, F. (1995): Intracellular immunization of human fetal blood cord blood stem cells with a ribozyme against human immunodeficiency virus type 1. Proc. Natl. Acad. Sci. U.S.A. 92:699–703.

Recombinant Vaccines

Aldovini, A., and Young, R.A. (1991): Humoral and cell-mediated immune responses to live recombinant BCG-HIV vaccines. Nature (London) 351:479–482.

Bloom, B.R. (1989): Vaccines for the third world. Nature (London) 342:115–120.

Brochier, B., Kieny, M.P., Costy, F., Coppens, P., Bauduin, B., Lecocq, J.P., Languet, B., Chappuis, G., Desmettre, P., Afiademanyo, K., Libois, R., and Pastoret, P.P. (1991): Large-scale eradication of rabies using recombinant vaccinia-rabies vaccine. Nature 354:520–522.

Fikrig, E., Barthold, S.W., Kantor, F.S., and Flavell, R.A. (1990): Protection of mice against the lyme disease agent by immunizing with recombinant OspA. Science 250:553–556.

Fynan, E.F., Webster, R.G., Fuller, D.H., Haynes, J.R., Santoro, J.C., and Robinson, H.L. (1993): DNA vaccines: Protective immunizations by parenteral, mucosal, and gene-gun inoculations. Proc. Natl. Acad. Sci. U.S.A. 90:11478–11482.

Kaslow, D.C., Isaacs, S.N., Quakyi, I.A., Gwadz, R.W., Moss, B., and Keister, D.B. (1991): Induction of *Plasmodium falciparum* transmission-blocking antibodies by recombinant vaccinia virus. Science 252:1310–1313.

Langermann, S., Palaszynski, S., Sadziene, A., Stover, C.K., and Koenig, S. (1994): Systemic and mucosal immunity induced by BCG vector expressing outer-surface protein A of Borrelia burgdorferi. Nature (London) 372:552–555.

Lowrie, D.B., Tascon, R.E., Colston, M.J., and Silva, C.L. (1994): Towards a DNA vaccine against tuberculosis. Vaccine 12:1537–1540.

Major, M.E., Vitvitski, L., Mink, M.A., Schleef, M., Whalen, R.G., Trépo, C., and Inchauspé, G. (1995): DNA-based immunization with chimeric vectors for the induction of immune responses against the hepatitis C virus nucleocapsid. J. Virol. 69:5798–5805.

Michel, M-L., Davis, H.L., Schleef, M., Mancini, M., Tiollais, P., and Whalen, R.G. (1995): DNA-mediated immunization to the hepatitis B surface antigen in mice: Aspects of the humoral response mimic hepatitis B viral infection in humans. Proc. Natl. Acad. Sci. U.S.A. 92:5307–5311.

Oehen, S., Hengartner, H., and Zinkernagel, R.M. (1991): Vaccination for disease. Science 251:195–198.

Schodel, F. (1992): Prospects for oral vaccination using recombinant bacteria expressing viral epitopes. Adv. Virus Res. 41:409–446.

Sedegah, M., Hedstrom, R., Hobart, P., and Hoffman, S.L. (1994): Protection against malaria by immunization with plasmid DNA encoding circumsporozoite protein. Proc. Natl. Acad. Sci. U.S.A. 91:9866–9870.

Shen, L., Chen, Z.W., Miller, M.D., Stallard, V., Mazzara, G.P., Panicali, D.L., and Letvin, N.L. (1991): Recombinant virus vaccine-induced SIV-specific CD8+ cytotoxic T lymphocytes. Science 252:440–443.

Sizemore, D.R., Branstrom, A.A., and Sadoff, J.C. (1995): Attenuated *Shigella* as a DNA delivery vehicle for DNA-mediated immunization. Science 270:299–302.

Stover, C.K., de la Cruz, V.F., Fuerst, T.R., Burlein, J.E., Benson, L.A., Bennett, L.T., Bansal, G.P., Young, J.F., Lee, M.H., Hatfull, G.F., Snapper, S.B., Barletta, R.G., Jacobs, Jr. W.R., and Bloom, B.R. (1991): New use of BCG for recombinant vaccines. Nature 351:456–460.

Ulmer, J.B., Donnelly, J.J., Parker, S.E., Rhodes, G.H., Felgner, P.L., Dwarki, V.J., Gromkowski, S.H., Deck, R.R., DeWitt, C.M., Friedman, A., Hawe, L.A., Leander, K.R., Martinez, D., Perry, H.C., Shiver, J.W., Montgomery, D.L., and Liu, M.A. (1993): Heterologous protection against influenza by injection of DNA encoding a viral protein. Science 259:1745–1749.

Xu, D., and Liew, F.Y. (1995): Protection against leishmaniasis by injection of DNA encoding a major surface glycoprotein, gp63, of L. major. Immunology 84:173–176.

Hepatic System

Batshaw, M.L., Yudkoff, M., McLaughlin, B.A., Gorry, E., Anegawa, N.J., Smith, I.A.S., Hyman, S.L., and Robinson, M.B. (1995): The sparse fur mouse as a model for gene therapy in ornithine-carbamyltransferase deficiency. Gene Ther. 2:743–749.

Cardoso, J.E., Branchereau, S., Jeyaraj, P.R., Houssin, D., Danos, O., and Heard, J.M. (1993): In situ retrovirus-mediated gene transfer into dog liver. Hum. Gene Ther. 4:411–418.

Chiang, P.W., Hu, C.P., Su, T.S., Lo, S.J., Chu, M.H.H., Chang, C. (1990): Encapsidation of truncated human hepatitis B virus genomes through trans-complementation of the core protein and polymerase. Virology 176:355–361.

Chowdhury, J.R., Grossman, M., Gupta, S., Chowdhury, N.R., Baker, J.R., and Wilson, J.M. (1991): Long-term improvement of hypercholesterolemia after ex vivo gene therapy in LDLR-deficient rabbits. Science 254:1802–1805.

Cristiano, R.J., Smith, L.C., and Kay, M.A., Brinkley, B.R., and Woo, S.L.C. (1993a): Hepatic gene therapy: Efficient gene delivery and expression in primary hepatocytes utilizing a conjugated adenovirus-DNA complex. Proc. Natl. Acad. Sci. U.S.A. 90:11548–11552.

Cristiano, R.J., Smith, L.C., and Woo, S.L. (1993b): Hepatic gene therapy: Adenovirus enhancement of receptor-mediated gene delivery and expression in primary hepatocytes. Proc. Natl. Acad. Sci. U.S.A. 90:2122–2126.

Fang, B., Eisensmith, R.C., Li, X.H.C., Finegold, M.J., Shedlovsky, A., Dove, W., and Woo, S.L.C. (1994): Gene therapy for phenylketonuria: Phenotypic correction in a genetically deficient mouse model by adenovirus-mediated hepatic gene transfer. Gene Ther. 1:247–254.

Ferry, N., Duplessis, O., Houssin, D., Danos, O., and Heard, J.M. (1991): Retroviral-mediated gene transfer into hepatocytes in vivo. Proc. Natl. Acad. Sci. U.S.A. 88:8377–8381.

Hoffmann, C., Sandig, V., Jennings, G., Rudolph, M., Schlag, P., and Strauss, M. (1995): Efficient gene transfer into human hepatocytes by baculovirus vectors. Proc. Natl. Acad. Sci. U.S.A. 92:10099–10103.

Jaffe, H.A., Danel, C., Longnecker, G., Metzger, M., Setoguchi, Y., Rosenfeld, M.A., Gant, T.W., Thorgeirsson, S.S., Stratford-Perricaudet, L.D., Perricaudet, M., Pavirani, A., Lecocq, J-P., and Crystal, R.G. (1992): Adenovirus-mediated in vivo gene transfer and expression in normal rat liver. Nature Genet. 1:372–378.

Kaleko, M., Garcia, J.V., and Miller, A.D. (1991): Persistent gene expression after retroviral gene transfer into liver cells in vivo. Hum. Gene Ther. 2:27–32.

Kay, M.A., Li, Q., Liu, T.-J., Leland, F., Toman, C., Finegold, M., and Woo, S.L. (1992): Hepatic gene therapy: Persistent expression of human α1-antitrypsin in mice after direct gene delivery in vivo. Hum. Gene Ther. 3:641–647.

Kozarsky, K., Grossman, M., and Wilson, J.M. (1993): Adenovirus-mediated correction of the genetic defect in hepatocytes from patients with familial hypercholesterolemia. Som. Cell Mol. Genet. 19:449–458.

Lieber, A., Vrancken Peeters, M-J.T.F.D., Meuse, L., Fausto, N., Perkins, J., and Kay, M.A. (1995): Adeno virus-mediated urokinase gene transfer induces liver regeneration and allows for efficient retrovirus transduction of hepatocytes in vivo. Proc. Natl. Acad. Sci. U.S.A. 92:6210–6214.

Miyanohara, A., Yee, J-K., Bouic, K., LaPorte, P., and Friedmann, T. (1995): Efficient in vivo transduction of the neonatal mouse liver with pseudotyped retroviral vectors. Gene Ther. 2:138–142.

Morsy, M.A., Alford, E.L., Bett, A., Graham, F.L., and Caskey, C.T. (1993): Efficient adenoviral-mediated ornithine transcarbamylase expression in deficient mouse and human hepatocytes. J. Clin. Invest. 92:1580–1586.

Raper, S.E., Wilson, J.M., and Grossman, M. (1992): Retroviral-mediated gene transfer in human hepatocytes. Surgery 112:333–340.

Strauss, M. (1994): Liver-directed gene therapy: Prospects and problems. Gene Ther. 1:156–164.

Blood-Clotting System

Anson, D.S., Austen, D.E.G., and Brownlee, G.G. (1985): Expression of active human clotting factor IX from recombinant DNA clones in mammalian cells. Nature (London) 315:683–685.

Axelrod, J.H., Read, M.S., Brinkhous, K.M., and Verma, I.M. (1990): Phenotypic correction of factor IX deficiency in skin fibroblasts of hemophiliac dogs. Proc. Natl. Acad. Sci. U.S.A. 87:5173–5177.

Brownlee, G.G. (1995): Prospects for gene therapy of hemophilia-A and -B. Br. Med. Bull. 51:91–105.

Connelly, S., Smith, T.A.G., Dhir, G., Gardner, J.M., Mehaffey, M.G., Zaret, K.S., McClelland, A., and Kaleko, M. (1995): In vivo gene delivery and expression of physiological levels of functional human Factor-VIII in mice. Hum. Gene Ther. 6:185–193.

Dai, Y., Roman, M., Naviaux, R.K., and Verma, I.M. (1992): Gene therapy via primary myoblasts: long-term expression of factor IX protein following transplantation in vivo. Proc. Natl. Acad. Sci. U.S.A. 89:10892–10895.

Dwarki, V.J., Belloni, P., Nijjar, T., Smith, J., Couto, L., Rabier, M., Clift, S., Berns, A., and Cohen, L.K. (1995): Gene therapy for hemophilia A: Production of therapeutic levels of human factor VIII in vivo in mice. Proc. Natl. Acad. Sci. U.S.A. 92:1023–1027.

Ferry, N., Duplessis, O., Houssin, D., Danos, O., and Heard, J-M. (1991): Retroviral-mediated gene transfer into hepatocytes in vivo. Proc. Natl. Acad. Sci. U.S.A. 88:8377–8381.

Hao, Q.L., Malik, P., Salazar, R., Tang, H., Gordon, E.M., and Kohn, D.B. (1995): Expression of biologically active human Factor-IX in human hematopoietic cells after retroviral vector-mediated gene transduction. Hum. Gene Ther. 6:873–880.

Hoeben, R.C., van der Jagt, R.C.M., Schoute, F., van Tilburg, N.H., Verbeet, M.Ph., Briet, E., van Ormondt, H., and van der Eb, A.J. (1990): Expression of functional factor VIII in primary human skin fibroblasts after retrovirus-mediated gene transfer. J. Biol. Chem. 265:7318–7323.

Hoeben, R.C., Fallaux, F.J., Tilburg, N.H.V., Cramer, S.J., van Ormondt, H., Briët, E., and van der Eb, A.J. (1993): Toward gene therapy for hemophilia: Long-term persistence of factor VIII-secreting fibroblasts after transplantation into immunodeficient mice. Hum. Gene Ther. 4:179–186.

Hoeben, R.C., Fallaux, F.J., Cramer, S.J., van den Wollenberg, D.J.M., van Ormondt, H., Briet, E., and van der Eb, A.J. (1995): Expression of the blood-clotting Factor-VIII cDNA is repressed by a transcriptional silencer located in its coding region. Blood 85:2447–2454.

Hsueh, J.L., Meng, P., Wang, J., Wang, X., Din, X., Qiu, X., Zhou, J., Dai, Y., Hu, Y., Lu, D., Al, X., Zheng, B., Jiang, Z., Wang, X., and Wang, J. (1992): Treatment of hemophilia B with autologous skin fibroblasts transduced with human clotting factor IX cDNA. Hum. Gene Ther. 3:543–552.

Kay, M.A., Rothenberg, S., Landen, C.N., Bellinger, D.A., Leland, F., Toman, C., Finegold, M., Thompson, A.R., Read, M.S., Brinkhous, K.M., and Woo, S.L.C. (1993): In vivo gene therapy of hemophilia B: Sustained partial correction in factor IX-deficient dogs. Science 262:117–119.

Kay, M.A., Landen, C.N., Rothenberg, S.R., Taylor, L.A., Leland, F., Wiehle, S., Fang, B., Bellinger, D., Finegold, M., Thompson, A.R., Read, M., Brinkhous, K.M., and Woo, S.L.C. (1994): In vivo hepatic gene therapy: Complete albeit transient correction of factor IX deficiency in hemophilia dogs. Proc. Natl. Acad. Sci. U.S.A. 91:2353–2357.

Kurachi, K., and Kurachi, S. (1995): Regulatory mechanism of the Factor-IX gene. Thromb. Haemostasis. 73:333–339.

Lozier, J.N., and Brinkhous, K.M. (1994): Gene therapy and the hemophilias. JAMA 271:47–51.

Lu, D.R., Zhou, J.M., Zheng, B., Qiu, X.F., Xue, J.L., Wang, J.M., Meng, P.L., Han, F.L., Ming, B.H., and Wang, X.P. (1993): Stage I clinical trial of gene therapy for hemophilia-B. Sci. China-B. 36:1342–1351.

Palmer, T.D., Thompson, A.R., and Miller, A.D. (1989): Production of human factor IX in animals by genetically modified skin fibroblasts: Potential therapy for hemophilia B. Blood 73:438–445.

Scharfmann, R., Axelrod, J.H., and Verma, I.M. (1991): Long-term in vivo expression of retrovirus-mediated gene transfer in mouse fibroblast implants. Proc. Natl. Acad. Sci. U.S.A. 88:4626–4630.

Smith, T.A.G., Mehaffey, M.G., Kayda, E.B., Saunders, J.M., Yei, S., Trapnell, B.C., McClelland, A., and Kaleko, M. (1993): Adenovirus-mediated expression of therapeutic plasma levels of human factor IX in mice. Nat. Genet. 5:397–402.

St. Louis, D. and Verma, M. (1988): An alternative approach to somatic cell gene therapy. Proc. Natl. Acad. Sci. U.S.A. 85:3150–3154.

Yao, S.N., and Kurachi, K. (1992): Expression of human factor IX in mice after injection of genetically modified myoblasts. Proc. Natl. Acad. Sci. U.S.A. 89:3357–3361.

Yao, S.N., Wilson, J.M., Nabel, E.G., Kurachi, S., Hachiya, H.L., and Kurachi, K. (1991): Expression of human factor IX in rat capillary endothelial cells: Toward somatic gene cell therapy for hemophilia B. Proc. Natl. Acad. Sci. U.S.A. 88:8105–8108.

Pulmonary System

Alton, E.W.F.W., and Geddes, D.M. (1995): Gene therapy for cystic fibrosis: a clinical perspective. Gene Ther. 2:88–95.

Boucher, R.C., Knowles, M.R., Johnson, L.G., Olsen, J.C., Pickles, R., Wilson, J.M., Engelhardt, J., Yang, Y., and Grossman, M. (1994): Gene therapy for cystic fibrosis using E1-deleted adenovirus: A phase I trial in the nasal cavity. Hum. Gene Ther. 5:615–639.

Caplen, N.J., Alton, E.W.F.W., Middleton, P.G., Dorin, J.R., Stevenson, B.J., Gao, X., Durham, S.R., Jeffery, P.K., Hodson, M.E., Coutelle, C., Huang, L., Porteous, D.J., Williamson, R., and Geddes, D.M. (1995): Liposome-mediated CFTR gene transfer to the nasal epithelium of patients with cystic fibrosis. Nat. Med. 1:39–46.

Collins, F.S. (1992): Cystic fibrosis: Molecular biology and therapeutic implications. Science 256:774–779.

Crystal, R.G. (1995): The gene as the drug. Nat. Med. 1:15–17.

Crystal, R.G., McElvaney, N.G., Rosenfield, M.A., Chu, C.S., Mastrangeli, A., and Hay, J.C. (1994): Administration of an adenovirus containing the human CFTR cDNA to the respiratory tract of individuals with cystic fibrosis. Nature Genet. 8:42–51.

Crystal, R.G., Jaffe, A., Brody, S., Mastrangeli, A., McElvaney, N.G., Rosenfeld, M., Chiu, C.S., Danel, C., Hay, J., and Eissa, T. (1995a): A phase 1 study, in cystic fibrosis patients, of the safety, toxicity, and biological efficacy of a single administration of a replication deficient, recombinant adenovirus carrying the cDNA of the normal cystic fibrosis transmembrane conductance regulator gene in the lung. Hum. Gene Ther. 6:643–666

Crystal, R.G., Mastrangeli, A., Sanders, A., Cooke, J., King, T., Gilbert, F., Henschke, C., Pascal, W., Herena, J., Harvey, B.G., Hirschowitz, E., Diaz, D., Ruissi, T., Pacheco, F., Sikand, V., and Brion, P. (1995b): Evaluation of repeat administration of a replication-deficient, recombinant adeno virus containing the normal cystic fibrosis transmembrane conductance regulator cDNA to the airways of individuals with cystic fibrosis. Hum. Gene Ther. 6:667–703.

Drumm, M.L., Pope, H.A., Cliff, W.H., Rommens, J.M., Marvin, S.A., Tsui, L.C., Collins, F.S., Frizzell, R.A., and Wilson, J.M. (1990): Correction of the cystic fibrosis defect in vitro by retrovirus-mediated gene transfer. Cell 62:1227–1233.

Dupuit, F., Bout, A., Hinnrasky, J., Fuchey, C., Zahm, J.M., Imler, J.L., Pavirani, A., Valerio, D., and Puchelle, E. (1995): Expression and localization of CFTR in the Rhesus monkey surface airway epithelium. Gene Ther. 2:156–163.

Engelhardt, J.F., Yang, Y., Stratford-Perricaudet, L.D., Allen, E.D., Kozarsky, K., Perricaudet, M., Yankaskas, J.R., and Wilson, J.M. (1993): Direct gene transfer of human CFTR into human bronchial epithelia of xenografts with E1-deleted adenoviruses. Nature Genet. 4:27–34.

Ferkol, T., Perales, J.C., Eckman, E., Kaetzel, C.S., Hanson, R.W., and Davis, P.B. (1995): Gene transfer into the airway epithelium of animals by targeting the polymeric immunoglobulin receptor. J. Clin. Invest. 95:493–502.

Goldman, M.J., Yang, Y., and Wilson, J.M. (1995a): Gene therapy in a xenograft model of cystic fibrosis lung corrects chloride transport more effectively than the sodium defect. Nature Genet. 9:126–131.

Goldman, M.J., Litzky, L.A., Engelhardt, J.F., and Wilson, J.M. (1995b): Transfer of the CFTR gene to the lung of nonhuman primates with E1-deleted, E2a-defective recombinant adenoviruses: A preclinical toxicology study. Hum. Gene Ther. 6:839–851.

Grubb, B.R., Pickles, R.J., Ye, H., Yankaskas, J.R., Vick, R.N., Engelhardt, J.F., Wilson, J.M., Johnson, L.G., and Boucher, R.C. (1994): Inefficient gene transfer by adenovirus vector to cystic fibrosis airway epithelia of mice and humans. Nature (London) 371:802–806.

Hyde, S.C., Gill, D.R., Higgins, C.F., Trezise, A.E., MacVinish, L.J., Cuthbert, A.W., Ratcliff, R., Evans, M.J., and Colledge, W.H. (1993): Correction of the ion transport defect in cystic fibrosis transgenic mice by gene therapy. Nature (London) 362:250–255.

Imler, J.L., Bout, A., Dreyer, D., Dieterle, A., Schultz, H., Valerio, D., Mehtali, M., and Pavirani, A. (1995): Trans-complementation of E1-deleted adenovirus: A new vector to reduce the possibility of codissemination of wild-type and recombinant adenoviruses. Hum. Gene Ther. 6:711–721.

Johnson, L.G., Olsen, J.C., Sarkadi, B., Moore, K.L., Swanstrom, R., and Boucher, R.C. (1992): Efficiency of gene transfer for restoration of normal airway epithelial function in cystic fibrosis. Nature Genet. 2:21–25.

Knowles, M.R., Hohneker, K.W., Zhou, Z., Olsen, J.C., Noah, T.L., Hu, P-C., Leigh, W.M., Engelhardt, J.F., Edwards, L.J., Jones, K.R., Grossman, M., Wilson, J.M., Johnson, L.G., and Boucher, R.C. (1995): A controlled study of adenoviral-vector-mediated gene transfer in the nasal epithelium of patients with cystic fibrosis. N. Engl. J. Med. 333:823–831.

Korst, R.J., Bewig, B., and Crystal, R.G. (1995): In vitro and in vivo transfer and expression of human surfactant SP-A- and SP-B-associated protein cDNAs mediated by replication-deficient, recombinant adenoviral vectors. Hum. Gene Ther. 6:277–287.

Logan, J.J., Bebok, Z., Walker, L.C., Peng, S., Felgner, P.L., Siegal, G.P., Frizzell, R.A., Dong, J., Howard, M., Matalon, S., Lindsey, J.R., DuVall, M., and Sorscher, E.J. (1995): Cationic lipids for reporter gene and CFTR transfer to rat pulmonary epithelium. Gene Ther. 2:38–49.

McCray, P.B., Jr., Armstrong, K., Zabner, J., Miller, D.W., Koretzky, G.A., Couture, L., Robillard, J.E., Smith, A.E., and Welsh, M.J. (1995): Adenoviral-mediated gene transfer to fetal pulmonary epithelia in vitro and in vivo. J. Clin. Invest. 95:2620–2632.

McElvaney, N.G., and Crystal, R.G. (1995): IL-6 release and airway administration of human CFTR cDNA adenovirus vector. Nat. Med. 1:182–184.

Pitt, B.R., Schwarz, M.A., Pilewski, J.M., Nakayama, D., Mueller, G.M., Robbins, P.D., Watkins, S.A., Albertine, K.H., and Bland, R.D. (1995): Retrovirus-mediated gene transfer in lungs of living fetal sheep. Gene Ther. 2:344–350.

Rich, D.P., Anderson, M.P., Gregory, R.J., Cheng, S.H., Paul, S., Jefferson, D.M., McCann, J.D., Klinger, K.W., Smith, A.E., and Welch, M.J. (1990): Expression of cystic fibrosis transmembrane conductance regulator corrects defective chloride channel regulation in cystic fibrosis airway epithelial cells. Nature (London) 347:358–363.

Rich, D.P., Couture, L.A., Cardoza, L.M., Guiggio, V.M., Armentano, D., Espino, P.C., Hehir, K., Welsh, M.J., Smith, A.E., and Gregory, R.J. (1993): Development and analysis of recombinant adenoviruses for gene therapy of cystic fibrosis. Hum. Gene Ther. 4:465–476.

Riordan, J.R., Rommens, J.M., Kerem, B.-S., Alon, N., Rozmahel, R., Grezelczak, Z., Zielenski, J., Lok, S., Plavsic, N., Chou, J.-L., Drumm, M.L., Iannuzzi, M.C., Collins, F.S., and Tsui, L.-C. (1989): Identification of the cystic fibrosis gene: Cloning and characterization of complementary DNA. Science 245:1066–1073.

Rosenfeld, M.A., Yoshimura, K., Trapnell, B.C., Yoneyama, K., Rosenthal, E.R., Dalemans, W., Fukayama, M., Bargon, J., Steir, L.E., Stratford-Perricaudet, L., Perricaudet, M., Guggino, W.B., Pavirani, A., Lecocq, C-P., and Crystal, R.G. (1992): In vivo transfer of the human cystic fibrosis transmembrane conductance regulator gene to the airway epithelium. Cell 68:143–155.

Ross, G.F., Morris, R.E., Ciraolo, G., Huelsman, K., Bruno, M., Whitsett, J.A., Baatz, J.E., and Korfhagen, T.R. (1995): Surfactant protein-A-polylysine conjugates for delivery of DNA to airway cells in culture. Hum. Gene Ther. 6:31–40.

Sorscher, E.J., Logan, J.J., Frizzell, R.A., Lyrene, R.K., Bebok, Z., Dong, J.Y., Duvall, M.D., Felgner, P.L., Matalon, S., Walker, L., and Wiatrak, B.J. (1994): Gene therapy for cystic fibrosis using cationic liposome mediated gene transfer: A phase I trial of safety and efficacy in the nasal airway. Hum. Gene Ther. 5:1259–1277.

Wagner, J.A., Chao, A.C., and Gardner, P. (1995): Molecular strategies for therapy of cystic fibrosis. Annu. Rev. Pharmacol. Toxicol. 35:257–276.

Welsh, M.J., Smith, A.E., Zabner, J., Rich, D.P., Graham, S.M., Gregory, R.J., Pratt, B.M., and Moscicki, R.A. (1994): Cystic fibrosis gene therapy using an adenovirus vector: In vivo safety and efficacy in nasal epithelium. Hum. Gene Ther. 5:209–219.

Welsh, M.J., Zabner, J., Graham, S.M., Smith, A.E., Moscicki, R., and Wadsworth, S. (1995): Adenovirus-mediated gene transfer for cystic fibrosis: Part A. Safety of dose and repeat administration in the nasal epithelium. Part B. Clinical efficacy in the maxillary sinus. Hum. Gene Ther. 6:205–218.

Wilmott, R.W., Whitsett, J.A., Trapnell, B., Wert, S., Baughman, R., Cuppoletti, J., and Tolstochev, P. (1994): Gene therapy for cystic fibrosis utilizing a replication deficient recombinant adenovirus vector to deliver the human cystic fibrosis transmembrane conductance regulator cDNA to the airways. A phase I trial. Hum. Gene Ther. 5:1019–1057.

Wilson, J.M., Engelhardt, J.F., Grossman, M., Simon, R.H., and Yang, Y. (1994): Gene therapy of cystic fibrosis lung disease using E1 deleted adenoviruses: A phase I trial. Hum. Gene Ther. 5:501–519.

Yang, Y., Nunes, F.A., Berencsi, K., Gonczol, E., Engelhardt, J.F., and Wilson, J.M. (1994): Inactivation of E2a in recombinant adenoviruses improves the prospect for gene therapy in cystic fibrosis. Nature Genet. 7:362–369.

Yang, Y., Li, Q., Ertl, H.C.J., and Wilson, J.M. (1995): Cellular and humoral immune responses to viral antigens create barriers to lung-directed gene therapy with recombinant adenoviruses. J. Virol. 69:2004–2015.

Yang, Y., Trinchieri, G., and Wilson, J.M. (1995): Recombinant IL-12 prevents formation of blocking IgA antibodies to recombinant adenovirus and allows repeated gene therapy to mouse lung. Nature Med. 1:890–893.

Zabner, J., Couture, L.A., Gregory, R.J., Graham, S.M., Smith, A.E., and Welsh, M.J. (1993): Adenovirus-mediated gene transfer transiently corrects the chloride transport defect in nasal epithelia of patients with cystic fibrosis. Cell 75:207–216.

Cardiovascular System

Chang, M.W., Barr, E., Seltzer, J., Jiang, Y-Q., Nabel, G.J., Nabel, E.G., Parmacek, M.S., and Leiden, J.M. (1995): Cytostatic gene therapy for vascular proliferative disorders with a constitutively active form of the retinoblastoma gene product. Science 267:518–522.

Feldman, L.J., Steg, P.G., Zheng, L.P., Chen, D., Kearney, M., McGarr, S.E., Barry, J.J., Dedieu, J.F., Perricaudet, M., and Isner, J.M. (1995): Low-efficiency of percutaneous adenovirus-mediated arterial gene transfer in the atherosclerotic rabbit. J. Clin. Invest. 95:2662-2671.

Flugelman, M.Y., Jaklitsch, M.T., Newman, K.D., Casscells, W., Bratthauer, G.L., and Dichek, D.A. (1992): Low level in vivo gene transfer into the arterial wall through a perforated balloon catheter. Circulation 85:1110-1117.

Grossman, M., Rader, D.J., Muller, D.W.M., Kolansky, D.M., Kozarsky, K., Clark, III., B.J., Stein, E.A., Lupien, P.J., Brewer, Jr., H.B., Raper, S.E., and Wilson, J.M. (1995): A pilot study of ex vivo gene therapy for homozygous familial hypercholesterolemia. Nature Med. 1:1148-1154.

Grossman, M., Raper, S.E., Kozarsky, K., Stein, E.A., Engelhardt, J.F., Muller, D., Lupien, P.J., and Wilson, J.M. (1994): Successful ex vivo gene therapy directed to liver in a patient with familial hypercholesterolemia. Nature Genet. 6:335-341.

Guzman, R.J., Hirschowitz, E.A., Brody, S.L., Crystal, R.G., Epstein, S.E., and Finkel, T. (1995): In vivo suppression of injury-induced vascular smooth muscle cell accumulation using adenovirus-mediated transfer of the herpes simplex virus thymidine-kinase gene. Proc. Natl. Acad. Sci. U.S.A. 91:10732-10736.

Indolfi, C., Avvedimento, E.V., Rapacciuolo, A., Di Lorenzo, E., Esposito, G., Stabile, E., Feliciello, A., Mele, E., Giuliano, P., Condorelli, G., and Chiariello, M. (1995): Inhibition of cellular ras prevents smooth muscle cell proliferation after vascular injury in vivo. Nat. Med. 1:541-545.

Isner, J.M., and Feldman, L.J. (1994): Gene therapy of arterial disease. Lancet 344:1653-1654.

Johns, D.C., Nuss, H.B., Chiamvimonvat, N., Ramza, B.M., Marban, E., and Lawrence, J.H. (1995): Adenovirus-mediated expression of a voltage-gated potassium channel in vitro (rat cardiac myocytes) and vivo (rat liver). J. Clin. Invest. 96:1152-1158.

Kashya, V.S., Santamarina-Fojo, S., Brown, D.R., Parrott, C.L., Applebaum-Bowden, D., Meyn, S., Talley, G., Paigen, B., Maeda, N., and Brewer, Jr., H.B. (1995): Apolipoprotein E deficiency in mice: Gene replacement and prevention of atherosclerosis using adenovirus vectors. J. Clin. Invest. 96:1612-1620.

Landau, C., Pirwitz, M.J., Willard, M.A., Gerard, R.D., Meidell, R.S., and Willard, J.E. (1995): Adenoviral mediated gene transfer to atherosclerotic arteries after balloon angioplasty. Am. Heart J. 129:1051-1057.

Leclere, G., Gal, D., Takeshita, S., Nikol, S., Weir, L., and Isner, J.M. (1992): Percutaneous arterial gene transfer in a rabbit model. Efficiency in normal and balloon-dilated athrosclerotic arteries. J. Clin. Invest. 90:936-944.

Li, J.J., Ueno, H., Tomita, H., Yamamoto, H., Kanegae, Y., Saito, I., and Takeshita, A. (1995): Adenovirus-mediated arterial gene transfer does not require prior injury for submaximal gene expression. Gene Ther. 2:351-354.

Lin, H., Parmacek, M.S., Morle, G., Bolloing, S., and Leiden, J.M. (1990): Expression of recombinant genes in myocardium in vivo after direct injection of DNA. Circulation 82:2217-2221.

Lin, K.F., Chao, J., and Chao, L. (1995): Human atrial natriuretic peptide gene delivery reduces blood pressure in hypertensive rats. Hypertension 26:847-853.

Linton, M.F., Atkinson, J.B., and Fazio, S. (1995): Prevention of atherosclerosis in apoprotein E-deficient mice by bone marrow transplantation. Science 267:1034-1037.

Mann, M.J., Gibbons, G.H., Kernoff, R.S., Diet, F.P., Tsao, P.S., Cooke, J.P., Kaneda, Y., and Dzau, V.J. (1995): Genetic engineering of vein grafts resistant to atherosclerosis. Proc. Natl. Acad. Sci. U.S.A. 92:4502-4506.

Milano, C.A., Allen, L.F., Rockman, H.A., Dolber, P.C., McMinn, T.R., Chien, K.R., Johnson, T.D., Bond, R.A., and Lefkowitz, R.J. (1994): Enhanced myocardial function in transgenic mice overexpressing the β-2-adrenergic receptor. Science 264:582-586.

Morishita, R., Gibbons, G.H., Horiuchi, M., Ellison, K.E., Nakajima, M., Zhang, L., Kaneda, Y., Ogihara, T., and Dzau, V.J. (1995): A gene therapy strategy using a transcription factor decoy of the E2F binding site inhibits smooth muscle proliferation in vivo. Proc. Natl. Acad. Sci. U.S.A. 92:5855-5859.

Muller, D.W. (1994): Gene therapy for cardiovascular disease. Br. Heart J. 72:309-312.

Nabel, E.G., Plautz, G., and Nabel, G.J. (1990): Site-specific gene expression in vivo by direct gene transfer into the arterial wall. Science 249:1285-1288.

Pages, J.C., Andreoletti, M., Bennoun, M., Vons, C., Elcheroth, J., Lehn, P., Houssin, D., Chapman, J., Briand, P., Benarous, R., Franco, D., and Weber, A. (1995): Efficient retroviral-mediated gene transfer into primary culture murine and human hepatocytes; expression of the LDL receptor. Hum. Gene Ther. 6:21-30.

von der Leyen, H.E., Gibbons, G.H., Morishita, R., Lewis, N.P., Zhang, L., Nakajima, M., Kaneda, Y., Cooke, J.P., and Dzau, V.J. (1995): Gene therapy inhibiting neointimal vascular lesion: In vivo transfer of endothelial cell nitric oxide synthetase gene. Proc. Natl. Acad. Sci. U.S.A. 92:1137-1141.

Wang, C., Chao, L., and Chao, J. (1995): Direct gene delivery of human tissue kallikrein reduces blood pressure in spontaneously hypertensive rats. J. Clin. Invest. 95:1710-1716.

Wilson, J.M., Grossman, M.A., Raper, S.E., Baker, J.R., Newton, R.S., and Thoene, J.G. (1992): Ex vivo gene therapy of familial hypercholesterolemia. Hum. Gene Ther. 3:179-222.

Xiong, W., Chao, J., and Chao, L. (1995): Muscle delivery of human tissue kallikrein reduces blood pressure in hypertensive rats. Hypertension 25:715-719.

Muscle

Acsadi, G., Dickson, G., Love, D.R., Jani, A., Walsh, F.S., Gurusinghe, A., Wolff, J.A., and Davies, K.E. (1991): Human dystrophin expression in MDX mice after intramuscular injection of DNA constructs. Nature (London) 352:815-818.

Acsadi, G., Massie, B., and Jani, A. (1995): Adenovirus-mediated gene transfer into striated muscles. J. Mol. Med. 73:165-180.

Barr, E., and Leiden, J.M. (1991): Systemic delivery of recombinant proteins by genetically modified myoblasts. Science 254:1507-1509.

Cox, G.A., Cole, N.M., Matsumura, K., Phelps, S.F., Hauschka, S.D., Campbell, K.P., Faulkner, J.A., and Chamberlain, J.S. (1993): Overexpression of dystrophin in transgenic mdx mice eliminates dystrophic symptoms without toxicity. Nature (London) 364:725-729.

Dahler, A., Wade, R.P., Muscat, G.E.O., and Waters, M.J. (1994): Expression vectors encoding human growth hormone (hGH) controlled by human muscle-specific promoters: Prospects for regulated production of hGH delivered by myoblast transfer or intravenous injection. Gene 145:305-310.

Dai, Y., Schwarz, E.M., Gu, D., Zhang, W., Sarvetnick, N., and Verma, I.M. (1995): Cellular and humoral immune responses to adenoviral vectors containing Factor-IX gene. Proc. Natl. Acad. Sci. U.S.A. 92:1401-1405.

Dhawan, J., Pan, L.C., Pavlath, G.K., Travis, M.A., Lanctot, A.M., and Blau, H.M. (1991): Systemic delivery of human growth hormone by injection of genetically engineered myoblasts. Science 254:1509-1512.

Dunckley, M.G., Wells, D.J., Walsh, F.S., and Dickson, G. (1993): Direct retroviral-mediated transfer of a dystrophin minigene into mdx mouse muscle in vivo. Hum. Mol. Genet. 2:717-723.

Ferrari, G., Salvatori, G., Rossi, C., Cossu, G., and Mavilio, F. (1995): A retroviral vector containing a muscle-specific enhancer drives gene expression only in differentiated muscle fibers. Hum. Gene Ther. 6:733-742.

Jiao, S., Williams, P., Berg, R.K., Hodgeman, B.A., Liu, L., Repetto, G., and Wolff, J.A. (1992): Direct gene transfer into nonhuman primate myofibers in vivo. Hum. Gene Ther. 3:21-33.

Koenig, M., Hoffman, E.P., Bertelson, C.J., Monaco, A.P., Feener, C., and Kunkel, L.M. (1987): Complete cloning of the Duchene muscular dystrophy (DMD) cDNA and preliminary genomic organization of the DMD gene in normal and affected individuals. Cell 50:509-517.

Lee, C.C., Pearlman, J.A., Chamberlain, J.S., and Caskey, C.T. (1991): Expression of recombinant dystrophin and its localization to the cell membrane. Nature (London) 349:334-336.

Mendell, J.R., Kissel, J.T., Amato, A.A., King, W., Signore, L., Prior, T.W., Sahenk, Z., Benson, S., McAndrew, P.E., Rice, R., Nagaraja, H., Stephens, R., Lantry, L., Morris, G.E., and Burghes, A.H.M. (1995): Myoblast transfer in the treatment of Duchenne's muscular dystrophy. N. Engl. J. Med. 333:832-838.

Miller, J.B., and Boyce, F.M. (1995): Gene therapy by and for muscle cells. Trends Genet. 11:163-165.

Partridge, T.A., and Davies, K.E. (1995): Myoblast-based gene therapies. Br. Med. Bull. 51:123-137.

Ragot, T., Vincent, N., Chafey, P., Vigne, E., Gilgenkrantz, H., Couton, D., Cartaud, J., Briand, P., Kaplan, J-C., Perricaudet, M., and Kahn, A. (1993): Efficient adenovirus-mediated transfer of a human minidystrophin gene to skeletal muscle of mdx mice. Nature (London) 361:647-650.

Salminen, A., Elson, H.F., Mickley, L.A., Fojo, A.T., and Gottesmann, M.M. (1993): Implantation of recombinant rat myocytes into adult skeletal muscle: a potential gene therapy. Hum. Gene Ther. 2:15-26.

Vincent, N., Ragot, T., Gilgenkrantz, H., Couton, D., Chafex, P., Grégoire, A., Briand, P., Kaplan, J-C., Kahn, A., and Perricaudet, M. (1993): Long-term correction of mouse dystrophic degeneration by adenovirus-mediated transfer of a minidystrophin gene. Nature Genet. 5:130-134.

Webster, C., and Blau, H.M. (1990): Accelerated age-related decline in replicative life-span of Duchene muscular dystrophy myoblasts: Implications for cell and gene therapy. Som. Cell Mol. Genet. 16:557-565.

Wells, D.J., Wells, K.E., Walsh, F.S., Davies, K.E., Goldspink, G., Love, D.R., Chan-Thomas, P., Dunckley, M.G., Piper, T., and Dickson, G. (1992): Human dystrophin expression corrects the myopathic phenotype in transgenic mdx mice. Hum. Mol. Genet. 1:35-40.

Wells, D.J., Wells, K.E., Asante, E.A., Turner, G., Sunada, Y., Campbell, K.P., Walsh, F.S., and Dickson, G. (1995): Expression of human full-length and minidystrophin in transgenic mdx mice: Implications for gene therapy of duchenne muscular dystrophy. Hum. Mol. Genet. 4:1245-1250.

Wolff, J.A., Malone, R.W., Williams, P., Chong, W., Acsadi, G., and Jani, A. (1990): Direct gene transfer into mouse muscle in vivo. Science 247:1465-1468.

Skin, Bone, and Joints

Andree, C., Swain, W.F., Page, C.P., Macklin, M.D., Slama, J., Hatzis, D., and Eriksson, E. (1994): In vivo transfer and expression of a human epidermal growth factor gene accelerates would repair. Proc. Natl. Acad. Sci. U.S.A. 91:12188–12192.

Bandara, G., Robbins, P.D., Georgescu, H.I., Mueller, G.M., Glorioso, S.C., and Evans, C.H. (1992): Gene transfer to synoviocytes: prospects for gene treatment of arthritis. DNA Cell Biol. 11:227–231.

Bandara, G., Mueller, G.M., Galea-Lauri, J., Tindal, M.H., Georgescu, H.I., Suchanek, M.K., Hung, G.L., Glorioso, J.C., Robbins, P.D., and Evans, C.H. (1993): Intraarticular expression of biologically active interleukin 1-receptor-antagonist protein by ex vivo gene transfer. Proc. Natl. Acad. Sci. U.S.A. 90:10764–10768.

Baragi, V.M., Renkiewicz, R.R., Jordan, H., Bonadio, J., Hartman, J.W., and Roessler, B.J. (1995): Transplantation of transduced chondrocytes protects articular cartilage from interleukin 1-induced extracellular matrix degradation. J. Clin. Invest. 96:2454–2460.

Chen, B.F., Chang, W.C., Chen, S.T., Chen, D.S., and Hwang, L.H. (1995): Long-term expression of the biologically active growth hormone in genetically modified fibroblasts after implantation into a hypophysectomized rat. Hum. Gene Ther. 6:917–926.

Chen, S-J., Wilson, J.M., Vallance, D.K., Hartman, J.M., Davidson, B.L., and Roessler, B.J. (1995): A recombinant adenoviral vector expressing a soluble form of VCAM-1 inhibits VCAM-1/VLA-4 adhesion in transduced synoviocytes. Gene Ther. 2:469–480.

Chernajovsky, Y., Feldman, M., and Maini, R.N. (1995): Gene therapy of rheumatoid arthritis via cytokine regulation: future perspectives. Br. Med. Bull. 51:503–516.

Doherty, P.J. (1995): Gene therapy and arthritis—methods and prospects. J. Rheumatol. 22:1220–1223.

Evans, C., and Robbins, P.D. (1994): Prospects for treating arthritis by gene therapy. J. Rheumatol. 21:779–782.

Fenjves, E.S. (1994): Approaches to gene transfer in keratinocytes. J. Invest. Dermatol. 103:70S–75S.

Fenjves, E.S., Smith, J., Zaradic, S., and Taichman, L.B. (1994): Systemic delivery of secreted protein by grafts of epidermal keratinocytes: Prospects for keratinocyte gene therapy. Hum. Gene Ther. 5:1241–1248.

Gerrard, A.J., Hudson, D.L., Brownlee, G.G., and Watt, F.M. (1993): Towards gene therapy for haemophilia B using primary human keratinocytes. Nature Genet. 3:180–183.

Greenhalgh, D.A., Rothnagel, J.A., and Roop, D.R. (1994): Epidermis: An attractive target tissue for gene therapy. J. Invest. Dermatol. 103:63S–69S.

Hengge, U.R., Chan, E.F., Foster, R.A., Walker, P.S., and Vogel, J.C. (1995): Cytokine gene expression in epidermis with biological effects following injection of naked DNA. Nature Genet. 10:161–166.

Hung, G.L., Galea-Lauri, J., Mueller, G.M., Georgescu, H.I., Larkin, L.A., Suchanek, M.K., Tindal, M.H., Robbins, P.D., and Evans, C.H. (1993): Suppression of intra-articular responses to interleukin-1 by transfer of the interleukin-1 receptor antagonist gene to synovium. Gene Ther. 1:1–6.

Kündig, T.M., Bachmann, M.F., DiPaolo, C., Simard, J.J.L., Battegay, M., Lother, H., Gessner, A., Kühlcke, K., Ohashi, P.S., Hengartner, H., and Zinkernagel. (1995): Fibroblasts as efficient antigen-presenting cells in lymphoid organs. Science 268:1343–1347.

Makarov, S.S., Olsen, J.C., Johnston, W.N., Schwab, J.H., Anderle, S.K., Brown, R.R., and Haskill, J.S. (1995): Retrovirus mediated in vivo gene transfer to synovium in bacterial cell wall-induced arthritis in rats. Gene Ther. 2:424–428.

Morgan, J.R., Barrandon, Y., Green, H., and Mulligan, R.C. (1987): Expression of an exogenous growth hormone gene by transplantable human epidermal cells. Science 237:1476–1479.

Navsaria, H.A., Myers, S.R., Leigh, I.M., and McKay, I.A. (1995): Culturing skin in vitro for wound therapy. Trends Biotechnol. 13:91–100.

Palmer, T.D., Rosman, G.J., Osborne, W.R.A., and Miller, A.D. (1991): Genetically modified skin fibroblasts persist long after transplantation but gradually inactivate introduced genes. Proc. Natl. Acad. Sci. U.S.A. 88:1330–1334.

Petersen, M.J., Kaplan, J., Jorgensen, C.M., Schmidt, L.A., Li, L., Morgan, J.R., Kwan, M.K., and Krueger, G.G. (1995): Sustained production of human transferrin by transduced fibroblasts implanted into athymic mice: A model for somatic gene therapy. J. Invest. Dermatol. 104:171–176.

Prockop, D.J., and Kivirikko, K.I. (1995): Collagens: Molecular biology, diseases and potentials for therapy. Annu. Rev. Biochem. 64:403–434.

Ramesh, N., Lau, S., Palmer, T.D., Storb, R., and Osborne, W.R.A. (1993): High level human adenosine deaminase expression in dog skin fibroblasts is not sustained following transplantation. Hum. Gene Ther. 4:3–7.

Roessler, B.J., Kerrick, G.P., Goldstein, S.A., and Bonadio, J.F. (1994): Focal transduction of adult osteogenic cells in vivo. Arthritis Rheum. 37(Suppl.):S186.

Selden, R.F., Skoskiewicz, M.J., Howie, K.B., Russell, P.S., and Goodman, H.M. (1987): Implantation of genetically engineered fibroblasts into mice: Implications for gene therapy. Science 236:714–718.

Veelken, H., Jesuiter, H., Mackensen, A., Kulmburg, P., Schultze, J., Rosenthal, F., Mertelsmann, R., and Lindemann, A. (1994): Primary fibroblasts from human adults as target cells for ex vivo transfection and gene therapy. Hum. Gene Ther. 5:1203–1210.

Vogt, P.M., Thompson, S., Andree, C., Liu, P., Breuning, K., Hatzis, D., Brown, H., Mulligan, R.C., and Eriksson, E. (1994): Genetically modified keratinocytes transplanted to wounds reconstitute the epidermis. Proc. Natl. Acad. Sci. U.S.A. 91:9307–9311.

Yovandich, J., O'Malley, Jr., B., Sikes, M., and Ledley, F.D. (1995): Gene transfer to synovial cells by intra-articular administration of plasmid DNA. Hum. Gene Ther. 6:603–610.

Endocrine System

Hayashi, Y., DePaoli, A.M., Burant, C.F., and Refetoff, S. (1994): Expression of a thyroid hormone-responsive recombinant gene introduced into adult mice livers by replication-defective adenovirus can be regulated by endogenous thyroid hormone receptor. J. Biol. Chem. 269:23872–23875.

Hughes, S.D., Johnson, J.H., Quaade, C., and Newgard, C.B. (1992): Engineering of glucose-stimulated insulin secretion and biosynthesis in nonislet cells. Proc. Natl. Acad. Sci. U.S.A. 89:688–692.

Ikemoto, S., Thompson, K.S., Takahashi, M., Itakura, H., Lane, M.D., and Ezaki, O. (1995): High fat diet-induced hyperglycemia: Prevention by low level expression of a glucose transporter (GLUT4) minigene in transgenic mice. Proc. Natl. Acad. Sci. U.S.A. 92:3096–3099.

Kolodka, T.M., Finegold, M., Moss, L., and Woo, S.L.C. (1995): Gene therapy for diabetes mellitus in rats by hepatic expression of insulin. Proc. Natl. Acad. Sci. U.S.A. 92:3293–3297.

Newgard, C.B. (1994): Cellular engineering and gene therapy strategies for insulin replacement in diabetes. Diabetes 43:341–350.

Simpson, A.M., Tuch, B.E., Swan, M.A., Tu, J., and Marshall, G.M. Functional expression of the human insulin gene in a human hepatoma cell line (HepG2). Gene Ther. 2:223–231.

Vitullo, J.C., Aron, D.C., and Miller, R.E. (1994): Control of insulin gene expression: Implications for insulin gene therapy. J. Lab. Clin. Med. 124:328–334.

Wang, F., Li, X., Annis, B., and Faustman, D.L. (1995): Tap-1 and Tap-2 gene therapy selectively restores conformationally dependent HLA class-I expression in type-I diabetic cells. Hum. Gene Ther. 6:1005–1017.

Gastrointestinal System

Grubman, S.A., Fang, S.L., Mulberg, A.E., Perrone, R.D., Rogers, L.C., Lee, D.W., Armentano, D., Murray, S.L., Dorkin, H.L., Cheng, S.H., Smith, A.E., and Jefferson, D.M. (1995): Correction of the cystic fibrosis defect by gene complementation in human intrahepatic biliary epithelial cell lines. Gastroenterology 108:584–592.

Lau, C., Soriano, H.E., Ledley, F.D., Finegold, M.J., Wolfe, J.H., Birkenmeier, E.H., and Henning, S.J. (1995): Retroviral gene transfer into the intestinal epithelium. Hum. Gene Ther. 6:1145–1151.

Ledley, F.D. (1992): Somatic gene therapy in gastroenterology: Approaches and applications. J. Pediatr. Gastroenterol. Nutr. 14:328–337.

Maeda, H., Danel, C., and Crystal, R.G. (1994): Adenovirus-mediated transfer of human lipase complementary DNA to the gallbladder. Gastroenterology 106:1638–1644.

Mastrangeli, A., O'Connell, B., Aladib, W., Fox, P.C., Baum, B.J., and Crystal, R.G. (1994): Direct in vivo adenovirus-mediated gene transfer to salivary glands. Am. J. Physiol. 266:1146–1155.

Ramakrishna, J., and Grand, R.J. (1994): Gene therapy for exocrine pancreatic insufficiency. Gastroenterology 106:1711–1713.

Urinary System

Kitamura, M., Taylor, S., Unwin, R., Burton, S., Shimizu, F., and Fine, L.G. (1994): Gene transfer into the rat glomerulus via a mesangial cell vector: Site-specific delivery, in situ amplification, and sustained expression of an exogenous gene in vivo. J. Clin. Invest. 94:497–505.

Nervous System and the Eye

Beutler, A.S., Banck, M.S., Bach, F.W., Gage, F.H., Porreca, F., Bilsky, E.J., and Yaksh, T.L. (1995): Retrovirus-mediated expression of an artificial beta-endorphin precursor in primary fibroblasts. J. Neurochem. 64:475–481.

Byrnes, A.P., Rusby, J.E., Wood, M.J.A., and Charlton, H.M. (1995): Adenovirus gene transfer causes inflammation in the brain. Neuroscience (Oxford). 66:1015–1024.

Dunaief, J.L., Kwun, R.C., Bhardwaj, N., Lopez, R., Gouras, P., and Goff, S.P. (1995): Retroviral gene transfer into retinal pigment epithelial cells followed by transplantation into the rat retina. Hum. Gene Ther. 6:1225–1229.

During, M.J., Naegele, J.R., O'Malley, K.L., and Geller, A.I. (1994): Long-term behavioral recovery in parkinsonian rats by an HSV vector expressing tyrosine hydroxylase. Science 266:1399–1403.

Frim, D.M., Uhler, T.A., Galpern, W.R., Beal, M.F., Breakefield, X.O., and Isacson, O. (1994): Implanted fibroblasts genetically engineered to produce brain-derived neurotrophic factor prevent 1-methyl-4-phenylpyridium toxicity to dopaminergic neurons in the rat. Proc. Natl. Acad. Sci. U.S.A. 91:5104–5108.

Gage, F.H., and Fisher, L.J. (1991): Intercerebral grafting: A tool for the neurobiologist. Neuron 6:1–12.

Gage, F., Kawaja, M.D., and Fisher, L.J. (1991): Genetically modified cells: Applications for cerebral grafting. Trends Neurosci. 14:328–333.

Ghadge, G.D., Roos, R.P., Kang, U.J., Wollmann, R., Fishman, P.S., Kalynych, A.M., Barr, E., and Leiden, J.M. (1995): CNS gene delivery by retrograde transport of recombinant replication-defective adenoviruses. Gene Ther. 2:132–137.

Horellou, P., Marlier, L., Privat, A., and Mallet, J. (1990): Behavioral effect of engineered cells that secrete L-dopa or dopamine after grafting into the rat neostriatum. Eur. J. Neurosci. 2:116–119.

Jiao, S., Gurevich, V., and Wolff, J.A. (1993): Long-term correction of rat model of Parkinson's disease by gene therapy. Nature (London) 362:450–453.

Jinnah, H.A., and Friedmann, T. (1995): Gene therapy and the brain. Br. Med. Bull. 51:138–148.

Jomary, C., Piper, T.A., Dickson, G., Couture, L.A., Smith, A.E., Neal, M.J., and Jones, S.E. (1994): Adenovirus-mediated gene transfer to murine retinal cells in vitro and in vivo. FEBS Lett. 347:117–122.

Jordan, J., Ghadge, G.D., Prehn, J.H.M., Toth, P.T., Roos, R.P., and Miller, R.J. (1995): Expression of human copper/zinc-superoxide-dismutase inhibits the death of rat sympathetic neurons caused by withdrawal of nerve growth factor. Mol. Pharmacol. 47:1095–1100.

Kaplitt, M.G., Kwong, A.D., Kleopoulos, S.P., Mobbs, C.V., Rabkin, S.D., and Pfaff, D.W. (1994a): Preproenkephalin promoter yields region-specific and long-term expression in adult brain after direct in vivo gene transfer via a defective herpes simplex viral vector. Proc. Natl. Acad. Sci. U.S.A. 91:8979–8983.

Kaplitt, M.G., Leone, P., Samulski, R.J., Xiao, X., Pfaff, D.W., and During, M.J. (1994b): Long-term gene expression and phenotypic correction using adeno-associated virus vectors in the mammalian brain. Nature Genet. 8:148–154.

Kojima, H., Inuzuka, S., Miwa, T., Furukawa, S., Hayashi, K., Kanegae, Y., Saito, I., Ohishi, N., Takamori, M., and Yagi, K. (1995): Construction and characterization of adenoviral vector expressing biologically active brain-derived neurotrophic factor. Biochem. Biophys. Res. Commun. 212:712–717.

Lawrence, M.S., Ho, D.Y., Dash, R., and Sapolsky, R.M. (1995): Herpes simplex virus vectors overexpressing the glucose transporter gene protect against seizure-induced neuron loss. Proc. Natl. Acad. Sci. U.S.A. 92:7247–7251.

Levatte, M.A., Weaver, L.C., York, I.A., Johnson, D., and Dekaban, G.A. (1995): Delivery of a foreign gene to sympathetic preganglionic neurons using recombinant herpes simplex virus. Neuroscience (Oxford). 66:737–750.

Martin, J.B. (1995): Gene therapy and pharmacological treatment of inherited neurological disorders. Trends Biotechnol. 13:28–35.

Mashhour, B., Couton, D., Perricaudet, M., and Briand, P. (1994): In vivo adenovirus-mediated gene transfer into ocular tissues. Gene Ther. 1:122–126.

Nakao, N., Frodl, E.M., Widner, H., Carlson, E., Eggerding, F.A., Epstein, C.J., and Brundin, P. (1995): Overexpressing Cu/Zn superoxide dismutase enhances survival of transplanted neurons in a rat model of parkinson's disease. Nat. Med. 1:226–231.

Rosenberg, R.N., and Iannaccone, S.T. (1995): The prevention of neurogenetic disease. Arch. Neurol. 52:356–362.

Sabate, O., Horellou, P., Vigne, E., Colin, P., Perricaudet, M., Buc-Caron, M.H., and Mallet, J. (1995): Transplantation to the rat brain of human neural progenitors that were genetically modified using adenoviruses. Nature Genet. 9:256–260.

Wax, M., and Patil, R. (1994): A rationale for gene targeting in glaucoma therapy. J. Ocul. Pharm. 10:403–410.

APPLICATIONS OF GENE THERAPY TO CANCER

Major advances in our understanding of how cancer occurs have shown that cancer is a genetic disease resulting in the abnormal proliferation of a clone of cells. Carcinogenesis appears to be a multistep process in which a series of genetic alterations occur within one cell, leading to malignancy (Fig. 6–1) (Cho and Vogelstein, 1992). The specific genetic alterations vary according to the histologic type of malignancy and different stages of growth. For instance, additional genetic changes are required for an autonomously growing clump of cells to metastasize. In general, a recessive mutation correlates with the loss of a function, such as a tumor suppressor gene, while a dominant mutation correlates with the gain of a function, such as the overexpression of an oncogene. Delineating the various underlying mechanisms of carcinogenesis in any one tumor will determine the type of gene transfer approach to be used. In general, current technologies are better at transferring a new function, than totally blocking overexpression of a gene. A marriage of tumor cell genotyping and gene therapy will be an increasingly important element for success in clinical trials.

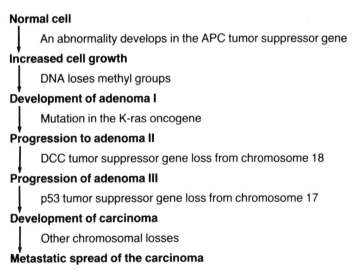

Fig. 6–1. A proposed model for the genetic basis of oncogenesis in colon cancer. Cancer is thought to be a series of genetic abnormalities that accumulate within a cell. The study of colon cancers has suggested a model for the sequence of genetic defects and their associated histologic and clinical changes.

The understanding of the genetic basis of cancer allows entirely new approaches to the treatment of cancer (Table 6–1). One of the greatest advantages of gene transfer, versus traditional cancer therapies, is that most gene transfer methods in development are not immunosuppressive. As a result, it is likely that the immune system can be used in a synergistic manner to augment the primary action of the transferred gene. Also, the deletion of tumor suppressor genes could theoretically be corrected by the insertion of a normal copy of the gene, perhaps before the development of cancer. Likewise, the overexpression of an oncogene could be blocked at the genetic level by the insertion of an antisense gene that would bind to the oncogene, disabling its ability to express. In fact, there is a wide variety of potential uses of gene therapy for the treatment of cancer, with more developing monthly. Seventy-nine of the 122 approved therapy trials target cancer. They are listed in Table 6-2. These possibilities and a growing enthusiasm for gene therapy have resulted in the majority of RAC approved trials being for cancer (Tables 6–2 and 6–3; Appendix B). The application of gene transfer to clinical oncology also began with the

Table 6–1.   Potential Applications for Gene Therapy for the Treatment of Cancer

1. Enhance the immunogeniticy of the tumor (e.g., foreign antigens, cytokines, B7 costimulatory molecule)
2. Genetically alter immune cells to increase function (e.g., cytokines, costimulatory molecules, a tumor-specific T-cell receptor)
3. Insert a "sensitivity" or "suicide" gene into the tumor (e.g., herpes simplex-thymidine kinase, cytosine deaminase)
4. Block oncogene expression (e.g., antisense K-*ras*, intracellular antibodies)
5. Insertion of a tumor suppressor gene (e.g., wild-type p53)
6. Protect tissues from the systemic toxicities of chemotherapy (e.g., multiple drug resistance type 1 gene, DNA repair enzymes, alkyltransferase, dihydrofolate reductase)
7. Induce normal tissues to produce antitumor substances (e.g., interferon)
8. Production of recombinant vaccines for the prevention and treatment of malignancy (e.g., direct injection of CEA DNA, BCG expressing tumor antigens)
9. Local radioprotection of normal bystander tissues with antioxidant overexpression (e.g., glutathione synthetase or transferase, manganese superoxide dismutase)
10. Insertion of genes to enhance tumor sensitivity to radiation (e.g., manganese superoxide dismutase, TNF-α)
11. Transfer of genes that block expression of receptors critical for tumor cell survival and growth (e.g., EGF, IGF-1 receptor)
12. Transfer genes to induce apoptosis (e.g., FAS or FAS ligand)
13. Enhancement of chemotherapeutic activity (e.g., transfer of cytochrome P-450)
14. Transfer of antimetastasis genes (e.g., nitric oxide synthetase)
15. Transfer of genes that block tumor-associated angiogenesis (e.g., antisense VEGF or PDECGF)

CEA = Carcinoembryonic antigen; EGF = epidermal growth factor; VEGF = vascular endothelial growth factor; PDECGF = platelet-derived endothelial cell growth factor.

Table 6–2. Active Human Gene Therapy Experiments for Cancer in the United States

Types of cancers	Tissue	Gene
Bladder cancer	Tumor cells	Retinoblastoma tumor suppressor gene[a]
Brain tumors	Tumor cells	HS-*tk*[a]
Brain tumors	Tumor cells	IL-2 or antisense IGF-1
Brain tumors	HSC[b]	*MDR-1*
Brain tumors	Tumor cells	IL-4
Brain tumors	Tumor cells	Antisense TGF-β_2
Breast cancer	Fibroblasts	IL-4 or IL-12
Breast cancer	HSC	*MDR-1*
Breast cancer	Tumor cells	Antisense c-*fos* or c-*myc* RNA[a]
Breast cancer	Tumor cells	IL-2 or TNF
Breast cancer	Tumor cells	HLA-B7 + β_2-microglobulin[a]
Breast cancer	Muscle	Carcinoembryonic antigen[a]
Breast cancer	Skin	Carcinoembryonic antigen[a]
Breast cancer	Tumor cells	E1A tumor suppressor gene[a]
Colorectal cancer	Tumor cells	IL-2, TNF, or wild-type p53
Colorectal cancer	Fibroblasts	IL-2 or IL-4
Colorectal cancer	Muscle	Carcinoembryonic antigen[a]
Colorectal cancer	Skin	Carcinoembryonic antigen[a]
Colorectal cancer	Tumor cells	HLA-B7 + β_2-microglobulin[a]
Colorectal cancer	Tumor cells	Cytosine deaminase
Head/neck cancer	Tumor cells	Wild-type p53[a]
Head/neck cancer	Tumor cells	HLA-B7 + β_2-microglobulin[a]
Head/neck cancer	Tumor cells	HS-*tk*[a]
Head/neck cancer	Fibroblasts	IL-12
Hepatocellular carcinoma	Tumor cells	Wild-type p53
Leptomeningeal carcinoma	Tumor cells	HS-*tk*[a]
Leukemia	T cells	HS-*tk*
Lung cancer	Tumor cells	Antisense k-*ras* or wild-type p53[a]
Lung cancer	Tumor cells	IL-2
Lung cancer	Muscle	Carcinoembryonic antigen[a]
Lung cancer	Skin	Carcinoembryonic antigen[a]
Lymphoma	Tumor cells	IL-2
Lymphoma	Fibroblasts	IL-12
Lymphoma	Tumor cells	HLA-B7 + β_2 microglobulin[a]
Malignant melanoma	T cells	TNF or HS-*tk*
Malignant melanoma	Tumor cells	TNF, IL-2, IL-4, IL-7 or GM-CSF
Malignant melanoma	Fibroblasts	IL-4 or IL-12
Malignant melanoma	Tumor cells	Interferon-γ[a]
Malignant melanoma	Tumor cells	B7 costimulatory molecule
Malignant melanoma	Tumor cells	HLA-B7[a]
Malignant melanoma	Tumor cells	HLA-B7 + β_2 microglobulin[c]
Malignant melanoma	Skin	MART-1 melanoma antigen
Mesothelioma	Tumor cells	HS-*tk*[a]
Multiple myeloma	T cells	HS-*tk*

Table 6–2. (continued)

Types of cancers	Tissue	Gene
Neuroblastoma	Tumor cells	IL-2 or Interferon-γ
Ovarian cancer	Tumor cells	IL-2
Ovarian cancer	T cells	Chimeric T cell receptor
Ovarian cancer	HSC	*MDR-1*
Ovarian cancer	Tumor cells	HS-*tk*
Ovarian cancer	Tumor cells	BRCA-1 tumor suppressor gene[a]
Ovarian cancer	Muscle	Carcinoembryonic antigen[a]
Ovarian cancer	Tumor cells	E1A tumor suppressor gene[a]
Ovarian cancer	Tumor cells	Anti-*erbβ*-2 single chain antibody[a]
Pancreatic cancer	Muscle	Carcinoembryonic antigen[a]
Prostate cancer	Tumor cells	GM-CSF, IL-2, or IL-2 + Interferon-γ
Prostate cancer	Tumor cells	HS-*tk*[a]
Prostate cancer	Tumor cells	Antisense c-*myc* RNA[a]
Prostate cancer	Skin	Prostate-specific antigen (PSA)
Renal cell carcinoma	Tumor cells	IL-2, TNF, or GM-CSF
Renal cell carcinoma	Tumor cells	HLA-B7 + β_2-microglobulin[c]
Renal cell carcinoma	Fibroblasts	IL-4
Solid tumors	Tumor cells	IL-2 or HLA-B7 + β_2-microglobulin[a]
Stomach cancer	Muscle	Carcinoembryonic antigen[a]
Stomach cancer	Skin	Carcinoembryonic antigen[a]

[a]*In vivo* gene transfer protocol.
[b]HSC = hematopoietic stem cells.
[c]*In vivo* and *ex vivo* gene transfer protocols.

genetic alteration of T lymphocytes and marrow stem cells just as with the genetic diseases. This focus on gene therapy applications for cancer is based on more than the fact that cancer is a major cause of morbidity and mortality. Cancer cells by virtue of their higher proliferative index are ideal targets for murine retroviral vectors, which require that the target cells be proliferating for gene integration and expression; tumor cells generally express vector genes at higher levels compared to primary cells and one gene may be useful for many cancers, unlike genetic diseases where each specific disorder requires a unique gene.

HEMATOPOIETIC STEM CELL GENE MARKING AND THERAPY PROTOCOLS

Hematopoietic Stem Cells: Marking Experiments

An early group of clinical studies has focused upon the insertion of marker genes into the bone marrow of patients who are undergoing autologous, purged bone marrow transplantation and are in remission from leukemia and

Table 6–3.   Active RAC Approved Gene Marking Experiments by Disease Category

Disease	Tissue	Gene
Acute leukemias	EBV-specific T cells	*NeoR*
Acute leukemias	Hematopoietic stem cells	*NeoR*
Acute lymphocytic leukemia	Marrow tumor cells	*NeoR*
Acute myelogenous leukemia	Marrow tumor cells	*NeoR*
Breast cancer	Hematopoietic stem cells	*NeoR*
Chronic lymphocytic leukemia	Marrow tumor cells	*NeoR*
Chronic myelogenous leukemia	Marrow tumor cells	*NeoR*
Chronic myelogenous leukemia	Hematopoietic stem cells	*NeoR*
HIV	T cells	*NeoR*
Hodgkin disease	Hematopoietic stem cells	*NeoR*
Hodgkin disease	T cells	*NeoR*
Malignant melanoma	T cells	*NeoR*
Multiple myeloma	Hematopoietic stem cells	*NeoR*
Neuroblastoma	Marrow tumor cells	*NeoR*
Non-Hodgkin lymphoma	Marrow tumor cells	*NeoR*
Non-Hodgkin lymphoma	Hematopoietic stem cells	*NeoR*
Ovarian cancer	T cells	*NeoR*
Renal cell carcinoma	T cells	*NeoR*
Solid tumors	Hematopoietic stem cells	*NeoR*

neuroblastoma (see Table 6–3). These studies have identified leukemic relapses that occurred from the gene-marked marrow, even though there was no evidence of leukemic cells in the infused marrow at the time of transplantation (Brenner et al., 1993a; Deisseroth et al., 1994; Rill et al., 1994). Apparently, the systemic chemotherapy was effective in eliminating the systemic cancer, but the marrow-purging techniques were suboptimal. This fundamental biological question could be answered adequately only with gene marking using retroviral vectors, because the vector will insert only into dividing tumor cells (the normal marrow cells generally do not proliferate actively, and this is why it has not been possible to move more quickly with marrow gene therapy clinical trials) and the gene is passed to all daughter cells unlike other forms of marking (e.g., radioactive labeling). A second series of clinical studies is in preparation to evaluate different methods of marrow purging in human autologous bone marrow transplantation using gene marking (Brenner et al., 1994). Marking studies might also be used to determine which combinations of cytokines added during transduction provide optimal engraftment.

Another series of hematopoietic stem cell gene marking experiments is aimed at evaluating possible differences in engraftment potential between the use of genetically altered bone marrow stem cells (BMSC) versus the use of peripheral blood stem cells (PBSC). Patients enrolled in these studies have solid tumors, disseminated breast cancer, multiple myeloma, lymphoma, or leukemia and will receive autologous stem cell transplants containing both BMSC and PBSC, each genetically marked with a different murine retroviral vector. The patients will then be evaluated for evidence of engraftment to determine whether one method is more advantageous. This is a very important question because PBSC can be harvested repeatedly with less expense and much less discomfort for the patient.

BMSCs are routinely harvested via multiple needle aspirations through the posterior iliac crests under local or general anesthesia. In contrast, PBSCs are harvested by apheresis from a vein (Fig. 6–2). To increase the yield of stem cells from the peripheral blood, the patient may be treated with injections of granulocyte-colony-stimulating factor (G-CSF) to induce marrow stem cells to move from the marrow compartment to the peripheral blood. Other stimuli such as pretreatment with chemotherapy, which induces marrow proliferation, will also produce a demargination of hematopoietic stem cells into the peripheral blood. Once the PBSC number has increased in the blood, they can be captured by apheresis through a central or peripheral vein. The ability to harvest and genetically alter PBSC would greatly facilitate the ease of widespread application of stem cell gene therapy. However, it is not certain if PBSCs contain sufficient totipotent stem cells to completely and permanently reconstitute all marrow lineages. The first published report from one of these gene marking studies suggested that PBSC transplants are as good as and perhaps better than marrow-derived stem cells for long-term marking (Dunbar et al., 1995). The results of long-term results from this and other studies will have profound significance for the application of gene therapy to all types of marrow disorders.

Hematopoietic Stem Cells: MDR Gene Experiments

The genetic manipulation of stem cells may also theoretically be used to protect them from the toxic effects of chemotherapy. This goal might be accomplished by the insertion of the multiple drug resistance type 1 (MDR-1) gene into hematopoietic stem cells prior to administration of high-dose, myelosuppressive chemotherapy. The *MDR1* gene was isolated from tumor cells and functions to pump chemotherapy drugs (i.e., daunorubicin, doxorubicin, vincristine, vinblastine, VP-16, VM-26, taxol, actinomycin D) from tumor cells. This tumor resistance mechanism represents one of the ways in which tumors develop resistance to chemotherapy drugs. The use of *ex vivo* retroviral vector-mediated insertion of the *MDR-1* gene into murine marrow cells has demonstrated significant protective effects *in vivo*, when animals were treated with high doses of taxol (Sorrentino et al., 1992). Several human clinical trials are in progress to study these properties in the high-dose chemotherapy treatment of brain tumors, progressive ovarian cancer, or disseminated breast cancer (Table 6–2 and Appendix B). No published data from these clinical trials are currently available.

Hematopoietic Stem Cells: Other Potential Uses for Cancer Therapy

Other potential uses include the following: (1) The insertion of genes that would selectively express genes in cytotoxic T cells. These might be cytokine genes or unique T cell receptor genes that are directed at specific tumor anti-

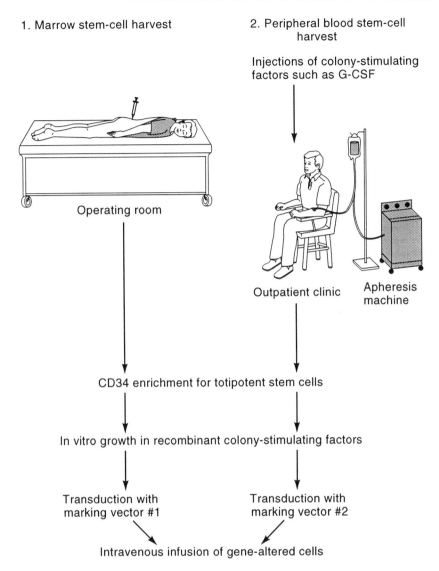

1. Marrow stem-cell harvest

2. Peripheral blood stem-cell harvest

Injections of colony-stimulating factors such as G-CSF

Operating room

Outpatient clinic

Apheresis machine

CD34 enrichment for totipotent stem cells

In vitro growth in recombinant colony-stimulating factors

Transduction with marking vector #1

Transduction with marking vector #2

Intravenous infusion of gene-altered cells

Fig. 6–2.   The methods for bone marrow stem cell (BMSC) and peripheral blood stem cell (PBSC) harvesting. The classical marrow harvest uses repeated needle aspirations through the iliac crest under general anesthesia. A PBSC harvest is accomplished through a large-bore IV on an outpatient basis following daily subcutaneous injections of G-CSF to mobilize stem cells from the marrow space into the bloodstream. Once the cells have been collected by either method, more differentiated progenitor cells are purified away from the totipotent reconstituting stem cells. This is accomplished by using a CD34 monoclonal antibody that selectively binds a population of cells containing totipotent stem cells. To attempt permanent genetic correction, the CD34$^+$ cells are cultured with growth factors to induce proliferation, allowing more efficient transduction with murine retroviral vectors. To determine which population of cells is reconstituting hematopoiesis and the duration of engraftment, two different marking vectors are used that can be easily distinguished by DNA analysis. The cells are then returned to the patient as an intravenous infusion.

gens (see the following T lymphocyte sections). (2) The insertion of genes that will selectively deplete tumor cells from the marrow before autologous marrow transplantation. This might include the transfer of tumor suppressor genes such as p53, which may induce apoptosis in proliferating p53-deficient tumor cells in the marrow. (3) Transfer of sensitivity genes (e.g., HS-*tk*) into the marrow after purging and before an autologous transplant so that if any tumor cells remain and begin to grow, the transduced tumor cells can be selectively destroyed *in vivo* without the need for systemic, myeloablative chemotherapy (Moolten, 1986).

T LYMPHOCYTE GENE MARKING AND THERAPY PROTOCOLS

T Lymphocytes: Marking Experiments

Another approach to the genetic therapy of cancer is gene transfer into T lymphocytes (Tables 6–2 and 6–3; Appendix B). Because T lymphocytes are critical for the prevention and elimination of tumors, investigators are growing T lymphocytes from tumor biopsies for use as a delivery vehicle for genes directly to tumor deposits *in situ*. Investigators first wanted to determine if tumor-derived T lymphocytes would "home" to tumor deposits. These early studies, which involved gene marking of tumor-infiltrating lymphocytes (TIL), demonstrated safety, but failed to demonstrate conclusively that the TIL homed to tumor cell deposits (Merrouche et al., 1995; Rosenberg et al., 1990a). Similar trials are in progress in patients with renal cell carcinoma and ovarian cancer (Nash et al., 1995) (Table 6–2). The protocol with renal carcinoma patients hopes to confirm the ability or inability of TIL to home to tumor deposits by marking both autologous peripheral blood-derived T cells and TIL with different vectors, as have been used in the hematopoietic stem cell experiments (Economou et al., 1992).

Investigators performing another nontherapeutic trial have inserted the *NeoR* marker gene with murine retroviral vectors into EBV-specific T cells (Table 6–3). The genetically altered T cells were then administered for the treatment or prevention of EBV lymphoproliferative disease following a T cell-depleted allogeneic bone marrow transplant. These investigators treated 10 patients with donor-derived, EBV-specific T cells without complication. The marker gene was identified by PCR for up to 10 weeks after infusion of the *NeoR*-marked T cells (Rooney et al., 1995). This study provides a scientific basis to add sensitivity genes (e.g., HS-*tk*) as a "safety" in the event the infused T cells produce an adverse effect, such as graft-versus-host disease (GVHD), so that the infused cells can be destroyed *in vivo* with ganciclovir.

T Lymphocytes: Therapy Experiments

Three different approaches to the use of gene transfer in T lymphocytes for cancer therapy are approved for clinical trials (see Table 6–2 and Appendix B). The first involves the insertion of a novel new T cell receptor gene. Scientists have produced a chimeric T cell receptor gene that confers a binding affinity to the folate binding protein, which is overexpressed on ovarian carcinoma cells (Hwu et al., 1995). Insertion of this gene into T cells with retroviral vectors functionally alters the specificity of the T cells, redirecting their cytotoxic functions to cells expressing the folate binding protein. No published clinical results are available at this time. The second type of trial uses the HS-*tk* gene as a method to deplete conditionally and selectively T lymphocyte populations *in vivo* that might harm the patient. In one approach, patients who received a T cell-depleted bone marrow transplant for multiple myeloma or leukemia and now have a recurrence will be eligible. They will receive donor T cells that have been genetically altered with retroviral vectors to contain the HS-*tk* gene. If any of the transferred T cells produce adverse side effects, such as graft vs. host disease (GVHD), the effector population can be destroyed *in vivo* with the administration of ganciclovir. In another effort, scientists are transferring the HS-*tk* gene into tyrosinase-specific T-cells from patients with melanoma. Tyrosinase is a potential tumor rejection antigen on melanoma cells that is also present on several normal tissues such as the eye, skin and brain. Therefore, the plan is to use the HS-tk gene as a means to follow the cells and as a way to deplete the genetically altered cells if they induce adverse reactions. No published clinical results are available at this time.

The final approved approach involves the insertion of the TNF-α gene into TIL cells (Rosenberg et al., 1990b). TNF is a cytokine that is normally produced by T lymphocytes and that, if infused in sufficient amounts in mice, can destroy tumors. Unfortunately, the intravenous infusion of TNF in humans has significant adverse side effects, significantly limiting the maximum tolerated dose. The initial experiment with TNF gene-modified TIL attempts to use genetically altered T lymphocytes to deliver high concentrations of TNF directly to the tumor. The hypothesis is that following an intravenous infusion of TIL expressing a TNF retroviral vector, these TIL will migrate back to tumor deposits in the body, delivering a high concentration of TNF directly to the tumor with minimal systemic side effects compared to intravenous TNF therapy. The pace of this human experiment has been slowed due to the poor efficiency of gene transfer into human TIL and a down-regulation of cytokine expression by the TIL (Hwu et al., 1993). There are no published clinical results to report at this time.

THE GENETIC ALTERATION OF TUMOR CELLS (AND FIBROBLASTS)

Approved clinical gene therapy applications involving the direct transfer of genes into tumor cells have been growing rapidly. Table 6–4 lists the variety of RAC methods in clinical trials and the cancers that are being targeted. This chapter will use this table format, combining both *ex vivo* and *in vivo* gene transfer methods under these subheadings. For a comprehensive list of investigators, see Appendix B.

Table 6–4. RAC Approved Clinical Approaches to the Direct Genetic Alteration of Tumor Cells and Immunization Strategies

Type of antitumor process	Tumor types
Direct enhancement of tumor immunogenicity	
Insertion of cytokine genes (i.e., IL-2, IL-4, IL-7, IL-12, TNF-α, interferon-γ, GM-CSF)	Brain, breast, colorectal, head/neck, lung, lymphoma, melanoma, neuroblastoma, ovarian, prostate, renal cell, solid tumors
Transfer of foreign MHC genes (i.e., HLA-B7)	Breast, colorectal, head/neck, lymphoma, melanoma, renal cell, solid tumors
Making the tumor "visible" to T cells (i.e., antisense IGF-1, antisense TGF-β2, B7 costimulatory molecule)	Brain, melanoma
Immunization approaches	
Vectors that transiently express tumor antigens on the surface of muscle cells (i.e., CEA MART-1, prostate specific antigen)	Breast, colorectal, lung, melanoma, ovarian, pancreatic, prostate, stomach
Direct tumor cell destruction	
Sensitivity genes (i.e., HS-*tk*, cytosine deaminase)	Brain, colorectal, head/neck, mesothelioma, leptomeningeal carcinomatosis, ovarian, prostate
Targeting the genetic basis of carcinogenesis	
Insertion of tumor suppressor genes (i.e., BRCAI, EIA, retinoblastoma, p53)	Bladder, colorectal, head/neck, liver, lung
Blocking oncogene expression (i.e., antisense c-fos, c-myc, or k-ras genes, anti-erbβ-2 intracellular antibodies)	Breast, lung, ovarian, prostate

Cytokine Gene Transfer into Tumor Cells and Fibroblasts

This area of clinical gene therapy research has been the most active for several reasons: (1) a variety of cytokine genes have been cloned and are available for experimentation; (2) they can be delivered by all current gene delivery methods, both *ex vivo* and *in vivo*; (3) cytokine genes alone may be sufficient to induce immunologic regression of certain malignancies, especially those that tend to be more immunoresponsive, such as melanoma, renal cell carcinoma, bladder, and colorectal cancer; and (4) the transfer of cytokine genes with tumor antigens may induce a potent immunizing response to eliminate minimal residual disease or prevent the progression from a premalignant to a malignant lesion. These possibilities have resulted in the approval to use a variety of cytokines in clinical trials for humans (Table 6–5).

The idea for the *ex vivo* genetic modification of patient tumor cells followed by reinjection *in vivo* for use as a vaccine was initially received with some skepticism. The thought of injecting a patient with viable human cancer cells made it seem as though we were moving in the wrong direction. However, animal experiments from a variety of centers have suggested that this form of gene therapy might be useful in vaccinating patients (Colombo and Forni, 1994). These investigations have focused on the genetic alteration of tumor cells with one or more cytokines. In brief, murine tumors were genetically altered *in vitro* with genes including IL-1β, IL-2, IL-4, IL-6, IL-7, IL-10, IL-12, TNF-α, IFN-γ, and/or GM-CSF, and then reimplanted into mice (see reference list). In each case, the genetically altered tumor cells either did not grow or grew and regressed. Most of the treated mice were then systemically immune to reimplantation of the non-gene-altered tumor. However, when animals with established, large tumors and/or metastases were treated, the results were much less satisfactory. Nonetheless, clinical trials have been initiated to study the immunobiology of this type of immunization system in humans (Table 6–2 and Appendix B). These initial experiments are an attempt to immunize tumor-bearing patients specifically against their own tumor by genetically altering their tumor with one of a variety of genes that are expected to increase the host immune reactivity to the tumor.

Human trials have been approved involving the *in vitro* insertion of seven cytokine genes involving 12 different types of cancer (Table 6–5 and Appendix B). These "tumor vaccines" are produced by surgically removing the tumor from the body and making genetic alterations in the tumor in the laboratory (Fig. 6–3). Once the tumor has been shown to produce large quantities of the inserted gene product, the tumor cells are reinjected subcutaneously into the patient. Booster injections of cells are commonly administered at intervals for a total of three to six injections. Melanoma, colorectal cancer, and renal cell carcinoma have been the primary focus of the tumor vaccine studies because they are believed to be inherently more immunogenic than other tumors and may therefore be more likely to respond to this type of therapeutic approach. Nearly all approved pro-

Table 6–5. Approved Cytokine Immune Stimulatory Genes for Clinical Trials

Gene	Cancers to be treated
Interleukin-2 (IL-2)	Brain, breast, colorectal, lung, lymphoma, melanoma, neuroblastoma, ovarian, prostate,[a] renal cell, solid tumors
Interleukin-4 (IL-4)	Brain, breast, colorectal, melanoma, renal cell
Interleukin-7 (IL-7)	Melanoma
Interleukin-12 (IL-12)	Breast, head/neck, lymphoma, melanoma
INF-γ	Melanoma, neuroblastoma, prostate[a]
Tumor necrosis factor (TNF)	Breast, colorectal, melanoma, renal cell
Granulocyte-macrophage colony-stimulating factor (GM-CSF)	Melanoma, prostate, renal cell

[a]One trial will combine IL-2 and Interferon-γ for the treatment of prostate cancer.

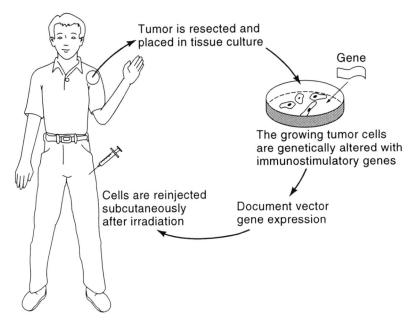

Tumor is resected and placed in tissue culture

Gene

The growing tumor cells are genetically altered with immunostimulatory genes

Cells are reinjected subcutaneously after irradiation

Document vector gene expression

Fig. 6–3. Production and use of autologous genetic tumor vaccines. The tumor is surgically removed from the patient and placed in tissue culture. The growing cells are then genetically altered to express genes that will induce increased immune responsiveness to the engineered tumor cells. The cells are confirmed to be producing the desired gene product and are usually irradiated as an added safety precaution to prevent tumor formation. The cells are then injected subcutaneously into the patient.

tocols have used autologous tumor even though this approach is complicated because it is difficult to grow tumor from many patients. Methods that stably integrate the vector genes (e.g., retroviral vectors) require tumor cell growth in the laboratory for several weeks. The use of nonintegrating vectors, such as adenovirus, or particle bombardment eliminates the need to grow cells *in vitro* for long periods, if needed at all, but the question of vector gene expression for a sufficient time period *in vivo* is of concern for these nonintegrating delivery methods. All but one of the currently approved trials use retroviral vectors because this system has been extensively tested, these vectors express well in tumor cells, and stable integration provides confidence that the vector genes will continue to be present in all tumor cells after reinjection.

The *in vitro* growth of tumor cells can be problematic, with less than 50% of tumor cell lines growing in long-term culture. In an effort to maximize the opportunity to treat patients, several investigators are using allogeneic tumor cells lines that are partially major histocompatibility complex (MHC)-matched or mixing nontransduced tumor cells with transduced autologous fibroblasts. The allogeneic tumors may express similar tumor antigens and, therefore, may be a good substitute. However, there is no reliable way to measure the variety of tumor antigens expressed on the cell surface, and it may be that only a few, if any, of the same tumor antigens expressed on the allogeneic cell line are the same as on the patient's own tumor. However, if this method demonstrates efficacy in patients, it is much less expensive and more practical for widespread application than growing each person's tumor in the laboratory. Two groups of investigators will insert cytokine genes into autologous fibroblast cell lines, which can be routinely adapted to long-term tissue culture. The IL-2, IL-4, and IL-12 immune stimulatory cytokine genes have been approved by the RAC for insertion into skin fibroblasts. These genetically altered fibroblasts are mixed with irradiated autologous tumor cells and injected subcutaneously. Researchers hope that the local production of cytokines by the fibroblasts will induce a vigorous immune response to the adjacent irradiated tumor cells, resulting in a systemic anticancer immunizing response (Tahara et al., 1994). It is unclear at this point if this approach reduces antitumor immunogenicity compared to irradiated tumor cells secreting the same cytokine (Shawler et al., 1995). Patients with melanoma, colorectal cancer, breast cancer, head/neck cancer, lymphoma, and renal cell carcinoma are to be enrolled in the trials (Tables 6–2 and 6–3; Appendix B).

There are no formal publications from the clinical trials using cytokine-transduced tumor cells or fibroblasts. However, there have been a number of progress reports presented at various meetings. The results are very similar. First, these approaches appear to be safe. Nothing more than a self-limited local inflammatory reaction has been seen in response to repeated injections of the cells. Second, there has been some evidence of enhanced antitumor immunity (e.g., increased antitumor T cell responses *in vitro*), but no significant sustained clinical benefit has been noted in any of the patients. This is not surprising because the majority of these patients have substantial tumor burdens and have received significant amounts of prior chemotherapy. For both of these reasons, these patients have suppressed immunologic response capabilities, even if these therapies were, under ideal circumstances, very effective vaccines. Until patients with very minimal disease can be treated and followed over the long term, this generation of cytokine vaccines will likely have unsatisfactory clinical results. The next steps, in addition to choosing healthier patients, will combine more genes (e.g., cytokines, tumor antigens, foreign antigens, and/or sensitivity genes), use inducible promoters to allow the transplanted tumor to engraft, and induce an immunologic response before triggering the high levels of cytokine production. The irradiation step may be eliminated to enhance immunologic reactivity and the treatment may be combined with traditional therapies, such as initial surgical patients who do not usually receive chemotherapy (e.g., early stages of lung cancer).

Transfer of Foreign MHC Genes into Tumor Cells

One of the most advanced gene therapy clinical trial efforts involves the direct intratumoral injection of liposomes to transfer HLA-B7 into the tumors of HLA-B7-negative patients. Liposomes are taken up by the tumor's cells by phagocytosis and the product of the transferred DNA is expressed transiently on the

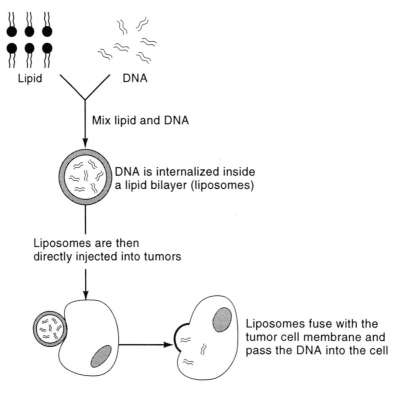

Lipid

DNA

Mix lipid and DNA

DNA is internalized inside
a lipid bilayer (liposomes)

Liposomes are then
directly injected into tumors

Liposomes fuse with the
tumor cell membrane and
pass the DNA into the cell

Fig. 6–4. *In vivo* liposome gene delivery. A lipid solution is mixed *in vitro* with DNA, which results in the internalization of DNA within a lipid bilayer (liposomes). The liposomes are then directly injected into tumor deposits. The liposomes fuse with the tumor cell membrane and pass their DNA contents into the tumor cells. The DNA then transiently expresses the genes encoded in the plasmid.

surface of the cancer cells (Fig. 6–4). Animal studies have shown a significant increase in the antitumor immune response when some of the tumor cells express foreign antigens on the cell surface (Ostrand-Rosenberg et al., 1990; Plautz et al., 1993). This first clinical trial was approved in 1992 for the transfer of HLA-B7 into melanoma (see Appendix B). Data from the first five patients were published in 1993 (Nabel et al., 1993). In one of the patients, the injected lesion as well as distant metastases regressed. A CD8$^+$ cellular infiltrate mediated the antitumor response. Only the injected lesion responded in the other four patients. All of the patients demonstrated evidence of gene transfer without evidence of toxicity related to the procedure. Subsequent patients with a variety of malignancies are being treated with a combination of HLA-B7 and β_2-microglobulin genes in an effort to enhance further the development of a cytotoxic immune response against the tumor (Nabel et al., 1994). These early findings suggest that the use of *in vivo* gene transfer of foreign HLA antigens with liposomes may have the potential for inducing a systemic antitumor immune response in some patients with melanoma.

This approach now includes 10 approved protocols for the experimental treatment of breast cancer, colon cancer, head/neck, melanoma, non-Hodgkin's lymphoma, and renal cell cancer (Table 6–2 and Appendix B). Seven of these protocols are attempting to characterize and optimize the best methods for the repeated delivery of the genes to induce a systemic antitumor immunologic response in different malignancies. One protocol will add the concurrent administration of low-dose intravenous IL-2 therapy in patients with renal cell carcinoma in an effort to develop a synergistic antitumor immune response. Two others are using the direct injection of HLA-B7 and β_2-microglobulin to induce an antitumor immune response and then harvesting the responding T cells from the injected lesion. These cells will then be expanded *in vitro* with anti-CD3 monoclonal antibody and readministered to the patient. Hopefully these combination therapies will demonstrate increasing efficacy in the treatment of one or more of the malignancies under investigation.

Making the Tumor "Visible" to T Lymphocytes

There are a variety of methods that allow tumors to grow progressively despite the presence of immunologic effector cells within the tumor mass. Some of these mechanisms are becoming better understood, allowing investigators to begin to alter the veil behind which tumors hide. These include the production of cytokines that prevent full immune responsiveness (e.g., IGF-1) and the downregulation of molecules needed to generate a full immunologic response against the tumor (e.g., B7 co-stimulatory molecule).

Many tumors (e.g., breast, brain, osteosarcoma) overexpress the insulin-like growth factor-1 (IGF-1). Insertion of an antisense IGF-1 gene will block tumor cell production of IGF-1 (Trojan et al., 1992). The antisense IGF-1 vector produces mirror image RNA molecules that will bind the ones being produced by the tumor cell. These RNA:RNA hybrids are then degraded by the cell, preventing translation and protein production (see Chapter 1). Animal experiments have demonstrated that the injection of tumor cells genetically altered with an antisense IGF-1 gene in the brain are immunologically rejected CD8$^+$ T cytotoxic lymphocytes. If non-genetically altered tumor is injected into the brain and antisense IGF-1-transfected tumor cells are injected subcutaneously, both tumors are destroyed by this immunologic response (Trojan et al., 1993). A trial has been approved and is currently enrolling patients for the treatment of glioblastoma multiforme using an *ex vivo* nonviral DNA transfer method (Appendix B). There are no published clinical results available at this time.

The development of a maximal cellular immune response to tumor antigens requires two signals (Linsley et al., 1991), one through an MHC class I:T cell receptor interaction and a second through a B7 co-stimulatory surface molecule that binds to the CD28 surface receptor on T lymphocytes. The B7 costimulatory molecule is distinctly different from MHC class I HLA B7 used in tissue typing. Transfection of the B7 costimulatory surface molecule into melanoma cells can greatly enhance antigen presentation and tumor eradication *in vivo* (Townsend and Allison, 1993). The antitumor response is mediated by CD8$^+$ T cells independently of CD4$^+$ T cells. This method of enhanced tumor antigen presentation may prove an effective way to enhance tumor immunogenicity across various histologic tumor cell types. One trial has been approved for the treatment of patients with metastatic melanoma using the *ex vivo* transfection of plasmid containing the B7 costimulatory gene (Fenton et al., 1995) (Appendix B). No published clinical data are available at this time.

Finally, a second antisense gene transfer approach has been approved for the experimental treatment of brain tumors (Appendix B). It is well known that glioblastoma tumors produce immunosuppressive compounds, transformig growth factor-beta (TGF-β) being one of them. Animal brain tumor experiments demonstrated the generation of substantial immunologic-mediated antitumor efficacy following the subcutaneous injection of tumors cells expressing an antisense TGF-β gene that eliminated TGF-β secretion (Fakhrai et al., 1996). In the clinical protocol, scientists will remove tumor, genetically alter the cells with a plasmid containing an antisense TGF-β gene using electroporation, irradiate the tumor cells to prevent regrowth in the patient, and reinject subcutaneously every 3 weeks for 4 doses. The goal is to surmount one of the methods tumors use to hide from the immune system in order to induce a vigorous, systemic antitumor immune response.

These approaches to the treatment of cancer are likely candidates for incorporation into combination therapies. It may be possible to combine cytokines, B7, and other genes to develop a very potent, tumor-specific antitumor immune response (Cayeux et al., 1995; Salvadori et al., 1995). Additional clinical experiments using these types of approaches are expected over the next several years.

Expression of Tumor Antigens on the Surface of Skin and Muscle Cells

Five clinical trials have been approved to use poxvirus vectors or the direct injection of plasmid into muscle (Tables 6–2 and 6–4; Appendix B). Three will transfer the carcinoembryonic antigen (CEA) gene into patients with CEA-positive tumors and one will transfer the prostate-specific antigen (PSA) gene. This is an effort to elicit a cytotoxic immune response against CEA or PSA positive cancer cells. In animal models, the vaccination of animals with this method will protect them from subsequent CEA-positive tumor challenges (Conry et al., 1995b). One trial has recently been approved using an adenovirus to transfer the MART-1 melanoma antigen into patients with metastatic melanoma. These trials have been recently approved and no clinical data are available. Additional trials using direct DNA or viral vector injection (e.g., vaccinia) are expected and may also contain cytokine genes in an attempt to enhance further the immune response to tumor antigens.

Transfer of Sensitivity Genes

Herpes Simplex-Thymidine Kinase (HS-*tk*) Gene.   The HS-*tk* gene produces an enzyme that confers a sensitivity to the antiherpes drug, ganciclovir (Cytovene or GCV) (Moolten, 1986). Figure 6–5 depicts the mechanism of cell destruction using the HS-*tk*/GCV system. This method of tumor cell killing is very potent. Importantly, the destruction of a tumor with HS-*tk*/GCV will also induce immunity to the subsequent challenges with the original tumor type (Culver et al., 1994). As described in Figure 6–5, there is also a significant by-stander tumor killing effect. This appears to occur because the toxic derivatives of GCV pass through gap junctions into neighboring, HS-*tk*-negative cells, destroying them as well (Bi et al., 1993; Elshami et al., 1996; Fick et al., 1995). Experimental studies in animals have suggested that the transfer of the HS-*tk* gene into more than 10% of cells will allow the destruction of the entire tumor in most of the animals (Culver et al., 1992). Other investigators have suggested that fragments of HS-*tk*-destroyed cells, termed "apoptotic vesicles," are phagocytized by neighboring tumor cells, resulting in their destruction (Freeman et al., 1993). Final elucidation of the mechanism(s) involved in the bystander killing effect may provide an opportunity to magnify the effect, perhaps converting a local therapy into a regional or systemic therapy. The presence of this bystander killing effect makes the HS-*tk* gene very appealing for human clinical studies. Because there are no *in vivo* gene transfer methods that are

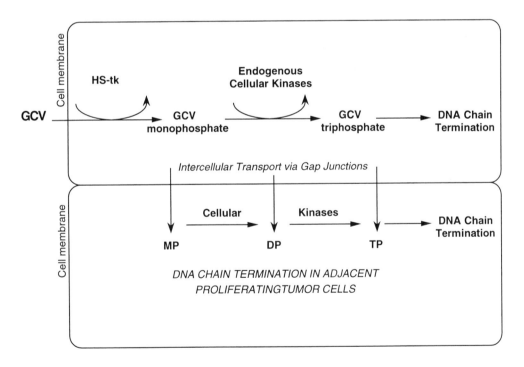

Fig. 6–5. The HS-tk/GCV sensitivity gene system. Following the intravenous administration of GCV, the HS-tk enzyme converts the drug to GCV-MP, an intracellular product. Endogenous cellular kinases then convert the GCV-MP to GCV-TP. GCV-TP destroys tumor cells by incorporating into the elongating DNA chain, inducing chain termination and DNA fragmentation. The leading hypothesis for the mechanism of the bystander tumor killing effect is the passage of phosphorylated derivatives of GCV through gap junctions.

100% efficient, the HS-*tk*/GCV bystander effect may compensate for less efficient gene delivery. As a result, HS-*tk* is the most used gene in RAC-approved cancer gene therapy clinical trials, with approved trials involving more than 20 different research centers.

The primary area of clinical application is in the treatment of brain tumors (Table 6–2). This choice of clinical circumstances resulted primarily because retroviral vectors and HS-*tk* both require a proliferating cell for gene transfer and cell destruction, respectively. In the brain, the normal resident tissues have a significantly lower rate of proliferation compared to tumor cells, providing a greater margin of safety. Table 6–6 lists the fundamental principles behind this intensive area of clinical investigation.

The first clinical attempt at the genetic modification of brain tumors *in situ* with retroviral vectors was initiated in December 1992 (Oldfield et al., 1993). In this protocol, murine fibroblast cells that are producing retroviral vectors (vector producer cells or VPC) are stereotactically implanted into growing brain tumors of the patients (Culver et al., 1992) (see Fig. 6–6). In a series of animal experiments, this technique resulted in gene transfer into 10%–55% of tumor cells (Ram et al., 1993b). No associated toxicity or evidence of systemic spread of the retroviral vectors with this form of *in vivo* gene transfer has been observed.

The stereotactic injection of experimental brain tumors in rats with HS-*tk* VPC demonstrated complete destruction of microscopic tumor in 80% of rats that received GCV administration (Culver et al., 1992). In survival experiments, 50%–60% of the rats survived long term, suggesting that this procedure may have the potential to be curative. There were no associated systemic toxicities related to the gene transfer with this form of *in vivo* gene delivery. Complete tumor ablation occurred despite the fact only 10%–55% of the tumor cells contained the HS-*tk* gene. This finding—the destruction of the adjacent HS-*tk*-negative tumor cells—

Table 6–6. Important Features of the HS-*tk* Brain Tumor Gene Therapy Trials

Central nervous system (CNS)	Immunologically privileged: allows longer survival of xenogeneic cells
	CNS tumors are usually localized and do not widely disseminate, so that local therapy may benefit patients
Murine retroviral vectors	Integrate only into dividing cells
	Normal tissues proliferate at much lower rates than tumor cells
Herpes simplex thymidine kinase (HS-*tk*)	Ganciclovir will destroy HS-*tk*-containing cells
	Ganciclovir crosses the blood–brain barrier in humans
	Tumor destruction is not immune-mediated
	HS-*tk* and GCV produce "bystander" tumor cell killing
Safety aspects	There is a vast excess of receptors in the area of injection that should bind any free vector
	Vector particles are inactivated by serum complement
	Vector producer cells are destroyed by GCV

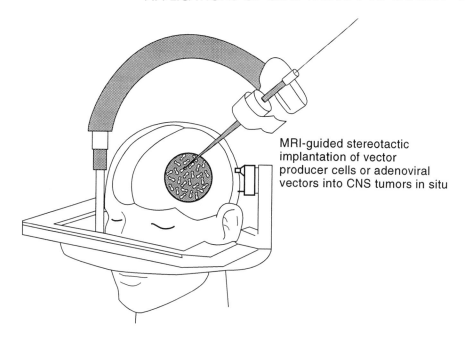

MRI-guided stereotactic implantation of vector producer cells or adenoviral vectors into CNS tumors in situ

Fig. 6–6. *In vivo* gene transfer into brain tumors. Retroviral vector producer cells (VPC) or adenoviral vectors are directly implanted into multiple areas within growing tumors using stereotactic injections guided by magnetic resonance (MR) imaging. Once injected, the VPC continuously produce retroviral vector particles within the tumor mass, transferring genes into surrounding tumor cells. The initial gene transfer studies have involved the transfer of the HS-*tk* gene into brain tumors, to allow tumor cell destruction with the anti-herpes drug ganciclovir.

is termed the "bystander" effect as described above. In none of the animal experiments reported has there been any evidence of destruction to surrounding normal tissues by the bystander phenomenon (Ram et al., 1993a).

In the initial phase I brain tumor gene therapy trial conducted at NIH, 15 patients with recurrent glioblastoma multiforme or metastatic tumors were treated. They had all failed external beam radiation and most had failed surgery and chemotherapy as well. Each of the 15 patients tolerated multiple intratumoral stereotactic injections of HS-*tk* VPC without evidence of toxicity related to the xenogeneic cells or treatment with GCV. The primary purpose of the trial was to determine the safety of the therapy (phase I trial); therefore, VPC were injected only into the gadolinium-enhancing portion of the tumor, so that changes in the tumor and surrounding brain could be visualized with MR scanning. In other words, no attempt was made to treat all of the tumor (infiltrating areas) in any of the patients. Four of the 13 evaluable patients demonstrated evidence of an antitumor effect based >50% in the size of the gadolinium-enhancing measure of the tumor. The change in size was accompanied by cystic changes within the tumor. Despite this limited approach, three patients lived more than 1 year after gene therapy, with one of the patients with a recurrent glioblastoma being

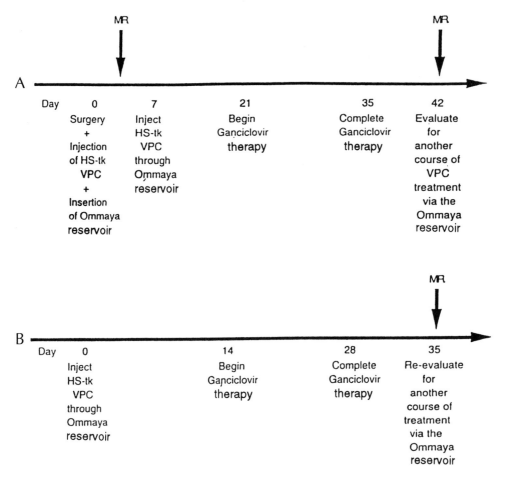

Fig. 6–7. Schematic representation of the multicenter trial combining gene transfer and surgery for recurrent glioblastoma multiforme. Initial treatment phase (A): Patients undergo a subtotal surgical resection. HS-*tk* VPC is injected into the unresectable tumor margin during the surgical procedure and an Ommaya reservoir is placed into the tumor cavity. Additional HS-*tk* VPC is infused into the tumor cavity through the Ommaya reservoir one week later if there is no evidence that the surgical cavity communicates with the subarachnoid space. IV GCV is administered twice daily for 14 days. At day 42, a repeat MR scan is made to determine safety and efficacy parameters. If the lesion is unchanged or smaller, the patient is eligible for additional injections of VPC. Retreatment cycle (B): The patient receives another dose of VPC through the Ommaya reservoir. After allowing 14 days for gene transfer to occur, the patient again receives a 14-day course of GCV. The MR scan is used to monitor therapy. Patients who tolerate the therapy and whose tumors do not progress significantly, are eligible to receive retreatments for 6 months.

more than 3 years status postinitiation of gene therapy treatment. Since patients with recurrent glioblastoma in general have a life expectancy of 5.8 months (range, 3.4–8.8) (Florell et al., 1992), we are encouraged that the further optimization of this approach to the treatment of glioblastoma multiforme may be an important advance over current therapies. This trial is closed for data analysis. Publication of the trial results are expected soon.

As a result of the encouraging safety data and the suggestion that this approach can produce an antitumor effect in human brain tumors, additional clinical trials have been approved. It appears that the primary limiting factor for successful therapy in these patients is poor efficiency of gene delivery. To try to improve gene transfer efficiency, two different gene therapy trials have been approved. The first modification involves the combination of surgical resection of tumor and gene transfer (Culver et al., 1993). This method attempts to deliver the VPC into the nonresectable areas of infiltrating tumor. Once the tumor is maximally resected (complete resection is not possible in these recurrent tumors), the VPC are injected 1 cm deep around the margins of the tumor bed, since the majority of infiltrating tumor is in this area. An Ommaya reservoir is then placed in the tumor bed. Two weeks after surgery, the patients receive additional VPC through the Ommaya reservoir in an attempt to transfer the gene into residual tumor cells. Figure 6–7 describes the schema for this protocol design.

Early results from this trial demonstrated risks associated with the direct and repeated injection of VPC into the Ommaya reservoir. It appears that if any of the VPC leak around the Ommaya catheter in the subarachnoid space, the patients can sustain an acute meningeal reaction, including high fever, meningismus, severe headache, and severe hypertension. The reaction is self-limited and responds to treatment with analgesics, glucocorticoids, and antihypertensives. These side effects were not predicted based upon studies in monkeys that involved the direct injection of VPC into the subarachnoid space. Modifications in the trial design, in which technetium is administered into the Ommaya reservoir, before injection of the cells, to make certain that the cavity has sealed, have decreased the frequency and severity of the reactions. These adverse reactions are not related to gene transfer, but appear to be a direct physiologic reaction to the infused xenogeneic cells. After a brief hold on patient accrual to develop safer procedures, patients are being enrolled at all five centers in this protocol. Additional sites in the United States and in Europe are expected to begin treatment with this approach during the next year.

A second possibility for increasing gene transfer efficiency with retroviral vector producer cells is to treat patients before the irradiation, because irradiation induces significant necrosis and gliosis that will limit the gene transfer efficiency and the bystander effect. Sufficient data must be accumulated in recurrent tumors before using this technique as an experimental up front therapy. However, children with recurrent astrocytomas do not routinely receive irradiation before age 6. A trial has been approved that will use both stereotactic delivery (Kun et al., 1995) and/or the surgery with gene transfer methods (Raffel et al., 1994) in children with recurrent supratentorial brain tumors. These studies may provide critical information that will facilitate the progression of the trials in children and adults to randomization with irradiation in selected patients.

Finally, gene transfer efficiency may be improved by switching to another type of gene transfer system. There are two approved trials using adenoviral vectors (Table 6-2 and Appendix B). This delivery system has the following advantages in the brain: (1) Transferring genes into both dividing and nondividing cells at very high efficiency. This is particularly important in recurrent brain tumors where <50% of cells are mitotically active (Yoshii et al., 1986). (2) High-level expression of the HS-*tk* gene (greater than the retroviral vectors). If a greater amount of HS-*tk* enzyme is produced, then more GCV-triphosphate may be produced resulting in a greater bystander effect. (3) Animal studies have not shown damage to the normal surrounding tissues because normal cells are not generally proliferating (Chen et al., 1994). However, these advantages must be balanced by the fact that HS-*tk* requires dividing cells to induce cell death and the GCV must be administered soon after gene transfer (within several days), because these vectors do not integrate and will be lost. Other disadvantages to this system include the induction of inflammatory responses in the brain (Byrnes et al., 1995) and inhibition of gene transfer and the bystander effect by necrosis and gliosis as with retrovirus-mediated gene transfer. Hopefully, the adenoviral vector system will provide a high degree of safety and antitumor efficacy in humans. These trials have only recently begun to treat patients and no published clinical results are available at this time.

Other potential modifications for improving antitumor efficacy include the use of a motile cell type (e.g., a glioma cell line) for the vector producer cell. Theoretically, this would allow the vector producer cells to infiltrate into the nonresectable areas of the tumor and transfer retroviral vectors into tumor cells outside the direct area of injection. Second, cytokines may be combined with HS-*tk*. IL-4 (Yu et al., 1993), interferon-β (Yoshida et al., 1992), and TNF (Mizuno et al., 1992) have been expressed safely in the brain, whereas IL-2 has been shown to be toxic (Ram et al., 1994a). Because HS-*tk* is a potent method for debulking tumors, HS-*tk* may substantially decrease the production of immunosuppressive factors elaborated by these malignancies, allowing the needed immunologic stimulation for destruction of residual tumor cells.

There are seven other approved trials using HS-*tk* for cancer therapy (Tables 6-2 and 6-4; Appendix B). One trial will use adenoviral vectors to deliver HS-*tk* into mesotheliomas (Smythe et al., 1994). Adenoviral vectors will also be injected into the peritoneal cavity for the treatment of ovarian cancer (Rosenfeld et al., 1995), into head/neck cancers, and into residual prostate cancer. Two will inject HS-*tk* VPC into either the ventricular space for treatment of leptomeningeal carcinomatosis (Oldfield et al., 1995) or into the peritoneal cavity for the treatment of stage III ovarian cancer patients. The initial injection of HS-*tk* VPC through an Ommaya reservoir into the ventricle resulted in a severe, transient acute meningeal reaction as discussed above. No more patients are expected to be enrolled into the trial until modifications can be made that will prevent the

Table 6–7.   Examples of "Sensitivity" Enzymes under Investigation

Prodrug	Enzyme activator	Toxic by-product
Doxorubicin phosphate	Alkaline phosphatase	Doxorubicin
E. coli DeoD	PNP	Toxic adenine analogs
Etoposide phosphate	Alkaline phosphatase	Etoposide
5-Fluorocytosine (5-FC)	Cytosine deaminase	5-Fluorouracil (5-FU)
Ganciclovir (GCV)	HS-tk	GCV-triphosphate
6-Methoxypurine arabinucleoside	HS-tk	Ara AMP, ADP, and ATP
Mitomycin phosphate	Alkaline phosphatase	Mitomycin C
Amygdalin	β-glucosidase	Cyanide
α-Peptidyl-methotrexate	Carboxypeptidase	Alanyl-methotrexate

significant toxicities associated with xenogoeneic VPC injection into the sub-arachnoid space.

Another approved ovarian cancer trial is based upon the use of HS-*tk* retroviral vector-transduced (*ex vivo*) allogeneic human ovarian cancer cells that are irradiated and delivered into the peritoneal cavity (Freeman et al., 1995). Investigators hope that the transduced tumor cells will randomly attach adjacent to the patient's tumor cells and with the administration of GCV will produce a bystander tumor cell killing effect that will destroy the patient's tumor and induce antitumor immunity. This therapeutic approach was evaluated in an intraperitoneal (IP) murine model in which mice bearing intraperitoneal tumors were treated with an IP injection of HS-*tk*-transduced tumor cells. Some of the animals had a significant reduction in tumor burden and a significant increase in survival, but all mice developed nontransduced tumors at the isolated site of needle injection. Patients are currently being added to the trial and no published information is available.

Cytosine Deaminase and Other Sensitivity Genes.   There are a variety of "sensitivity" genes in addition to HS-*tk*. One is cytosine deaminase (CD), a bacterial gene that converts the relatively nontoxic antifungal drug 5-fluorocytosine (5-FC) to the toxic drug 5-fluorouracil (5-FU) within the genetically altered cells. When murine retroviral vectors are used to insert the CD gene into tumor cells, the genetically altered cells can be killed *in vitro* (Mullen et al., 1992) and in mice (Mullen et al., 1994) with nontoxic doses of 5-FC. The animals also developed systemic immunity to the cancers that were destroyed *in vivo* with the CD/5-FC system, suggesting that when combined with cytokine genes they may be synergistic (Mullen et al., 1996). Bystander tumor cell killing is expected because the 5-FU is liberated to the extracellular space as the CD-containing cell is destroyed with 5-FC (Huber et al., 1994). However, the bystander effect appears to be generally less potent than HS-*tk*, depending on cell type. One other limitation in this approach to cancer therapy is that many tumor cells types have a rather high resistance to 5-FU and cannot be destroyed with nontoxic doses of 5-FC (Harris et al., 1994). This may be overcome by using 5-FC/CD to radiosensitize the tumor (Khil et al., 1996). A human clinical trial using CD has been recently approved (Tables 6–2 and 6–4; Appendix B). Investigators plan to inject adenoviral vectors that encode CD directly into colorectal metastases in the liver. There are no published data available on the results from this trial.

There are a number of other sensitivity genes under investigation (see Table 6–7). In each, a relatively nontoxic prodrug is administered systemically that is selectively converted into a toxic by-product within the genetically altered cell. Each has its own problems with pharmacokinetics, efficacy, and toxicities. For example, the *E. coli DeoD* gene, which produces purine nucleoside phosphorylase (PNP), apparently has very potent bystander killing *in vitro*, perhaps even greater than HS-*tk*, but the toxicities of the by-products (i.e., toxic purines) may substantially limit their clinical utility (Sorscher et al., 1994). Because these types of prodrug systems have many advantages, there will be many more that will be evaluated and some will certainly become clinically applicable for the management of cancer patients.

Other Potential Uses of HS-*tk*: Alone or in Combination as Therapy for Cancer. Animal studies have shown that the direct injection of HS-*tk* VPC into solid tumors in the liver (Caruso et al., 1993) or for the treatment of hepatic metastases (Hurford et al., 1995) may be feasible. Another group of investigators has injected HS-*tk* retroviral vectors IV into mice with melanoma metastases producing a substantial antitumor effect, presumably from the combination of direct tumor destruction and induction of systemic antitumor immunity (Vile et al., 1994). Because a number of studies have shown that the HS-*tk*/GCV destruction of tumors *in vivo* will result in tumor-specific immunity, one logical result is to combine HS-*tk* with cytokine genes in an attempt to further the potential of the antitumor immune response.

HS-*tk* is a very potent method for tumor cell destruction, has a tumor cell killing bystander effect, and can induce antitumor immunity; thus it is very likely that this gene will continue to be a mainstay in gene therapy clinical trials and one of the first genes to be FDA approved for the treatment of human malignancy.

Insertion of Tumor Suppressor Genes

One of the major genetic components leading to the development of cancer is the loss or functional inactivation of tumor suppressor genes. Many tumor suppressor genes have been discovered. Four have been approved for human clinical trials (Table 6–2 and 6–4; Appendix B). The first is based upon the observation that the insertion of WTp53 into p53-deficient cells results in the induction of apoptosis and tumor cell death (Baker et al., 1990). One group has approval to inject retroviral vectors or adenoviral vectors containing WTp53 directly into endobronchial lung cancers. Animal studies have demonstrated complete ablation of human tumors growing in immunodeficient animals using this approach (Fujiwara et al., 1994). These results suggest that there is a bystander effect, but no definite bystander mechanism has been confirmed in these immunodeficient mice (Cai et al., 1993).

Two other protocols have been approved in which adenoviral vectors will be used to transfer WTp53 into either head/neck cancers or primary liver tumors (hepatoma) and colorectal metastases in the liver. The direct injection of WTp53-containing adenoviral vectors into human squamous cell carcinomas in immunodeficient mice can produce complete regressions with this gene transfer method (Clayman et al., 1995). Other approved trials include the transfer of the retinoblastoma tumor suppressor gene by adenoviral vectors into bladder cancer and the transfer of BRCA-1 with MRV into ovarian cancer deposits. No published preliminary data are available on the clinical results from these trials.

E1A is an adenovirus tumor suppressor gene that is known to mediate its effect through the HER-2/neu oncogene. Transfer of the E1A gene into human or rodent HER-2/neu-positive tumors *in vitro* or *in vivo* inhibits tumor cell growth (Yu et al., 1995). One protocol has been approved to use liposomes to transfer the E1A gene into the peritoneal cavity or the pleural cavity for the treatment of ovarian or beast cancer respectively. This trial was only recently approved and no published clinical results are available. There are an ever-growing number of tumor suppressor genes and cell cycle regulatory genes (e.g., APC, ATM, p21, p16) that have potent influences on cell growth and the process of carcinogenesis (Friedman et al., 1994; Jin et al., 1995; Savitsky et al., 1995; Yang et al., 1995). Hopefully, these will be further developed alone or in combination with other strategies for use in genetic therapeutics and as preventive therapies.

Insertion of Antisense Oncogenes and Intracellular Antibody Genes

The rationale for these efforts is similar to the insertion of tumor suppressor genes, in that investigators are attempting to block the genetic mechanisms that underlie the development of malignancy. Animal experiments have shown that if the expression of oncogenes can be blocked with an antisense gene, apoptosis and tumor cell death will result (Mukhopadhyay et al., 1991). The first approach, antisense genes, is discussed in Chapter 1. The second approach is to produce an antibody within the tumor cell that will block oncogene-induced oncogenesis by binding critical elements in the oncogene cell growth activation pathway (Beerli et al., 1994).

Antisense Oncogene Approaches.   Two approved clinical trials will transfer an antisense k-*ras* gene into k-*ras* overexpressing endobronchial lung cancers with either retroviral or adenoviral vectors in the same manner as WTp53 is being used (Table 6–2 and Appendix B). Animal studies have shown this method to be capable of complete elimination of human lung cancers growing in immunodeficient mice (Georges et al., 1993). This trial is currently enrolling patients, but no published information is available regarding clinical results from the treatments.

There are two other approved trials that attempt to block oncogene expression through an antisense mechanism (Table 6–2 and Appendix B). The first is directed at the c-*fos* or c-*myc* oncogenes that are often overexpressed in breast cancer cells. In this experiment, the retroviral vectors that contain the antisense genes to c-*fos* or c-*myc* are under the control of a mammary cell-specific promoter and will be injected directly into tumor deposits (Arteaga and Holt, 1996). Because of the use of a retroviral vector that can transfer genes only into proliferating cells and the tissue-specific promoter, the antisense genes should be expressed only in malignant mammary cells. Antisense c-*myc* is also being used in the same manner for the experimental treatment of prostate cancer patients. These trials are early in the clinical phase of experimentation and no published preliminary data are available.

Intracellular Antibody Techniques. This approach to cancer therapy is similar to several HIV protocols (see Chapter 5). One trial has been approved to use an adenovirus vector to transfer an anti-*erbB*-2 single-chain antibody gene into the peritoneal space of women with ovarian cancer (Table 6–2 and Appendix B). The product of the *erbB*-2 oncogene is bound by the vector-derived single-chain antibody, blocking cellular activation by *erbB*-2 and inducing apoptosis (Deshane et al., 1994). Elimination of *erbB*-2-positive tumor cells has been safely achieved in animal models. As a result, a human clinical trial has been approved, but no published clinical data are available at this time. It is expected that there will be a number of related trials that will be devised in an effort to induce apoptosis in tumor cells *in vivo*, because this is a very effective, selective process for tumor cell destruction.

OTHER CANCER GENE THERAPY METHODS IN DEVELOPMENT

Induction of Apoptosis

Apoptosis, or programmed cell death, is a very hot area of research because triggering the apoptosis pathway results in DNA fragmentation and unequivocal cell death without apparent damage to surrounding tissues (Steller, 1995). This is one of the methods that the body uses naturally to eliminate tumor cells, virus-infected cells, and autoreactive cells. One of the first components of the apoptosis pathway identified was a cell-surface structure termed APO-1 (now also known as FAS antigen or CD95). Treatment of an APO-1-positive tumor cell with anti-APO-1 monoclonal antibody results in apoptosis (Trauth et al., 1989). Efforts to determine factors that will trigger this receptor have identified a FAS ligand (Suda et al., 1993). The combination of the FAS antigen and FAS ligand will also trigger apoptosis. Infusion of the FAS ligand into mice was lethal due to fulminant hepatitis (Ogasawara et al., 1993). Therefore, gene transfer might be used to deliver selectively genes whose intracellular product will act functionally as if it were a ligand bound to APO-1, and restore APO-1 on tumor cell surfaces and/or down-regulate oncogenes that block apoptosis (e.g., *Bcl*-2), with limited potential adverse side effects (Lacronique et al., 1996). Once the various intracellular pathways involved in apoptosis have been fully defined, there will likely be multiple different targets for which transfer genes may be used to trigger apoptosis selectively in tumor cells.

Enhancement of Chemotherapeutic and Radiation Activity

Gene therapy also may be used to potentiate standard forms of chemotherapy and radiation therapy to achieve either the same effect with a lower dose or to protect nonmalignant tissues, so that higher doses can be delivered to the tumor without increased systemic toxicities. For instance, investigators have shown that transfer of the cytochrome P-450 genes into tumor cells enhances the cytotoxic effect of cyclophosphamide (Chen and Waxman, 1995). The antitumor effects of cyclophosphamide are dependent on liver cytochrome P-450, which converts cyclophosphamide to the toxic derivative 4-hydroxycyclophosphamide. Therefore, gene transfer may allow a potentiation of this conversion within the local area of gene transfer, increasing activity and limiting the systemic side effects.

A second approach is to alter the effect of ionizing radiation. One method is to link a TNF-α gene to a radiation-inducible promoter such as the *Egr*-1 gene. Experiments *in vivo* have shown the degree of tumor killing is greater than either treatment alone without increased local toxicity (Weichselbaum et al., 1994; Hallahan et al., 1995). Another possibility is the transfer of the manganese superoxide dismutase gene, which has been demonstrated to decrease the tumorigenicity of tumor cells *in vitro* and *in vivo* (Urano et al., 1995). While the goal of gene therapy is to eliminate the need for systemic, toxic chemotherapy and radiation therapy, the further development of these methods could be an important step along the path to that goal.

THE GENETIC PREVENTION OF CANCER

Because cancer has a significant genetic component, individuals can be identified who have a known predisposition to cancer (e.g., patients with mutations in p53 or BRAC1). Integrating vectors theoretically could be used to insert genes stably into mammary epithelial cells in patients at risk. Insertion of a normal copy of the gene or repair of the defective gene will likely become a primary approach to the treatment of loss of tumor suppressor gene function in the future. However, when there is a gain of function (i.e., overexpression of an oncogene), the oncogene needs to be disabled. The oncogene's expression may be blocked with antisense genes or intracellular antibodies as described above.

Further clarification of the seeming multitude of genetic abnormalities that predispose to cancer will certainly provide insight into a variety of potential genetic manipulations that may function to prevent the onset of malignancy. Developing the ability to prevent cancer will always be superior to any therapy applied after the onset of the disease. Just as for therapy, the potential uses of gene transfer and gene repair for the prevention of cancer are limited only by our imagination.

SUMMARY

Our growing understanding of the molecular basis of cancer has led us into a new era in cancer therapy. As a massive gene therapy attack mounts against all forms of malignancy, there is reason to be optimistic. For the first time, scientists and clinicians have joined together to target directly the molecular basis of tumorigenesis through the restoration of tumor suppressor gene function or the inhibition of oncogene expression. In addition, scientists mapping the genomes of viruses, bacteria, fungi, and humans have provided us with a number of genes that can be used to destroy cancer cells selectively (e.g., HS-*tk*), induce a potent antitumor immune response (e.g., IL-2), and provide protection for normal tissues against the toxic effects of systemic chemotherapy (e.g., *MDR-1*). These new anticancer tools provide new opportunities for selective tumor cell destruction *in vivo* without the common regional and systemic side effects related to standard forms of chemotherapy, radiation, and surgery. Over the next 5 to 10 years, gene therapy is likely to become a standard therapy for certain forms of cancer. In addition to effective cancer therapies, the development of genetic cancer prevention strategies is needed. As the genome project progresses, many genetic abnormalities will be identified that predispose individuals to cancer. The further development of efficient *in vivo* gene delivery methods may furnish us with the opportunity to reestablish genetic health in susceptible cells, providing an opportunity to achieve our ultimate goal of cancer prevention.

REFERENCES

General

Chambers, R., Gillespie, G.Y., Soroceanu, L., Andreansky, S., Chatterjee, S., Chou, J., Roizman, B., and Whitley, R.J. (1995): Comparison of genetically engineered herpes simplex viruses for the treatment of brain tumors in a scid mouse model of human malignant glioma. Proc. Natl. Acad. Sci. U.S.A. 92:1411–1415.

Cho, K.R. and Vogelstein, B. (1992): Genetic alterations in the adenoma-carcinoma sequence. Cancer 70 (Suppl):1727–1731.

Gutierrez, A.A., Lemoine, N.R., and Sikora, K. (1992): Gene therapy for cancer. Lancet 339:715–721.

Herrmann, F. (1995): Cancer gene therapy: Principles, problems, and perspectives. J. Mol. Med. 73:157–163.

Hu, G., Liu, W., Hanania, E.G., Fu, S., Wang, T., and Deisseroth, A.B. (1995): Suppression of tumorigenesis by transcription units expressing the antisense E6 and E7 messenger RNA (mRNA) for the transforming proteins of the human papilloma virus and the sense mRNA for the retinoblastoma gene in cervical carcinoma cells. Cancer Gene Ther. 2:19–32.

Kinzler, K.W., and Vogelstein, B. (1992): The colorectal gene hunt: current findings. Hosp. Pract. 27:51–58.

Randrianarison-Jewtoukoff, V., and Perricaudet, M. (1995): Recombinant adenoviruses as vaccines. Biologicals 23:145–157.

Roth, J.A., Mukhopadhyay, T., Zhang, W.W., Fujiwara, T., and Georges, R. (1994): Gene replacement strategies for the prevention and therapy of cancer. Eur. J. Cancer. 30:2032–2037.

Schmidt-Wolf, G. and Schmidt-Wolf, I.G.H. (1995): Cytokines and clinical gene therapy. Eur. J. Immunol. 25:1137–1140.

Shillitoe, E.J., Kamath, P., and Chen, Z. (1994a): Papilloma viruses as targets for cancer gene therapy. Cancer Gene Ther. 1:193–204.

Shillitoe, E.J., Lapeyre, J-M., and Adler-Storthz, K. (1994b): Gene therapy-its potential in the management of oral cancer. Eur. J. Cancer 30B:143–145.

Spooner, R.A., and Epenetos, A.A. (1995): Genetic delivery of enzymes for cancer therapy. Gene Ther. 2:235–244.

Xie, K., Huang, S., Dong, Z., Juang, S.H., Gutman, M., Xie, Q., Nathan, C., and Fidler, I.J. (1995): Transfection with the inducible nitric-oxide-synthase gene suppresses tumorigenicity and abrogates metastasis by K-1735 murine melanoma cells. J. Exp. Med. 181:1333–1343.

Hematopoietic Stem Cells

Allay, J.A., Dumenco, L.L., Koc, O.N., Liu, L., and Gerson, S.L. (1995): Retroviral transduction and expression of the human alklytransferase cDNA provides nitrosourea resistance to hematopoietic cells. Blood 85:3342–3351.

Barquinero, J., Kiem, H.P., van Kalle, C., Darovsky, B., Goehle, S., Graham, T., Seidel, K., Storb, R., and Schuening, F.G. (1995): Myelosuppressive conditioning improves autologous engraftment of genetically marked hematopoietic repopulating cells in dogs. Blood 85:1195–1201.

Brenner, M.K., Rill, D.R., Moen, R.C., Krance, R.A., Mirro, J., Jr., Anderson, W.F., and Ihle, J.N. (1993a): Gene-marking to trace origin of relapse after autologous bone-marrow transplantation. Lancet 341:85–86.

Brenner, M.K., Rill, D.R., Holladay, M.S., Heslop, H.E., Moen, R.C., Buschle, M., Krance, R.A., Santana, V.M., Anderson, W.F., and Ihle, J.N. (1993b): Gene marking to determine whether autologous marrow infusion restores long-term haemopoiesis in cancer patients. Lancet 342:1134–1137.

Brenner, M.K., Rill, D.R., Heslop, H.E., Rooney, C.M., Roberts, W.M., Li, C., Nilson, T., and Krance, R.A. (1994): Gene marking after bone marrow transplantation. Eur. J. Cancer 30A: 1171–1176.

Brenner, M.K. (1995): Human somatic gene therapy: Progress and problems. J. Intern. Med. 237:229–239.

Cardarelli, C.O., Aksentijevich, I., Pastan, I., and Gottesman, M.M. (1995): Differential effects of P-glycoprotein inhibitors on NIH3T3 cells transfected with wild-type(G185) or mutant (V185) multidrug transporters. Cancer Res. 55:1086–1091.

Deisseroth, A.B., Zu, Z., Claxton, D., Hanania, E.G., Fu, F., Ellerson, D., Goldberg, L., Thomas, M., Janicek, K., Anderson, W.F., Hester, J., Korbling, M., Durett, A., Moen, R., Berenson, R., Heimfeld, S., Hamer, J., Calvert, L., Tibbits, P., Talpaz, M., Kantarjian, H., Champlin, R., and Reading, C. (1994): Genetic marking shows that Ph+ cell present in autologous transplants of chronic myelogenous leukemia (CML) contribute to relapse after autologous bone marrow in CML. Blood 83:3068–3076.

Dunbar, C.E., Cottler-Fox, M., O'Shaughnessy, J.A., Doren, S., Carter, C., Berenson, R., Brown, S., Moen, R.C., Greenblatt, J., Stewart, F.M., Leitman, S.F., Wilson, W.H., Cowan, K., Young, N.S., and Nienhuis, A.W. (1995): Retrovirally marked CD34-enriched peripheral blood and bone marrow cells contribute to long-term engraftment after autologous transplantation. Blood 85:3048–3057.

Galaski, H., Sullivan, M., Willingham, M.C., Chin, K-V., Gottesman, M., Pastan, I., and Merlino, G.T. (1989): Expression of a human multidrug resistance cDNA (MDR1) in the bone marrow of transgenic mice: Resistance to daunomycin-induced leukopenia. Mol. Cell. Biol. 9:4357–4363.

Hanania, E.G., Fu, S., Zu, Z., Hegewisch-Becker, S., Korbling, M., Hester, J., Durett, A., Andreeff, M., Mechetner, E., Holtzmayer, T., Robinson, I.B., Giles, R.E., Berenson, R., Heimfeld, S., and Deisseroth, A.B. (1995a): Chemotherapy resistance to taxol in clonogenic progenitor cells following transduction of CD34 selected marrow and peripheral blood cells with a retrovirus that contains the MDR-1 chemotherapy resistance gene. Gene Ther. 2:285–294.

Hanania, E.G., Fu, S., Robinson, I., Zu, Z., Gottesman, M.M., and Deisseroth, A.B. (1995b): Resistance to taxol chemotherapy produced in mouse marrow cells by safety-modified retroviruses containing a human MDR-1 transcription unit. Gene Ther. 2:279–284.

Hegewisch-Becker, S., Hanania, E.G., Fu, S., Koerbling, M., Deisseroth, A.B., and Andreeff, M. (1995): Transduction of MDR1 into human and mouse hematopoietic progenitor cells: Use of rhodamine (Rh123) to determine transduction frequency and in vivo selection. Br. J. Haematol. 90:876–883.

Licht, T., Aksentijevich, I., Gottesman, M.M., and Pastan, I. (1995): Efficient expression of functional human MDR1 gene in murine bone marrow after retroviral transduction of purified hematopoietic stem cells. Blood 86:111–121.

May, C., Gunther, R., and McIvor, R.S. (1995): Protection of mice from lethal doses of methotrexate by transplantation with transgenic marrow expressing drug-resistant dihydrofolate reductase activity. Blood 86:2439–2448.

Metz, M.Z., Best, D.M., and Kane S.E. (1995): Harvey murine sarcoma virus/MDR1 retroviral vectors: Efficient virus production and foreign gene transduction using MDR1 as a selectable marker. Virology 208:634–643.

Moolten, F.L. (1986): Tumor chemosensitivity conferred by inserted herpes thymidine kinase genes: Paradigm for a prospective cancer control strategy. Cancer Res. 46:5276–5281.

Moritz, T., Mackay, W., Glassner, B.J., Williams, D.A., and Samson, L. (1995): Retrovirus-mediated expression of a DNA repair protein in bone marrow protects hematopoietic cells from nitrosourea-induced toxicity in vitro and in vivo. Cancer Res. 55:2608–2614.

Richardson, C., Ward, M., and Bank, A. (1995): MDR gene transfer into live mice. J. Mol. Med. 73:189–195.

Rill, D.R., Santana, V.M., Roberts, W.M., Nilson, T., Bowman, L.C., Krance, R.A., Heslop, H.E., Moen, R.C., Ihle, J.N., and Brenner, M.K. (1994): Direct demonstration that autologous bone marrow transplantation for solid tumors can return a multiplicity of tumorigenic cells. Blood 84:380–383.

Sorrentino, B.P., Brandt, S.J., Bodine, D., Gottesman, M., Pastan, I., Cline, A., and Nienhuis, A.W. (1992): Selection of drug-resistant bone marrow cells in vivo after retroviral transfer of human MDR1. Science 257:99–103.

T Lymphocytes

Bordignon, C., Bonini, C., Verzeletti, S., Nobili, N., Maggioni, D., Traversari, C., Giavazzi, R., Servida, P., Zappone, E., Benazzi, E., Bernadi, M., Porta, F., Ferrari, G., Mavilio, F., Rossini, S., Blaese, R.M., and Candotti, F. (1995): Transfer of the HSV-tk gene into donor peripheral blood lymphocytes for in vivo modulation of donor anti-tumor immunity after allogeneic bone marrow transplantation. Hum. Gene Ther. 6:813–819.

Bunnell, B.A., Muul, L.M., Donahue, R.E., Blaese, R.M., and Morgan, R.A. (1995): High-efficiency retroviral-mediated gene transfer into human and nonhuman primate peripheral blood lymphocytes. Proc. Natl. Acad. Sci. U.S.A. 92:7739–7743.

Cai, Q., Rubin, J.T., and Lotze, M.T. (1995): Genetically marking human cells. Results of the first clinical gene transfer studies. Cancer Gene Ther. 2:125–136.

Cesano, A., Visonneau, S., and Santoli, D. (1995): Treatment of experimental glioblastoma with a human major histocompatibility complex non restricted cytotoxic T cell line. Cancer Res. 55:96–101.

Culver, K., Cornetta, K., Morgan, R., Morecki, S., Aebersold, P., Kasid, A., Lotze, M., Rosenberg, S.A., Anderson, W.F., and Blaese, R.M. (1991): Lymphocytes as cellular vehicles for gene therapy in mouse and man. Proc. Natl. Acad. Sci. U.S.A. 88:3155–3159.

Economou, J.S., Belldegrun, A., Figlin, R.A., Holmes, E.C., Jacobs, E., Kohn, D., Golub, S., Shau, H., DeKernion, J., McBride, W.H., and Moen, R.C. (1992): The treatment of patients with metastatic melanoma and renal cell cancer using in vitro expanded and genetically-engineered (neomycin phosphotransferase) bulk, CD8(+) and/or CD4(+) tumor infiltrating leukocytes and bulk, CD8(+) and/or CD4(+) peripheral blood leukocytes in combination with recombinant interleukin-2 alone, or with recombinant interleukin-2 and recombinant alpha interferon. Hum. Gene Ther. 3:411–430.

Hwu, P., Yang, J.C., Cowherd, R., Treisman, J., Shafer, G.E., Eshhar, Z., and Rosenberg, S.A. (1995): In vivo antitumor activity of T-cells redirected with chimeric antibody/T-cell receptor genes. Cancer Res. 55:3369–3373.

Hwu, P., Yannelli, J., Kriegler, M., Anderson, W.F., Perez, C., Chiang, Y., Schwarz, S., Cowherd, R., Delgado, C., Mule, J., and Rosenberg, S.A. (1993): Functional and molecular characterization of tumor-infiltrating lymphocytes transduced with tumor necrosis factor-α cDNA for the gene therapy of cancer in humans. J. Immunol. 150:4104–4115.

Kasid, A., Morecki, S., Aebersold, P., Cornetta, K., Culver, K., Freeman, S., Director, E., Lotze, M.T., Blaese, R.M., Anderson, W.F., and Rosenberg, S.A. (1990): Human gene transfer: Characterization of human tumor infiltrating lymphocytes as vehicles for retroviral-mediated gene transfer in man. Proc. Natl. Acad. Sci. U.S.A. 87:473–477.

Marincola, F.M., Ettinghausen, S., Cohen, P.A., Cheshire, L.B., Restifo, N.P., Mule, J.J., and Rosenberg, S.A. (1994): Treatment of established lung metastases with tumor-infiltrating lymphocytes derived from a poorly immunogenic tumor engineered to secrete human TNFα. J. Immunol. 152:3501–3513.

Merrouche, Y., Negrier, S., Bain, C., Combaret, V., Mercatello, A., Coronel, B., Moskovtchenk, J.F., Tolstoshev, P., Moen, R., Philip, T., and Favrot, M.C. (1995): Clinical application of retroviral gene transfer in oncology: results of a French study with tumor infiltrating lymphocytes transduced with the gene of resistance to neomycin. J. Clin. Oncol. 13:410–418.

Nakamura, Y., Wakimoto, H., Abe, J., Kanegae, Y., Saito, I., Aoyagi, M., Hirakawa, K., and Hamada, H. (1994): Adoptive immunotherapy with murine tumor-specific T-lymphocytes engineered to secrete interleukin-2. Cancer Res. 54:5757–5760.

Nash, M.A., Platsoucas, C.D., Wong, B.Y., Wong, P.M.C., Cottler-Fox, M., Otto, E., and Freedman, R.S. (1995): Transduction of rIL-2 expanded CD4+ and CD8+ ovarian TIL-derived T cell lines with the G1Na (neoR) replication-deficient retroviral vector. Hum. Gene Ther. 6:1379–1389.

Rooney, C.M., Smith, C.A., Ng, C.Y.C., Loftin, S., Li, C., Krance, R.A., Brenner, M.K., and Heslop, H.E. (1995): Use of gene-modified virus-specific T-lymphocytes to control Epstein-Barr virus-related lymphoproliferation. Lancet. 345:9–13.

Rosenberg, S.A., Aebersold, P., Cornetta, K., Kasid, A., Morgan, R., Moen, R., Karson, E., Lotze, M.T., Yang, J.C., Topalian, S., Merino, M.J., Culver, K., Miller, A.D., Blaese, R.M., and Anderson, W.F. (1990a): Gene transfer into humans—Immunotherapy of patients with advanced melanoma, using tumor-infiltrating lymphocytes modified by retroviral gene transduction. N. Engl. J. Med. 323:570–578.

Rosenberg, S.A., Kasid, A., Anderson, W.F., Blaese, R.M., Aebersold, P., Yang, J., Topalian, S., Kreigler, M., Maiorella, B., Moen, R, and Chiang, Y. (1990b): TNF/TIL human gene therapy clinical protocol. Hum. Gene Ther. 1:443–462.

Salvadori, S., Gansbacher, B., and Zier, K. (1994): Functional defects are associated with abnormal signal transduction in T cells of mice inoculated with parental but not IL-2 secreting tumor cells. Cancer Gene Ther. 1:165–170.

Schendel, D.J., and Gansbacher, B. (1993): Tumor-specific lysis of human renal cell carcinomas by tumor-infiltrating lymphocytes: Modulation of recognition through retroviral transduction of tumor cells with interleukin 2 complementary DNA and exogenous α interferon treatment. Cancer Res. 53:4020–4025.

Treisman, J., Hwu, P., Minamoto, S., Shafer, G.E., Cowherd, R., Morgan, R.A., and Rosenberg, S.A. (1995): Interleukin-2-transduced lymphocytes grow in an autocrine fashion and remain responsive to antigen. Blood 85:139–145.

Wahl, W.L., Strome, S.E., Nabel, G.J., Plautz, G.E., Cameron, M.J., San, H., Fox, B.A., Shu, S., and Chang, A.E. (1995): Generation of therapeutic T-lymphocytes after in vivo tumor transfection with an allogeneic class-I major histocompatibility complex gene. J. Immunother. 17:1–11.

Yamaue, H., Kashmiri, S.V.S., De Filippi, R., Nieroda, C., Yannelli, J.R., Tsang, K.Y., and Schlom, J. (1994): Enhanced interleukin-2 production in human tumor infiltrating lymphocytes engineered by 3'-truncated interleukin-2 gene. J. Immunother. 16:262–274.

Cytokine Gene Transfer into Tumor Cells

Abdel-Wahab, Z., Li, W.P., Osanto, S., Darrow, T.L., Hessling, J., Vervaert, C.E., Burrascano, M., Barber, J., and Seigler, H.F. (1994): Transduction of human melanoma cells with interleukin-2 gene reduces tumorigenicity and enhances host antitumor immunity: A nude mouse model. Cell Immunol. 159:26–39.

Abdel-Wahab, Z.A., Osanto, S., Darrow, T.L., Barber, J.R., Vevaert, C.E., and Gangavalli, R. (1995): Transduction of human melanoma cells with the gamma interferon gene enhances cellular immunity. Cancer Gene Ther. 1:171–179.

Addison, C.L., Braciak, T., Ralston, R., Muller, W.J., Gauldie, J., and Graham, F.L. (1995): Intratumoral injection of an adenovirus expressing interleukin 2 induces regression and immunity in a murine breast cancer model. Proc. Natl. Acad. Sci. U.S.A. 92:8522–8526.

Allione, A., Consalvo, M. N., Hock, H., Blankenstein, T., Rosenthal, F.M., Gansbacher, B., Bosco, M.C., Musso, T., Gusella, L., and Forni, G. (1994): Immunizing and curative potential of replicating and nonreplicating murine mammary adenocarcinoma cells engineered with interleukin (IL)-2, IL-4, IL-6, IL-7, IL-10. Cancer Res. 54:6022–6026.

Asher, A.L., Mule, J.J., Kasid, A., Restifo, N.P., Salo, J.C., Reichert, C.M., Jaffe, G., Fendly, B., Kriegler, M., and Rosenberg, S.A. (1991): Murine tumor cells transduced with the gene for tumor necrosis factor-a. J. Immunol. 146:3227.

Bubenik, J., Simova, J., Bubenikova, D., Zeuthen, J., and Indrova, M. (1995): Interleukin-2 gene therapy of residual EL-4 leukemia potentiates the effect of cyclophosphamide pretreatment. J. Cancer Res. Clin. Oncol. 121:39–43.

Colombo, M.P. and Forni, G. (1994): Cytokine gene transfer in tumor inhibition and tumor therapy: Where are we now? Immunol. Today 15:48–51.

Cordier, L., Duffour, M.T., Sabourin, J.C., Lee, M.G., Cabannes, J., Ragot, T., Perricaudet, M., and Haddada, H. (1995): Complete recovery of mice from a preestablished tumor by direct intratumoral delivery of an adenovirus vector harboring the murine IL-2 gene. Gene Ther. 2:16–21.

Dranoff, G., Jaffee, E., Lazenby, A., Golumbek, P., Levitsky, H., Brose, K., Jackson, V., Hamada, H., Pardoll, D., and Mulligan, R.C. (1993): Vaccination with irradiated tumor cells engineered to secrete murine granulocyte-macrophage colony-stimulating factor stimulates potent, specific, and long-lasting anti-tumor immunity. Proc. Natl. Acad. Sci. U.S.A. 90:3539–3543.

Fakhrai, H., Shawler, D.L., Gjerset, R., Naviaux, R.K., Koziol, J., Royston, I., and Sobol, R.E. (1995): Cytokine gene therapy with interleukin-2-transduced fibroblasts: Effects of IL-2 dose on anti-tumor immunity. Hum. Gene Ther. 6:591–601.

Fearon, E.R., Pardoll, D.M., Itaya, T., Golumbek, P., Levitsky, H.I., Simons, J.W., Karasuyama, H., Vogelstein, B., and Frost, P. (1990): Interleukin-2 production by tumor cells bypasses T helper function in the generation of an antitumor response. Cell. 60:397–403.

Ferrantini, M., Giovarelli, M., Modesti, A., Musiani, P., Modica, A., Venditti, M., Peretti, E., Lollini, P.L., Nanni, P., Forni, G., and Belardelli, F. (1994): IFN-alpha-1 gene expression into a metastatic murine adenocarcinoma (TS/A) results in CD8+ T-cell-mediated tumor rejection and development of antitumor immunity: comparative studies with IFN-gamma-producing TS/A cells. J. Immunol. 153:4604–4615.

Gansbacher, B., Bannerji, R., Daniels, B., Zier, K., Cronin, K., and Gilboa, E. (1990): Retroviral vector-mediated γ-interferon gene transfer into tumor cells generates potent and long lasting antitumor immunity. Cancer Res. 50:7820-7825.

Golumbek, P.T., Lazenby, A.J., Levitsky, H.I., Jaffee, L.M., Karasuyama, H., Baker, M., and Pardoll, D.M. (1991): Treatment of established renal cell cancer by tumor cells engineered to secrete interleukin-4. Science 254:713-716.

Hurford, R.K., Dranoff, G., Mulligan, R.C., and Tepper, R.I. (1995): Gene therapy of metastatic cancer by in vivo retroviral targeting. Nature Genet. 10:430-435.

Kaido, T., Bandu, M.T., Maury, C., Ferrantini, M., Belardelli, F., and Gresser, I. (1995): IFN-alpha-1 gene transfection completely abolishes the tumorigenicity of murine B16 melanoma cells in allogeneic DBA/2 mice and decreases their tumorigenicity in syngeneic C57BL/6 mice. Int. J. Cancer 60:221-229.

Krauss, J.C., Cameron, M.J., Park, A.N., Forslund, K., and Chang, A.E. (1995): Efficient transduction of early passage human melanoma to secrete IL-4. J. Immunol. Methods 183(2):239-250.

Laning, J., Kawasaki, H., Tanaka, E., Luo, Y., and Dorf, M.E. (1994): Inhibition of in vivo tumor growth by the beta-chemokine, TCA3. J. Immunol. 153:4625-4635.

Lollini, P.L., D'Errico, A., De Giovanni, C., Landuzzi, L., Frabetti, F., Nicoletti, G., Cavallo, F., Giovarelli, M., Grigioni, W.F., and Nanni, P. (1995): Systemic effects of cytokines released by gene-transduced tumor cells: marked hyperplasia induced in small bowel by gamma-interferon transfectants through host lymphocytes. Int. J. Cancer 61:425-430.

Maass, G., Schmidt, W., Berger, M., Schilcher, F., Koszik, F., Schneeberger, A., Stingl, G., Birnstiel, M.L., and Schweighoffer, T. (1995): Priming of tumor-specific T cells in the draining lymph nodes after immunization with interleukin-2-secreting tumor cells: Three consecutive stages may be required for successful tumor vaccination. Proc. Natl. Acad. Sci. U.S.A. 92:5540-5544.

Martinotti, A., Stoppacciaro, A., Vagliani, M., Melani, C., Spreafico, F., Wysocka, M., Parimani, G., Trinchieri, G., and Colombo, M.P. (1994): CD4 T-cells inhibit in vivo the CD8-mediated immune response against murine colon carcinoma cells transduced with interleukin-12 genes. Eur. J. Immunol. 25:137-146.

McAdam, A.J., Pulaski, B.A., Harkins, S.S., Hutter, E.K., Lord, E.M., and Frelinger, J.G. (1995): Synergistic effects of co-expression of the TH1 cytokines IL-2 and IFN-gamma on generation of murine tumor-reactive cytotoxic cells. Int. J. Cancer 61:628-634.

McBride, W.H., Thacker, J.D., Comora, S., Economou, J.S., Kelley, D., Hogge, D., Dubinett, S.M., and Dougherty, G.J. (1992): Genetic modification of a murine fibrosarcoma to produce interleukin-7 stimulates host cell infiltration and tumor immunity. Cancer Res. 52:3931-3937.

Mullen, C.A., Coale, M.M., Levy, A.T., Stetler-Stevenson, W.G., Liotta, L.A., Brandt, S., and Blaese, R.M. (1992): Fibrosarcoma cells transduced with the IL-6 gene exhibit reduced tumorigenicity, increased immunogenicity and decreased metastatic potential. Cancer Res. 52:6020-6024.

Nabel, G.J., Chang, A., Nabel, E.G., and Plautz, G. (1992): Immunotherapy of malignancy by in vivo gene transfer into tumors. Hum. Gene Ther. 3:399-410.

Nishihara, K., Barth, R.F., Wilkie, N., Lang, J.C., Oda, Y., Kikuchi, H., Everson, M.P., and Lotze, M.T. (1995): Increased in vitro and in vivo tumoricidal activity of a macrophage cell line genetically engineered to express IFN-gamma, IL-4, IL-6 or TNF-alpha. Cancer Gene Ther. 2:113-124.

Pericle, F., Giovarelli, M., Colombo, M.P., Ferrari, G., Musiani, P., Modesti, A., Cavallo, F., Di Pierro, F., Novelli, F., and Forni, G. (1994): An efficient Th2-type memory follows CD8+ lymphocyte-driven and eosinophil-mediated rejection of a spontaneous mouse mammary adenocarcinoma engineered to release IL-4. J. Immunol. 153:5659-5673.

Reszka, R., Zhu, J.H., Weber, F., Walther, W., Greferath, R., and Dyballa, S. (1995): Liposome mediated transfer of marker and cytokine genes into rat and human glioblastoma cells in vitro and in vivo. J. Liposome Res. 5:149-167.

Rosenthal, F.M., Cronin, K., Bannerji, R., Golde, D.W., and Gansbacher, B. (1994): Augmentation of antitumor immunity by tumor cells transduced with a retroviral vector carrying the interleukin-2 and interferon-γ cDNAs. Blood 83:1289-1298.

Saito, S., Bannerji, R., Gansbacher, B., Rosenthal, F.M., Romanenko, P., Heston, W.D.W., Fair, W.R., and Gilboa, E. (1994): Immunotherapy of bladder cancer with cytokine gene-modified tumor vaccines. Cancer Res. 54:3516-3520.

Schmidt, W., Schweighoffer, T., Herbst, E., Maass, G., Berger, M., Schilcher, F., Schaffner, G., and Birnstiel, M.L. (1995): Cancer vaccines: The interleukin-2 dosage effect. Proc. Natl. Acad. Sci. U.S.A. 92:4711-4714.

Shawler, D.L., Dorigo, O., Gjerset, R.A., Royston, I., Sobol, R.E., and Fakhrai, H. (1995): Comparison of gene therapy with interleukin-2 gene modified fibroblasts and tumor cells in the murine CT-26 model of colorectal carcinoma. J. Immunother. 17:201-208.

Sobol, R.E., Fakhrai, H., Shawler, D., Gjerset, R., Dorigo, O., Carson, C., Khaleghi, T., Koziol, J., Shiftan, T.A., and Royston, I. (1995): Interleukin-2 gene therapy in a patient with glioblastoma. Gene Ther. 2:164–167.

Sparmann, G., Walther, W., Gunzburg, W.H., Uckert, W., and Salmons, B. (1994): Conditional expression of human TNF-alpha: A system for inducible cytotoxicity. Int. J. Cancer. 59:103–107.

Suminam, Y., Elder, E.M., Lotze, M.T., and Whiteside, T.L. (1995): In situ interleukin-4 gene expression in cancer patients treated with genetically modified tumor vaccine. J. Immunother. 17:238–248.

Sun, W.H., Burkholder, J.K., Sun, J., Culp, J., Turner, J., Lu, X.G., Pugh, T.D., Ershler, W.B., and Yang, N.S. (1995): In vivo cytokine gene transfer by gene gun reduces tumor growth in mice. Proc. Natl. Acad. Sci. U.S.A. 92:2889–2893.

Tahara, H., and Lotze, M.T. (1995): Antitumor effects of interleukin-12 (IL-12): Applications for the immunotherapy and gene therapy of cancer. Gene Ther. 2:96–106.

Tahara, H., Zeh, III.H.J., Storkus, W.J., Pappo, I., Watkins, S.C., Gubler, U., Wolf, S.F., Robbins, P.D., and Lotze, M.T. (1994): Fibroblasts genetically engineered to secrete interleukin-12 can suppress tumor growth and induce antitumor immunity to a murine melanoma in vivo. Cancer Res. 54:182–189.

Tahara, H., Zitvogel, L., Storkus, W.J., Zeh, III.H.J., McKinney, T.G., Schreiber, R.D., Gubler, U., Robbins, P.D., and Lotze, M.T. (1995): Effective eradication of established murine tumors with IL-12 gene therapy using a polycistronic retroviral vector. J. Immunol. 154:6466–6474.

Tanaka, N., Sivanandham, M., and Wallack, M.K. (1994): Immunotherapy of a vaccinia colon oncolysate prepared with interleukin-2 gene-encoded vaccinia virus and interferon-alpha increases the survival of mice bearing syngeneic colon adenocarcinoma. J. Immunother. 16:283–293.

Tepper, R.I., Pattengale, P.K., and Leder, P. (1989): Murine interleukin-4 displays potent anti-tumor activity in vivo. Cell 57:503.

Vieweg, J., Boczkowski, D., Roberson, K.M., Edwards, D.W., Philip, M., Philip, R., Rudoll, T., Smith, C., Robertson, C., and Gilboa, E. (1995): Efficient gene transfer with adeno-associated virus-based plasmids complexed to cationic liposomes for gene therapy of human prostate cancer. Cancer Res. 55:2366–2372.

Walther, W., Stein, U., and Pfeil, D. (1995): Gene transfer of human TNF alpha into glioblastoma cells permits modulation of mdr1 expression and potentiation of chemosensitivity. Int. J. Cancer 61:832–839.

Wei, M.X., Tamiya, T., Hurford, Jr.R.K., Boviatsis, E.J., Tepper, R.I., and Chiocca, E.A. (1995): Enhancement of interleukin-4-mediated tumor regression in athymic mice by in situ retroviral gene transfer. Hum. Gene Ther. 6:437–443.

Xing, Z., Braciak, T., Jordana, M., Croitoru, K., Graham, F.L., and Gauldie, J. (1994): Adenovirus-mediated cytokine gene transfer at tissue sites: Over-expression of IL-6 induces lymphocytic hyperplasia in the lung. J. Immunol. 153:405–469.

Zitvogel, L., Tahara, H., Robbins, P.D., Storkus, W.J., Clarke, M.R., Nalesnik, M.A., and Lotze, M.T. (1995): Cancer immunotherapy of established tumors with IL-12. J. Immunol. 155:1393–1403.

Transfer of Foreign MHC Genes into Tumor Cells

De Giovanni, C., Nicoletti, G., Sensi, M., Santoni, A., Palmieri, G., and Landuzzi, L. (1994): H-2Kb and H-2Db gene transfections in B16 melanoma differently affect non-immunological properties relevant to the metastatic process. Involvement of integrin molecules. Int. J. Cancer. 59:269–274.

Hock, R.A., Reynolds, B.D., Tucker-McClung, C.L., and Kwok, W.W. (1995): Human class-II major histocompatibility complex gene transfer into murine neuroblastoma leads to loss of tumorigenicity, immunity against subsequent tumor challenge, and elimination of microscopic preestablished tumors. J. Immunother. 17:12–18.

Leach, D.R., and Callahan, G.N. (1995): Fibrosarcoma cells expressing allogeneic MHC class II antigens induce protective antitumor immunity. J. Immunol. 154:738–743.

Leong, C.C., Robinson, B.W.S., and Garlepp, M.J. (1994): Generation of an antitumor immune response to a murine mesothelioma cell line by the transfection of allogeneic MHC genes. Int. J. Cancer 59:212–216.

Nabel, G.J., Nabel, E.G., Yang, Z-Y., Fox, B.A., Plautz, G.E., Gao, X., Huang, L., Shu, S., Gordon, D., and Chang, A.E. (1993): Direct gene transfer with DNA-liposome complexes in melanoma: Expression, biologic activity, and lack of toxicity in humans. Proc. Natl. Acad. Sci. U.S.A. 90:11307–11311.

Nabel, E.G., Tang, Z., Muller, D., Chang, A.E., Gao, X., Huang, L., Cho, K.J., and Nabel, G.J. (1994): Safety and toxicity of catheter delivery to the pulmonary vasculature in a patient with metastatic melanoma. Human Gene Ther. 5:1089–1094.

Ostrand-Rosenberg, S., Thakur, A., and Clements, V. (1990): Rejection of mouse sarcoma cells after transfection of MHC class II genes. J. Immunol. 144:4068–4071.

Plaskin, D., Porgador, A., Vadai, E., Feldman, M., Schirrmacher, V., and Eisenbach, L. (1994): Effective anti-metastatic melanoma vaccination with tumor cells transfected with MHC genes and/or infected with Newcastle-disease virus (NDV). Int. J. Cancer 59:796–801.

Plautz, G.E., Yan, Z-Y., Wu, B-Y., Gao, X., Huang, L., and Nabel, G.J. (1993): Immunotherapy of malignancy by in vivo gene transfer into tumors. Proc. Natl. Acad. Sci. U.S.A. 90:4645–4649.

Making the Tumor "Visible" to T Lymphocytes: Antisense IGF-1

Long, L., Rubin, R., Baserga, R., and Brodt, P. (1995): Loss of the metastatic phenotype in murine carcinoma cells expressing an antisense RNA to the insulin-like growth factor receptor. Cancer Res. 55:1006–1009.

Trojan, J., Blossey, B.K., Johnson, T.R., Rudin, S.D., Tykocinski, M., Ilan, J., and Ilan, J. (1992): Loss of tumorigenicity of rat glioblastoma directed by episome-based antisense cDNA transcription of the insulin-like growth factor-1. Proc. Natl. Acad. Sci. U.S.A. 89:4874–4878.

Trojan, J., Johnson, T.R., Rudin, S.D., Ilan, J., Tykocinski, M.L., and Ilan, J. (1993): Treatment and prevention of rat glioblastoma by immunogenic C6 cells expressing antisense insulin-like growth factor 1 RNA. Science 259:94–97.

Making the Tumor "Visible" to T Lymphocytes: B7 Costimulatory Molecule

Baskar, S., Glimcher, L., Nabavi, N., Jones, R.T., and Ostrand-Rosenberg, S. (1995): Major histocompatibility complex class II+B7-1+ tumor cells are potent vaccines for stimulating tumor rejection in tumor-bearing mice. J. Exp. Med. 181:619–629.

Cayeux, S., Beck, C., Aicher, A., Dörken, B., and Blankenstein, T. (1995): Tumor cells cotransfected with interleukin-7 and B7.1 genes induce CD25 and CD28 on tumor-infiltrating lymphocytes and are strong vaccines. Eur. J. Immunol. 25:2325–2331.

Chen, L., McGowan, P., Ashe, S., Johnston, J., Li, Y., Hellström, I., and Hellström, K.E. (1994): Tumor immunogenicity determines the effect of B7 costimulation on T cell-mediated tumor immunity. J. Exp. Med. 179:523–532.

Fenton, R.T., Sznol, M., Luster, D.G., Taub, D.D., and Longo, D.L. (1995): A phase I trial of B7-transfected or parental lethally irradiated allogeneic melanoma cell lines to induce cell-mediated immunity against tumor-associated antigen presented by HLA-A2 or HLA-A1 in patients with stage IV melanoma. Hum. Gene Ther. 6:87–106.

Katsanis, E., Xu, Z., Bausero, M.A., Dancisak, B.B., Gorden, K.B., Davis, G., Gray, G.S., Orchard, P.J., and Blazar, B.R. (1995): B7-1 expression decreases tumorigenicity and induces partial systemic immunity to murine neuroblastoma deficient in major histocompatibility complex and costimulatory molecules. Cancer Gene Ther. 2:39–46.

Linsley, P.S., Brady, W., Grosmaire, L., Aruffo, A., Damle, N.K., and Ledbetter, J.A. (1991): Binding of the B cell activation antigen B7 to CD28 costimulates T cell proliferation and interleukin-2 mRNA accumulation. J. Exp. Med. 173:721–730.

Matulonis, U.A., Dosiou, C., Lamont, C., Freeman, G.J., Mauch, P., Nadler, L.M., and Griffin, J.D. (1995): Role of B7-1 in mediating an immune response to myeloid leukemia cells. Blood 85:2507–2515.

Salvadori, S., Gansbacher, B., Wernick, I., Tirelli, S., and Zier, K. (1995): B7-1 amplifies the response to interleukin-2-secreting tumor vaccines in vivo, but fails to induce a response by naive cells in vitro. Hum. Gene Ther. 6:1299–1306.

Townsend, S.E., and Allison, J.P. (1993): Tumor rejection after direct costimulation of CD8+ T cells by B7-transfected melanoma cells. Science 259:368–370.

Making the Tumor "Visible" to T Lymphocytes: Antisense TGF-β

Fakhrai, H., Dorigo, O., Shawler, D.L., Lin, H., Mercola, D., Black, K.L., Royston, I., and Sobol, R.E. (1996): Eradication of established intracranial rat gliomas by transforming growth factor β antisense gene therapy. Proc. Natl. Acad. Sci. U.S.A. 93:2909–2914.

Expression of Tumor Antigens on the Surface of Muscle Cells

Conry, R.M., LoBuglio, A.F., Loechel, F., Moore, S.E., Sumerel, L.A., Barlow, D.L., Pike, J., and Curiel, D.T. (1995a): A carcinoembryonic antigen polynucleotide vaccine for human clinical use. Cancer Gene Ther. 2:33–38.

Conry, R.M., LoBuglio, A.F., Loechel, F., Moore, S.E., Sumerel, L.A., Barlow, D.L., and Curiel, D.T. (1995b): A carcinoembryonic antigen polynucleotide vaccine has in vivo antitumor activity. Gene Ther. 2:59–65.

Horn, N.A., Meek, J.A., Budahazi, G., and Marquet, M. (1995): Cancer gene therapy using plasmid DNA: Purification of DNA for human clinical trials. Hum. Gene Ther. 6:565–573.

Lee, S.S., Eisenlohr, L.C., McCue, P.A., Mastrangelo, M.J., and Lattime, E.C. (1994): Intravesical gene therapy: In vivo gene transfer using recombinant vaccinia vectors. Cancer Res. 54:3325–3328.

Lew, D., Parker, S.E., Latimer, T., Abai, A.M., Kuwahara-Rundell, A., Doh, S.G., Yang, Z.H., Laface, D., Gromkowski, S.H., Nabel, G.J., Manthorpe, M., and Norman, J. (1995): Cancer gene therapy using plasmid DNA: Pharmacokinetic study of DNA following injection in mice. Hum. Gene Ther. 6:553–564.

Park, J.W., Hong, K., Carter, P., Asgari, H., Guo, L.Y., Keller, G.A., Wirth, C., Shalaby, R., Kotts, C., Wood, W.I., Papahadjopoulos, D., and Benz, C.C. (1995): Development of anti-p185HER2 immunoliposomes for cancer therapy. Proc. Natl. Acad. Sci. U.S.A. 92:1327–1331.

Parker, S.E., Vahlsing, H.L., Serfilippi, L.M., Franklin, C.L., Doh, S.G., Gromkowski, S.H., Lew, D., Manthorpe, M., and Norman, J. (1995): Cancer gene therapy using plasmid DNA: Safety evaluation in rodents and non-human primates. Hum. Gene Ther. 6:575–590.

Spooner, R.A., Deonarain, M.P., and Epenetos, A.A. (1995): DNA vaccination for cancer treatment. Gene Ther. 2:173–180.

Wang, B., Merva, M., Dang, K., Ugen, K.E., Williams, W.V., and Weiner, D.B. (1995): Immunization by direct DNA inoculation induces rejection of tumor cell challenge. Hum. Gene Ther. 6:407–418.

The Herpes Simplex-Thymidine Kinase (HS-tk) Gene

Barba, D., Hardin, J., Ray, J., and Gage, F.H. (1993): Thymidine kinase-mediated killing of rat brain tumors. J. Neurosurg. 79:729–735.

Bi, W.L., Parysek, L.M., Warnick, R., and Stambrook, P.J. (1993): In vitro evidence that metabolic cooperation is responsible for the bystander effect observed with HSV tk retroviral gene therapy. Hum. Gene Ther. 4:725–732.

Bonnekoh, B., Greenhalgh, D.A., Bundman, D.S., Eckhardt, J.N., Longley, M.A., Chen, S.H., Woo, S.L.C., and Roop, D.R. (1995): Inhibition of melanoma growth by adenoviral-mediated HSV thymidine-kinase gene transfer in vivo. J. Invest. Dermatol. 104:313–317.

Boviatsis, E.J., Park, J.S., Sena-Esteves, M., Kramm, C.M., Chase, M., Efird, J.T., Wei, M.X., Breakefield, X.O., and Chiocca, E.A. (1994): Long-term survival of rats harboring brain neoplasms treated with ganciclovir and a herpes simplex virus vector that retains an intact thymidine-kinase gene. Cancer Res. 54:5745–5751.

Byrnes, A.P., Rusby, J.E., Wood, M.J.A., and Charlton, H.M. (1995): Adenovirus gene transfer causes inflammation in the brain. Neuroscience (Oxford). 66:1015–1024.

Caruso, M., Panis, Y., Gagandeep, S., Houssin, D., Salzmann, J-L., and Klatzmann, D. (1993): Regression of established macroscopic liver metastases after in situ transduction of a suicide gene. Proc. Natl. Acad. Sci. U.S.A. 90:7024–7028.

Chen, S-H., Shine, H.D., Goodman, J.C., Grossman, R.G., and Woo, S.L.C. (1994): Gene therapy for brain tumors: Regression of experimental gliomas by adenovirus-mediated gene transfer in vivo. Proc. Natl. Acad. Sci. U.S.A. 91:3054–3057.

Culver, K.W., Ram, Z., Walbridge, S., Ishii, H., Oldfield, E.H., and Blaese, R.M. (1992): In vivo gene transfer with retroviral vector producer cells for treatment of experimental brain tumors. Science 256:1550–1552.

Culver, K.W., Van Gilder, J., Link, C.J. Jr., Carlstrom, T., Buroker, T., Yuh, W., Koch, K., Schabold, K., Doornbas, S., and Wetjen, B. (1993): Gene therapy for the treatment of malignant brain tumors with in vivo tumor transduction with the herpes simplex thymidine kinase gene/ganciclovir system. Hum. Gene Ther. 5:343–377.

Culver, K.W., Moorman, D.W., Muldoon, R.R., Paulsen, R.M., Jr., Lamsam, J.L., Walling, H.W., and Link, C.J., Jr. (1994): Toxicity and immunologic effects of in vivo retrovirus-mediated gene transfer of the herpes simplex-thymidine kinase gene into solid tumors. Cold Spring Harbor Symp. Quant. Biol. 59:685–690.

Culver, K.W., Vickers, T.M., Lamsam, J.L., Walling, H.W., and Seregina, T. (1995): Gene therapy for solid tumors. Br. Med. Bull. 51:192–204.

Elion, G.B. (1980): The chemotherapeutic exploitation of virus-specified enzymes. Adv. Enzyme Reg. 18:53–66.

Elshami, A.A., Saavedra, A., Zhang, H., Kucharczuk, J.C., Spray, D.C., Fishman, G.I., Amin, K.M., Kaiser, L.R., and Albelda, S.M. (1996): Gap junctions play a role in the "bystander effect" of the herpes simplex virus thymidine kinase/ganciclovir system in vitro. Gene Ther. 3:85–92.

Fick, J., Barker, II, F.G., Dazin, P., Westphale, E.M., Beyer, E.C., and Israel, M.A. (1995): The extent of heterocellular communication mediated by gap junctions is predictive of bystander tumor cytotoxicity in vitro. Proc. Natl. Acad. Sci. U.S.A. 92:11071–11075.

Florell, R.C., MacDonald, D.R., Irish, W.D., Bernstein, M., Leibel, S.A., Gutin, P.H., and Cairncross, J.G. (1992): Selection bias, survival, and brachytherapy for glioma. J. Neurosurg. 76:179–183.

Freeman, S.M., Abboud, C.N., Whartenby, K.A., Packman, C.H., Koeplin, D.S., Moolten, F.L., and Abraham, G.N. (1993): The "bystander effect": Tumor regression when a fraction of the tumor mass is genetically modified. Cancer Res. 53:5274–5283.

Freeman, S.M., McCune, C., Robinson, W., Abboud, C.N., Abraham, G.N., Angel, C., and Marrogi, A. (1995): The treatment of ovarian cancer with a gene modified cancer vaccine: A phase-I study. Hum. Gene Ther. 6:927–939.

Heyman, R.A., Borrelli, E., Lesley, J., Anderson, D., Richman, D.D., Baird, S.M., Hyman, R., and Evans, R.M. (1989): Thymidine kinase obliteration: Creation of transgenic mice with controlled immunodeficiency. Proc. Natl. Acad. Sci. U.S.A. 86:2698–2702.

Hurford, R.K., Dranoff, G., Mulligan, R.C., and Tepper, R.I. (1995): Gene therapy of metastatic cancer by in vivo retroviral targeting. Nature Genet. 10:430–435.

Izquierdo, M., Cortes, M., de Felipe, P., Martin, V., Diez-Guerra, J., Talavera, A., and Perez-Higueras, A. (1995): Long-term rat survival after malignant brain tumor regression by retroviral gene therapy. Gene Ther. 2:66–69.

Kun, L.E., Gajjar, A., Muhlbauer, M., Heideman, R.L., Sanford, R., Brenner, M., Walter, A., Langston, J., Jenkins, J., and Facchini, S. (1995): Stereotactic injection of herpes simplex thymidine kinase vector producer cells (PA317-G1Tk1SvNa.7) and intravenous ganciclovir for the treatment of progressive or recurrent primary supratentorial pediatric malignant brain tumors. Hum. Gene Ther. 6:1231–1255.

Mizuno, M., Yoshida, J., Ommaya, H., and Sugita, K. (1992): Growth inhibition of glioma cells by liposome-mediated cell transfection with tumor necrosis factor-α gene. Neurol. Medicochir. 32:873–876.

Moolten, F.L. (1986): Tumor chemosensitivity conferred by inserted herpes thymidine kinase genes: Paradigm for a prospective cancer control strategy. Cancer Res. 46:5276–5281.

Moolten, F.L., and Wells, J.M. (1990): Curability of tumors bearing herpes thymidine kinase genes transferred by retroviral vectors. J. Natl. Cancer Inst. 82:297–300.

Oldfield, E.H., Ram, Z., Culver, K.W., Blaese, R.M., and DeVroom, H.L. (1993): Gene therapy for the treatment of brain tumors using intra-tumoral transduction with the thymidine kinase gene and intravenous ganciclovir. Hum. Gene Ther. 4:39–69.

Oldfield, E.H., Ram, Z., Chiang, Y., and Blaese, R.M. (1995): Intrathecal gene therapy for the treatment of leptomeningeal carcinomatosis. Hum. Gene Ther. 6:55–85.

O'Malley, B.W., Jr., Chen, S.H., Schwartz, M.R., and Woo, S.L.C. (1995): Adenovirus-mediated gene therapy for human head and neck squamous cell cancer in nude mouse model. Cancer Res. 55:1080–1085.

Oshiro, E.M., Viola, J.J., Oldfield, E.H., Walbridge, S., Bacher, J., Frank, J.A., Blaese, R.M., and Ram, Z. (1995): Toxicity studies and distribution dynamics of retroviral vectors following intrathecal administration of retroviral vector-producer cells. Cancer Gene Ther. 2:87–95.

Raffel, C., Culver, K.W., Kohn, D., Nelson, M., Siegel, S., Gillis, F., Link, C.J. Jr., and Villablanca, J.G. (1994): Gene therapy for the treatment of recurrent pediatric malignant astrocytomas using in vivo tumor transduction with the herpes simplex thymidine kinase gene/ganciclovir system. Hum. Gene Ther. 5:863–890.

Ram, Z., Culver, K.W., Walbridge, S., Frank, J.A., Blaese, R.M., and Oldfield, E.H. (1993a): Toxicity studies of retroviral-mediated gene transfer for the treatment of brain tumors. J. Neurosurg. 79:400–407.

Ram, Z., Culver, K.W., Walbridge, S., Blaese, R.M., and Oldfield, E.H. (1993b): In situ retroviral-mediated gene transfer for the treatment of brain tumors in rats. Cancer Res. 53:83–88.

Ram, Z., Walbridge, S., Heiss, J.D., Culver, K.W., Blaese, R.M., and Oldfield, E.H. (1994a): In vivo transfer of the human interleukin-2 gene: Negative tumoricidal results in experimental brain tumors. J. Neurosurg. 80:535–540.

Ram, Z., Walbridge, S., Shawker, T., Culver, K.W., Blaese, R.M., and Oldfield, E.H. (1994b): The effect of thymidine kinase transduction and ganciclovir therapy on tumor vasculature and growth of 9L gliomas in rats. J. Neurosurg. 81:256–260.

Rosenfeld, M.E., Feng, M., Michael, S.I., Siegal, G.P., Alvarez, R.D., and Curiel, D.T. (1995): Adenoviral-mediated delivery of the herpes simplex virus thymidine kinase gene selectively sensitizes human ovarian carcinoma cells to ganciclovir. Clin. Cancer Res. 1:1571–1580.

Seth, P., Brinkman, U., Schwartz, G.N., Katayose, D., Gress, R., Pastan, I., and Cowan, K. (1996): Adenovirus-mediated gene transfer to human breast tumor cells: An approach for cancer gene therapy and bone marrow purging. Cancer Res. 56:1346–1351.

Smythe, W.R., Hwang, H.C., Amin, K.M., Eck, S.L., Davidson, B.L., Wilson, J.M., Kaiser, L.R., and Albelda, S.M. (1994): Use of recombinant adenovirus to transfer the herpes simplex virus thymidine kinase (HSVtk) gene to thoracic neoplasms: An effective in vitro drug sensitization system. Cancer Res. 54:2055–2059.

Vile, R.G., and Hart, I.R. (1993): Use of tissue-specific expression of the herpes simplex virus thymidine kinase gene to inhibit growth of established murine melanomas following direct intratumoral injection of DNA. Cancer Res. 53:3860–3864.

Vile, R.G., Nelson, J.A., Castleden, S., Chong, H., and Hart, I.R. (1994): Systemic gene therapy of murine melanoma using tissue-specific expression of HSVtk gene involves an immune component. Cancer Res. 54:6228–6234.

Yoshida, J., Mizuno, M., and Yagi, K. (1992): Cytotoxicity of human β-interferon produced in human glioma cells transfected with its gene by means of liposomes. Biochem. Int. 28:1055–1061.

Yoshii, Y., Maki, Y., Tsuboi, K., Tomono, Y., Nakagawa, K., and Hoshino, T. (1986): Estimation of the growth fraction with bromodeoxyuridine in human central nervous system tumors. J. Neurosurg. 65:659–663.

Yu, J.S., Wei, M.X., Chiocca, E.A., Martuza, R.L., and Tepper, R.I. (1993): Treatment of glioma by engineered interleukin-4 secreting cells. Cancer Res. 53:3125–3128.

Cytosine Deaminase and Other Sensitivity Genes

Harris, J.D., Gutierrez, A.A., Hurst, H.C., Sikora, K., and Lemoine, N.R. (1994): Gene therapy for cancer using tumor-specific prodrug activation. Gene Ther. 1:170–175.

Hirschowitz, E.A., Ohwada, A., Pascal, W.R., Russi, T.J., and Crystal, R.G. (1995): In vivo adenovirus-mediated gene transfer of the Escherichia coli cytosine deaminase gene to human colon carcinoma-derived tumors induces chemosensitivity to 5-fluorocytosine. Hum. Gene Ther. 6:1055–1063.

Huber, B.E., Austin, E.A., Richards, C.A., Davis, S.T., and Good, S.S. (1994): Metabolism of 5-fluorocytosine to 5-fluorouracil in human colorectal tumor cells transduced with the cytosine deaminase gene: Significant antitumor effects when only a small percentage of tumor cells express cytosine deaminase. Proc. Natl. Acad. Sci. U.S.A. 91:8302–8306.

Khil, M.S., Kim, J.H., Mullen, C.A., Kim, S.H., and Freytag, S.O. (1996): Radiosensitization by 5-fluorocytosine of human colorectal carcinoma cells in culture transduced with cytosine deaminase gene. Clin. Cancer Res. 2:53–57.

Kuefner, U., Lohrmann, U., Montejano, Y.D., Vitols, K.S., and Huennekens, F.M. (1989): Carboxypeptidase-mediated release of methotrexate for methotrexate α-peptides. Biochemistry 28:2288–2297.

Mullen, C.A., Coale, M.M., Lowe, R., and Blaese, R.M. (1994): Tumors expressing the cytosine deaminase gene can be eliminated in vivo with 5-fluorocytosine and induce protective immunity to wild type tumor. Cancer Res. 54:1503–1506.

Mullen, C.A., Kilstrup, M., and Blaese, R.M. (1992): Transfer of the bacterial gene for cytosine deaminase to mammalian cells confers lethal sensitivity to 5-fluorocytosine: A negative selection system. Proc. Natl. Acad. Sci. U.S.A. 89:33–37.

Mullen, C.A., Petropoulos, D., and Lowe, R.M. (1996): Treatment of microscopic pulmonary metastases with recombinant autologous tumor vaccine expressing interleukin 6 and Escherichia coli cytosine deaminase suicide genes. Cancer Res. 56:1361–1366.

Senter, P.D. (1990): Activation of prodrugs by antibody-enzyme conjugates: A new approach to cancer therapy. FASEB. J. 4:188–193.

Senter, P.D., Schreiber, G.J., Hirschberg, D.L., Ashe, S.A., Hellström, K.E., and Hellström, I. (1989): Enhancement of the in vitro and in vivo antitumor activities of phosphorylated mitomycin C and etoposide derivatives by monoclonal antibody-alkaline phosphatase conjugates. Cancer Res. 49:5789–5792.

Sorscher, E.J., Peng, S., Bebok, Z., Allan, P.W., Bennett, L.L., Jr., and Parker, W.B. (1994): Tumor cell bystander killing in colonic carcinoma utilizing the Escherichia coli DeoD gene to generate toxic purines. Gene Ther. 1:233–238.

Combination Therapies

Cao, X., Wang, J., Zhang, W., Chen, G., Kong, X., and Tani, K. (1995): Treatment of human hepatocellular carcinoma by fibroblast-mediated human interferon α gene therapy in combination with adoptive chemoimmunotherapy. J. Cancer Res. Clin. Oncol. 121:457–462.

Chen, S., Chen, X.H.L., Wang, Y., Kosai, K., Finegold, M.J., Rich, S.S., and Woo, S.L.C. (1995): Combination gene therapy for liver metastasis of colon carcinoma in vivo. Proc. Natl. Acad. Sci. U.S.A. 92:2577–2581.

Sugimoto, Y., Hrycyna, C.A., Aksentijevich, I., Pastan, I., and Gottesman, M.M. (1995): Coexpression of a multidrug-resistance gene (MDR1) and herpes simplex virus thymidine-kinase gene as part of a bicistronic messenger RNA in a retrovirus vector. Clin. Cancer Res. 1:447–457.

Insertion of Tumor Suppressor Genes

Baker, S.J., Markowitz, S., Fearon, E.R., Wilson, J.K.V., and Vogelstein, B. (1990): Suppression of human colorectal carcinoma cell growth by wild-type p53. Science 249:912–915.

Bertelsen, A.H., Beaudry, G.A., Stoller, T.J., Trotta, P.P., and Sherman, M.I. (1995): Tumor suppressor genes: Prospects for cancer therapies. Bio/Technology 13:127–131.

Cai, D.W., Mukhopadhyay, T., Liu, Y., Fujiwara, T., and Roth, J.A. (1993): Stable expression of the wild-type p53 gene in human lung cancer cells after retrovirus-mediated gene transfer. Hum. Gene Ther. 4:617–624.

Clayman, G.L., El-Naggar, A.K., Roth, J.A., Zhang, W.W., Goepfert, H., Taylor, D.L., and Liu, T.J. (1995): In vivo molecular therapy with p53 adenovirus for microscopic residual head and neck squamous carcinoma. Cancer Res. 55:1–6.

Friedman, L.S., Ostermeyer, E.A., Szabo, C.I., Dowd, P., Lynch, E.D., Rowell, S.E., and King, M.C. (1994): Confirmation of BRCA1 by analysis of germline mutations linked to breast and ovarian cancer in ten families. Nature Genet. 8:399–400.

Fujiwara, T., Grimm, E.A., Cai, D.W., Owen-Schaub, L.B., and Roth, J.A. (1993): A retroviral wild-type p53 expression vector penetrates human lung cancer spheroids and inhibits growth by inducing apoptosis. Cancer Res. 53:4129–4133.

Fujiwara, T., Cai, D.W., Georges, R.N., Mukhopadhyay, T., Grimm, E.A., and Roth, J.A. (1994): Therapeutic effect of a retroviral wild-type p53 expression vector in an orthotopic lung cancer model. J. Natl. Cancer Inst. 86:1458–1462.

Groden, J. Joslyn, G., Samowitz, W., Jones, D., Bhattacharyya, N., Spirio, L., Thliveris, A., Robertson, M., Egan, S., Meuth, M., and White, R. (1995): Response of colon cancer cell lines to the introduction of APC, a colon-specific tumor suppressor gene. Cancer Res. 55:1531–1539.

Hollstein, M., Sidransky, D., Vogelstein, B., and Harris, C.C. (1991): p53 mutations in human cancer. Science 253:49–53.

Jin, X., Nguyen, D., Zhang, W-W., Kyritsis, A.P., and Roth, J.A. (1995): Cell cycle arrest and inhibition of tumor cell proliferation by the p16^{INK4} gene mediated by an adenovirus vector. Cancer Res. 55:3250–3253.

Lesoon-Wood, L.A., Kim, W.H., Kleinman, H.K., Weintraub, B.D., and Mixson, A.J. (1995): Systemic gene therapy with p53 reduces growth and metastases of a malignant human breast cancer in nude mice. Hum. Gene Ther. 6:395–405.

Liu, T-J., El-Naggar, A.K., McDonnell, T.J., Steck, K.D., Wang, M., Taylor, D.L., and Clayman, G.L. (1995): Apoptosis induction mediated by wild-type p53 adenoviral gene transfer in squamous cell carcinoma of the head and neck. Cancer Res. 55:3117–3122.

Savitsky, K., Sfez, S., Tagle, D.A., Ziv, Y., Sartiel, A., Collins, F.S., Shiloh, Y., and Rotman, G. (1995): The complete sequence of the coding region of the ATM gene reveals similarity to the cell cycle regulators in different species. Hum. Mol. Genet. 4:2025–2032.

Skuse, G.R., and Ludlow, J.W. (1995): Tumor suppressor genes in disease and therapy. Lancet 345:902–906.

Wang, J., Bucana, C.D., Roth, J.A., and Zhang, W.W. (1995): Apoptosis induced in human osteosarcoma cells is one of the mechanisms for the cytocidal effect of Ad5CMV-p53. Cancer Gene Ther. 2:9–17.

Yang, Z-Y., Perkins, N.D., Ohno, T., Nabel, E.G., and Nabel, G.J. (1995): The p21 cyclin-dependent kinase inhibitor suppresses tumorigenicity in vivo. Nature Med. 1:1052–1056.

Yu, D., Matin, A., Xia, W., Sorgi, F., Huang, L., and Hung, M-C. (1995): Liposome-mediated in vivo E1A gene transfer suppressed dissemination of ovarian cancer cells that overexpress HER-2.neu. Oncogene 10:1947–1954.

Insertion of Antisense Oncogenes

Aoki, K., Yoshida, T., Sugimura, T., and Terada, M. (1995): Liposome-mediated in vivo gene transfer of antisense K-ras construct inhibits pancreatic tumor dissemination in the murine peritoneal cavity. Cancer Res. 55:3810–3816.

Arteaga, C.L. and Holt, J.T. (1996): Tissue-targeted antisense c-fos retroviral vector inhibits established breast cancer xenografts in nude mice. Cancer Res. 56:1098–1103.

Georges, R.N., Mukhopadhyay, T., Zhang, Y., Yen, N., and Roth, J.A. (1993): Prevention of orthotopic human lung cancer growth by intratracheal instillation of a retroviral antisense K-ras construct. Cancer Res. 53:1743–1746.

Mukhopadhyay, T., Tainsky, M., Cavender, A.C. and Roth, J.A. (1991): Specific inhibition of K-ras expression and tumorigenicity of lung cancer cells by antisense RNA. Cancer Res. 51:1744–1748.

Vaughn, J.P., Iglehart, J.D., Demirdji, S., Babiss, L.E., Caruthers, M.H., and Marks, J.R. (1995): Antisense DNA downregulation of the erbB-2 oncogene measured by a flow cytometric assay. Proc. Natl. Acad. Sci. U.S.A. 92:8338–8342.

Zhang, Y., Mukhopadhyay, T., Donehowe, L.A., Georges, R.N., and Roth, J.A. (1993): Retroviral vector-mediated transduction of K-ras antisense RNA into human lung cancer cells inhibits expression of the malignant phenotype. Hum. Gene Ther. 4:451–460.

Insertion of Intracellular Antibody Genes

Beerli, R.R., Wels, W., and Hynes, N.E. (1994): Intracellular expression of single chain antibodies reverts ErbB-2 transformation. J. Biol. Chem. 269:23931–23936.

Deshane, J., Loechel, F., Conry, R.M., Siegal, G.P., King, C.R., and Curiel, D.T. (1994): Intracellular single-chain antibody directed against erbB2 down-regulates cell surface erbB2 and exhibits a selective anti-proliferative effect in erbB2 over-expressing cancer cell lines. Gene Ther. 1:332–337.

Induction of Apoptosis

Bies, J., and Wolff, L. (1995): Acceleration of apoptosis in transforming growth factor-beta-1-treated M1 cells ectopically expresing B-myb. Cancer Res. 55:501–504.

Bissonnette, R.P., Echeverri, F., Mahboubi, A., and Green, D.R. (1992): Apoptotic cell death induced by c-myc is inhibited by bcl-2. Nature (London) 359:552–554.

Lacronique, V., Mignon, A., Fabre, M., Viollet, B., Rouquet, N., Molina, T., Porteu, A., Henrion, A., Bouscary, D., Varlet, P., Juolin, V., and Kahn, A. (1996): Bcl-2 protects from lethal hepatic apoptosis induced by an anti-Fas antibody in mice. Nature Med. 2:80–86.

Lowe, S.W., Schmitt, E.M., Smith, S.W., Osborne, B.A., and Jacks, T. (1993): p53 is required for radiation induced apoptosis in mouse thymocytes. Nature (London) 362:847–849.

Ogasawara, J., Watanabe-Fukunaga, R., Adachi, M., Matsuzawa, A., Kasugai, T., Kitamura, Y., Itoh, N., Suda, T., and Nagata, S. (1993): Lethal effect of the anti-FAS antibody in mice. Nature (London) 364:806–809.

Rieux-Laucat, F., Le Deist, F., Hivroz, C., Roberts, A.G., Debatin, K.M., Fischer, A., and de Villartay, J.P. (1995): Mutations in fas associated with human lymphoproliferative syndrome and autoimmunity. Science 268:1347–1350.

Steller, H. (1995): Mechanisms and genes of cellular suicide. Science 267:1445–1449.

Suda, T., Takahashi, T., Golstein, P., and Nagata, S. (1993): Molecular cloning and expression of the fas ligand, a novel member of the tumor necrosis factor family. Cell 75:1169–1178.

Trauth, B.C., Klas, C., Peters, A.M.J., Matzku, S., Möller, P., Falk, W., Debatin, K-M., and Krammer, P.H. (1989): Monoclonal antibody-mediated tumor regression by induction of apoptosis. Science 245:301–304.

Weller, M., Malipiero, U., Rensing-Ehl, A., Barr, P.J., and Fontana, A. (1995): Fas/APO-1 gene transfer for human malignant glioma. Cancer Res. 55:2936–2944.

Enhancement of Chemotherapeutic or Radiation Activity

Al-Nabulsi, I., Takamiya, Y., Voloshin, Y., Dritschilo, A., Martuza, R.L., and Jorgensen, T.J. (1994): Expression of thymidine kinase is essential to low dose radiation resistance of rat glioma cells. Cancer Res. 54:5614–5617.

Chen, L., and Waxman, D.J. (1995): Intratumoral activation and enhanced chemotherapeutic effect of oxazaphosphorines following cytochrome-P450 gene transfer: Development of a combined chemotherapy/cancer gene therapy strategy. Cancer Res. 55:581–589.

Hallahan, D.E., Mauceri, H.J., Seung, L.P., Dunphy, E.J., Wayne, J.D., Hanna, N.N., Toledano, A., Hellman, S., Kufe, D.W., and Weichselbaum, R.R. (1995): Spatial and temporal control of gene therapy using ionizing radiation. Nature Med. 1:786–791.

Nabulsi, I., Takamiya, Y., Voloshin, Y., Dritschilo, A., Martuza, R.L., and Jorgensen, T.J. (1994): Expression of thymidine-kinase is essential to low dose radiation resistance of rat glioma cells. Cancer Res. 54:5614–5617.

Urano, M., Kuroda, M., Reynolds, R., Oberley, T.D., and St. Clair, D.K. (1995): Expression of manganese superoxide-dismutase reduces tumor control radiation dose: Gene-radiotherapy. Cancer Res. 55:2490–2493.

Weichselbaum, R.R., Hallahan, D.E., Beckett, M.A., Mauceri, H.J., Lee, H., Sukhatme, V.P., and Kufe, D.W. (1994): Gene therapy targeted by radiation preferentially radiosensitizes tumor cells. Cancer Res. 54:4266–4269.

REGULATORY AND ETHICAL CONSIDERATIONS IN HUMAN GENE THERAPY

REGULATORY ISSUES

The United States is a leader in the development of safeguards for the clinical application of human gene therapy. In 1976, federal guidelines for research involving recombinant DNA molecules were issued. These included both biological and physical containment standards and a regulatory process for oversight of recombinant DNA research by researchers supported directly or indirectly by funds from the National Institutes of Health (NIH). The guidelines require that supported institutions establish an institutional biosafety committee (IBC) to monitor the use of recombinant DNA in the laboratory, in microorganisms, in animals, and in humans. The Office of Recombinant DNA Activities (ORDA) at the NIH monitors the status of the local IBC committees and provides administrative functions for the Recombinant DNA Advisory Committee (RAC). The RAC is an advisory committee to the director of NIH that discusses human gene therapy trial proposals in a public forum.

There are a number of approvals that are required for a proposed human clinical gene therapy trial to be approved and allow patient accrual. First, the protocol must be approved by the local Institutional Review Board (IRB) and IBC. Reports from these committees are then forwarded to the FDA and the RAC. The RAC meets at 3-month intervals where the members discuss all aspects of each protocol in an open session. There are no restrictions on who can attend, and noncommittee members may request an opportunity to speak on a particular issue. RAC membership includes clinicians, scientists, attorneys, ethicists, theologians, patient advocates, business persons, etc. The diverse composition of the RAC is an attempt to involve as many perspectives as possible so that the best interests of patients, society, and the investigators can be served. Countries in Europe and Asia have developed or are in the process of developing similar ethical and scientific review panels to regulate the application of gene therapy to humans. Some are listed in Appendix A.

To facilitate documentation, review, and discussion, the RAC prepared a "Points to Consider" document that lists a series of questions to be answered (see Appendix E). As part of an effort to streamline the review process between the FDA and the RAC, the Points to Consider document, now called Appendix M, is submitted to both entities. The RAC sends the results of its comprehensive review to the Director of the NIH. Once the RAC and the NIH director have approved the trial, investigators are required to make regular reports to the RAC of all adverse events, changes in investigators, patient eligibility criteria, etc., and comprehensive progress reports are required on an annual basis. The progress reports are reviewed at the RAC public meeting, so that the committee members can monitor the progress of the clinical research projects.

Each of the vector delivery systems used in human gene transfer trials is considered a biologic and requires the filing of an investigation new drug (IND) application for each specific vector. The IND is submitted to the Cellular and Gene Therapy Division of the Center for Biologics Evaluation and Research (CBER) at the FDA. CBER makes a detailed evaluation of the proposal and works with investigators to produce a final version that maximizes safety and the accrual of scientific information necessary for product approval.

Ongoing data monitoring of approved protocols by the RAC has not identified significant, unexpected side effects related to gene transfer since they began approving experiments in humans in 1989. During the past 7 years, several protocols have been submitted that use the same vector for a different clinical circumstance (e.g., IL-2 for several different malignancies). Therefore, changes have been made to expedite the review process for these similar protocols.

The most significant alteration in the review process was initiated following the June 1995 RAC meeting, a move that partially consolidated the FDA and RAC reviews. Investigators now submit their IND with Appendix M to the FDA only. The FDA forwards a copy to ORDA, which performs a review to determine if the protocol is sufficiently different from other approved trials or raises new safety concerns (e.g., new vector delivery system). If the ORDA review finds a sufficient basis for RAC review, the protocol goes to the full committee. However, if the protocol is not novel and does not raise new safety concerns, ORDA sends the protocol on for exclusive review by the FDA and no subsequent approval by the NIH director is required. The use of this system has resulted in 30 of the last 38 protocols submitted to RAC being sent directly to the FDA without formal RAC review. The average time for this RAC review process is 11 days. These changes are very important and represent another step taken by the NIH, ORDA, RAC, and FDA to revise continually the gene therapy review process so that transfer of preclinical information to clinical trials can be facilitated.

ETHICAL ISSUES

The only form of human gene therapy being conducted today in the United States is somatic cell gene therapy. The RAC will not currently consider approving any germline gene therapy protocols. At this point in history, the technology for human germ line manipulation is too inefficient and too early in development to be considered practically. However, the RAC has initiated scientific and ethical discussions about germline manipulation, so that when the technology becomes available RAC will be prepared to provide a useful public discussion about the potential risks and benefits of germline manipulation. Therefore, at present, we are dealing only with ethical issues regarding somatic cell gene transfer.

Early human gene transfer experiments conducted around the world have involved patients with known fatal diseases, using gene transfer methods that will affect only that specific individual. Because these experiments are limited to single individuals with terminal illnesses, the ethical issues are essentially the same as those for other heroic measures such as bone marrow and solid organ transplantation. Concerns about the use of this technology for the "wrong" reasons has not been a major issue for limiting human gene therapy experiments.

The development of human gene therapy is in its infancy. However, as the technology advances over the next 50 years, the possibilities for enhancement engineering (i.e., improving an individual's aptitude for certain skills such as music) or the theoretical risk of creating a "superior" race may become a realistic concern. We must not forget that prohibiting the use of gene therapy for the benefit of sick people will in no way prevent the use of genetic technologies for the "wrong" reasons if a devious person or government chooses to do so. Therefore, the use of somatic cell gene therapy for patients without recourse to any satisfactory therapies must be allowed to continue. The worldwide use of recombinant DNA technology must be as closely monitored as nuclear power has been. In this kind of environment, gene therapy should prosper safely and provide great benefit to all of humankind.

REFERENCES

Culliton, B. (1995): Politics and genes. Nat. Med. 1:181.

Davis, B.D. (1992): Germ-line gene therapy: Evolutionary and moral considerations. Hum. Gene Ther. 3:361-364.

Fletcher, J.C. (1990): Evolution of ethical debate about human gene therapy. Hum. Gene Ther. 1:55-68.

Gavaghan, H. (1995): Future perfect or imperfect? Nat. Med. 1:186-187.

Gustafson, J.M. (1994): A Christian perspective on genetic engineering. Hum. Gene Ther. 5:747-754.

Keenan, J.F. (1990): What is morally new in genetic manipulation. Hum. Gene Ther. 1:289-298.

Lindemann, A., Rosenthal, F.M., Hase, S., Markmeyer, P., and Mertelsmann, R. (1995): Guidelines for the design and implementation of clinical studies in somatic cell therapy and gene therapy. J. Mol. Med. 73:207-211.

Macer, D.R.J., Akiyama, S., Tan Alora, A., Asada, Y., Azariah, J., Azariah, H., Boost, M.V., Chatwachirawong, P., Kato, Y., Kaushik, V., Leavitt, F.J., Macer, N.Y., Ong, C.C., Srinives, P., and Tsuzuki, M. (1995): International perceptions and approval of gene therapy. Hum. Gene Ther. 6:791-803.

MacKay, C.R. (1993): Discussion points to consider in research related to the human genome. Hum. Gene Ther. 4:477-495.

Miller, H.I. (1994): Gene therapy for enhancement. Lancet 344:316-317.

Murray, T.H. (1990): Human gene therapy, the public and public policy. Hum. Gene Ther. 1:49-54.

Nelson, J.R. (1990): The role of religions in the analysis of ethical issues in gene therapy. Hum. Gene Ther. 1:43-48.

Ridgway, A. (1995): Regulation of gene therapy: The Canadian approach. Biologicals 23:31-36.

Taylor, A.J. and Lloyd, J. (1995): The role of the gene therapy advisory committee in the oversight of gene therapy research in the United Kingdom. Biologicals 23:37-38.

Wivel, N.A. and Walters, L. Germline gene modification and disease prevention: some medical and ethical perspectives. Science 262:533-538.

CONCLUSIONS

Throughout this book, I have attempted to summarize the current status of gene therapy trials in the United States. There continues to be tremendous growth in the number of approved clinical trials in the United States, now totaling 122. There are now 24 individual trials for 10 genetic diseases, 16 gene therapy trials for HIV infection, and 79 separate attempts at gene therapy for cancer. It can be expected that certain of these avenues of clinical experiments will lead to FDA-approved therapeutics. Hopefully, this book has provided you with a familiarity with the tools of gene therapy as a first step in the preparation for major changes in the practice of medicine. The reference lists at the end of each chapter and Appendix A list additional resources for more in-depth study. Appendix A also lists resources for updated information about gene mapping and the status of human clinical gene therapy trials. A table of the RAC approved trials as of March 1996 along with a list of published clinical trials in the United States and Europe is included in Appendix B.

Appendix D lists all of the disease genes that have been mapped as of September, 1995. If a disease gene does not appear on the list, it is very unlikely that there is an approved clinical gene therapy trial for that specific genetic disorder. Unfortunately, months to years are required after the gene is mapped to develop a clinically appropriate gene therapy protocol.

We have turned a corner in science to view a new horizon, the dawning of the era of genetic healing. The exact manner by which human gene therapy will evolve to benefit people around the world remains an unknown. However, there is no question but that one can have renewed confidence in the expectation that we as physicians may soon have the potential to cure our patients instead of merely treating their symptoms.

Resources for Further Information

Journals and Periodicals

Genetic Engineering News
Mary Ann Liebert, Inc., Publishers
2 Madison Ave.
Larchmont, NY 10538
914-834-3100
FAX: 914-834-3771

Human Gene Therapy
Mary Ann Liebert, Inc., Publishers
2 Madison Ave.
Larchmont, NY 10538
914-834-3100
FAX: 914-834-3771

Gene Therapy
Stockton Press Ltd.
345 Park Ave. South, 10th Fl.
New York, NY 10010-1707
212-689-9200
FAX: 212-689-9200

Cancer Gene Therapy
Appleton and Lange
25 Van Zant Street
Norwalk, CT 06855
203-406-4500
FAX: 203-406-4603

Gene Therapy Advisory Committees

*NIH Office of
Recombinant DNA
Activities (U.S.)*
Nelson Wivel, M.D., Director
6000 Executive Blvd, MSC 7052
Bethesda, MD 20892-7052

301-496-9838
FAX: 301-496-9839

*European Working Group on Human
Gene Transfer and Therapy*
Dr. Odile Cohen-Haguenauer
Scientific Secretariat
Hôpital Saint Louis
75475 Paris Cédex 10 France
33-1-42069214
FAX: 33-1-42414256

*Gene Therapy Advisory Committee
(GTAC)*
Department of Health
Room 417
Wellington House
133-155 Waterloo Road
London SE1 8UG
44-171-972-4021
FAX: 44-171-972-4196

*International Society for
the Advancement of Biotechnology*
4405 East West Highway, Suite 401
Bethesda, MD 20814
301-718-2544
FAX: 301-652-4951

Organizations

*National Organization for Rare
Disorders (NORD)*
Abbey S. Meyers, Executive Director
Fairwood Professional Building
P.O. Box 8923
New Fairfield, CT 06812
203-746-6518
FAX: 203-746-6481

Immune Deficiency Foundation
Thomas L. Moran, President
25 West Chesapeake Ave, Suite 206
Towson, MD 21204
800-296-4433
FAX: 410-321-9165

Information on Gene Mapping

The National Center for Human Genome Research
Office of Communications
Building 31 Room B1C35
9000 Rockville Pike
Bethesda, MD 20892
301-402-0911
FAX: 301-402-2218

Videotapes by Carolina Biological Supply Co. 800-334-5551

1. "Map of life: Science, Society and the Human Genome Project" (46 min.) 1992
2. "Molecular Miracles: Human Gene Therapy and the Future of Molecular Medicine" (47 min.) 1993

APPENDIX B

GENE THERAPY PROTOCOLS APPROVED BY THE RAC

RAC-Approved Gene Therapy Protocols for Genetic Diseases

RAC protocol approval number(s)	Disorder	Cells altered	Gene transferred (vector system)	Contact person, institution, telephone number
9306-46	Gaucher disease	Hematopoietic stem cells	Glucocerebrosidase gene (MRV)	John A. Barranger, M.D., Ph.D.* University of Pittsburgh 412-624-4623 FAX: 412-624-1032
9512-139	Partial ornithine transcarbamy-lase (OTC) deficiency	Liver	OTC gene (adenovirus)	Mark Batshaw, M.D. University of Pennsylvania 215-349-8600 FAX: 215-349-8623
9007-02	Adenosine deaminase (ADA) deficiency	T cells and hematopoietic stem cells	ADA gene (MRV)	R. Michael Blaese, M.D. NIH 301-496-5396 FAX: 301-496-7184
9303-42	Cystic fibrosis	Respiratory epithelium	CFTR gene (adenovirus)	Richard C. Boucher, M.D. University of North Carolina 919-966-1077 FAX: 919-966-7524
9403-70	α_1-Antitrypsin deficiency	Respiratory epithelium	α_1-Antitrypsin gene (liposomes)	Kenneth L. Brigham, M.D. Vanderbilt University 615-322-3412 FAX: 615-343-7448
9212-34 9409-85	Cystic fibrosis	Respiratory epithelium	CFTR gene (adenovirus)	Ronald G. Crystal, M.D. Cornell Medical Center 212-746-2250 FAX: 212-746-8383
9409-91 9412-94	Cystic fibrosis	Respiratory epithelium	CFTR gene (adenovirus)	Henry L. Dorkin, M.D. Tufts University[a] Harvard Medical School Massachusetts General Hospital New England Med Ctr. 617-956-5085 FAX: 617-636-7760
9409-83	Cystic fibrosis	Respiratory epithelium	CFTR gene (AAV)	Terence R. Flotte, M.D. Johns Hopkins 410-955-2035 FAX: 410-955-1030

These Footnotes apply to all tables in Appendix B.

Approval numbers are the year and month approved (first 4 digits) followed by the number in consecutive order approved by the RAC.

NB: More than one approval number means that this group of investigators has more than one trial approved for the same or a similar indication.

*Listed alphabetically by principal investigator.

[a]Denotes the institution represented by the contact person for trials approved with multiple trial sites.

[b]Direct DNA transfer immunization protocols (relates to Gene Therapy Protocols for Cancer table only).

145

RAC-Approved Gene Therapy Protocols for Genetic Diseases (*continued*)

RAC protocol approval number(s)	Disorder	Cells altered	Gene transferred (vector system)	Contact person, institution, telephone number
9507-114	Cystic fibrosis	Respiratory epithelium	CFTR gene (AAV)	Phyllis Gardner, M.D. Stanford University 415-723-6086 FAX: 415-725-2952
9306-47	Gaucher disease	Hematopoietic stem cells	Glucocerebrosidase gene (MRV)	Stefan Karlsson, M.D., Ph.D. NIH[a] Childrens Hospital (LA, CA) 301-496-8236 FAX: 301-496-9480
9406-78	Fanconi anemia	Hematopoietic stem cells	Complementation group C gene (MRV)	Johnson M. Liu, M.D. NIH 301-496-5093 FAX: 301-496-8396
9503-104	Chronic granulomatous disease	Hematopoietic stem cells	p47phox gene (MRV)	Harry L. Malech, M.D. NIH 301-480-6916 FAX: 301-402-0789
9506-111	Purine nucleoside phosphorylase (PNP) deficiency	T cells	PNP gene (MRV)	R. Scott McIvor, Ph.D. University of Minnesota 612-626-1497 FAX: 612-626-7031
9312-61	Gaucher disease	Hematopoietic stem cells	Glucocerebrosidase gene (MRV)	Friedrich G. Schuening, M.D. University of Wisconsin[a] Fred Hutchinson Cancer Ctr. 608-265-8690 FAX: 608-262-0759
9312-66	Cystic fibrosis	Respiratory epithelium	CFTR gene (liposomes)	Eric J. Sorscher, M.D. University of Alabama (Birm. 205-934-4715 FAX: 205-934-7593
9212-36 9312-67 9512-139	Cystic fibrosis	Respiratory epithelium	CFTR gene (adenovirus or liposomes)	Michael J. Welsh, M.D. University of Iowa[a] University of Washington 319-335-7619 FAX: 319-335-7623
9409-87	Mucopoly-saccharidosis type II (Hunter syndrome)	T cells	Iduronate-2-sulfatase gene (MRV)	Chester B. Whitley, M.D., Ph.D University of Minnesota 612-625-7422 FAX: 612-624-2682
9303-41	Cystic fibrosis	Respiratory epithelium	CFTR gene (adenovirus)	Robert W. Wilmott, M.D. University of Cincinnati 513-559-6771 FAX: 513-559-4615
9212-35	Cystic fibrosis	Respiratory epithelium	CFTR gene (adenovirus)	James M. Wilson, M.D., Ph.D. University of Pennsylvania 215-349-8600 FAX: 215-349-8623
9110-12	Familial hyper-cholesterolemia	Hepatocytes	LDLr gene (MRV)	James M. Wilson, M.D., Ph.D. University of Pennsylvania 215-349-8600 FAX: 215-349-8623

RAC-Approved Gene Therapy Protocols for Cancer

RAC protocol approval number(s)	Cancers to be treated	Therapeutic genes to be transferred	Vector systems	Contact person, institution, telephone numbers
Ex Vivo Gene Transfer into Hematopoietic Stem Cells				
9601-143	Breast	MDR-1 gene	MRV	Kenneth H. Cowan, M.D. NIH 301-496-4916 FAX: 301-402-0172
9306-44 9406-77	Breast Ovarian	MDR-1 gene	MRV	Albert B. Deisseroth, M.D. M.D. Anderson Cancer Center 713-792-8750 FAX: 713-794-4902
9306-051	Brain Breast Ovarian	MDR-1 gene	MRV	Charles S. Hesdorffer, M.D. Columbia University 212-305-4907 FAX: 212-305-6798
9309-54	Breast	MDR-1 gene	MRV	Joyce A. O'Shaughnessy, M.D. Kentucky Medical Oncology Assoc. 502-582-3735 FAX: 502-582-9968
Ex Vivo Gene Transfer into T Lymphocytes				
9506-109	Ovarian	Chimeric T cell receptor gene	MRV	Patrick Hwu, M.D. NIH 301-402-1156 FAX: 301-496-0011
9602-146	Leukemia	HS-tk gene	MRV	Charles J. Link, Jr., M.D. Iowa Methodist Medical Center[a] Northwestern University 515-241-8787 FAX: 515-241-8788
9506-107	Multiple myeloma	HS-tk gene	MRV	Nikhil C. Munshi, M.D. University of Arkansas 501-686-5222 FAX: 501-686-8165
9007-03	Melanoma	TNF-α gene	MRV	Steven A. Rosenberg, M.D., Ph.D. NIH 301-496-4164 FAX: 301-402-1738
9511-136	Melanoma	HS-tk gene	MRV	Cassian Yee, M.D. Fred Hutchinson Cancer Research 206-543-8306 FAX: 206-685-3128
Ex Vivo Gene Transfer into Fibroblasts				
9209-33	Breast Colon Melanoma Renal cell	IL-4 gene	MRV	Michael T. Lotze, M.D. University of Pittsburgh 412-624-9375 FAX: 412-624-1172
9406-81	Breast Head/neck Lymphoma Melanoma	IL-12 gene	MRV	Michael T. Lotze, M.D. University of Pittsburgh 412-624-9375 FAX: 412-624-1172

RAC-Approved Gene Therapy Protocols for Cancer (*continued*)

RAC protocol approval number(s)	Cancers to be treated	Therapeutic genes to be transferred	Vector systems	Contact person, institution, telephone numbers
9312-60	Colon	IL-2 gene	MRV	Robert E. Sobol, M.D. San Diego Regional Cancer Center 619-450-5990 FAX: 619-450-3251

Ex Vivo Gene Transfer into Tumor Cells

RAC protocol approval number(s)	Cancers to be treated	Therapeutic genes to be transferred	Vector systems	Contact person, institution, telephone numbers
9506-110	Ovarian	IL-2 gene	Liposomes	Andres Berchuck, M.D. Duke University 919-684-3618 FAX: 919-684-8719
9512-138	Brain	Antisense TGF-β gene	Electroporation	Keith L. Black, M.D. UCLA[a] 310-206-5687 FAX: 310-206-9486
9508-116	Malignant gliomas	IL-4 gene	MRV	Michael Bozik, M.D. University of Pittsburgh 412-692-2600 FAX: 412-692-2610
9205-18 9511-133	Neuroblastoma	IL-2 gene	MRV or adenovirus	Malcolm K. Brenner, M.D., Ph.D. St. Jude Children's Res. Hosp. 901-522-0410 FAX: 901-521-9005
9309-53	Small cell lung cancer	IL-2 gene	Liposomes, calcium-phosphate, or dextran	Peter A. Cassileth, M.D. University of Miami 305-548-4929 FAX: 305-548-4975
9312-65	Melanoma	GM-CSF gene	MRV	Alfred E. Chang, M.D. University of Michigan 313-936-4392 FAX: 313-936-5830
9309-56	Melanoma	IL-2 gene	MRV	Tapas K. Das Gupta, M.D. University of Illinois (Chicago) 312-996-9479 FAX: 312-996-6415
9411-93	Melanoma	GM-CSF gene	MRV	Glen Dranoff, M.D. Dana-Farber Cancer Institute 617-632-5051 FAX: 617-632-5167
9309-58 9503-101	Melanoma	IL-2 or IL-7 gene	MRV	James S. Economou, M.D., Ph.D. UCLA 310-825-2644 FAX: 310-825-7575
9202-16	Ovarian	HS-*tk* gene	MRV	Scott M. Freeman, M.D. Tulane University[a] University of Rochester 504-588-5224 FAX: 504-587-7389
9206-21 9206-22	Melanoma Renal cell	IL-2 gene	MRV	Bernd Gansbacher, M.D. Memorial-Sloan-Kettering Cancer Center 212-639-5019 FAX: 212-717-3132

RAC-Approved Gene Therapy Protocols for Cancer (*continued*)

RAC protocol approval number(s)	Cancers to be treated	Therapeutic genes to be transferred	Vector systems	Contact person, institution, telephone numbers
9503-102	Prostate	IL-2 and interferon-γ genes	MRV	Bernd Gansbacher, M.D. Memorial-Sloan-Kettering Cancer Center 212-639-5019 FAX: 212-717-3132
9306-52	Glioblastoma	Antisense IGF-1 gene	Liposomes	Joseph Ilan, Ph.D. Case Western Reserve University 216-368-3590 FAX: 216-368-1300
9409-86	Breast	IL-2 gene	Liposomes	H. Kim Lyerly, M.D. Duke University 919-681-8350 FAX: 919-681-7970
9510-132	Prostate	IL-2 gene	LIposomes	David F. Paulson, M.D. Duke University 919-684-5057 FAX: 919-684-4611
9110-10 9110-11	Breast Colon Melanoma Renal cell	IL-2 or TNF-α genes	MRV	Steven A. Rosenberg, M.D., Ph.D. NIH 301-496-4164 FAX: 301-402-1738
9403-68	Neuroblastoma	Interferon-γ gene	MRV	Joseph D. Rosenblatt, M.D. UCLA[a] Childrens Hospital of Los Angeles 310-825-2745 FAX: 310-825-6192
9306-43	Melanoma	Interferon-γ gene	MRV	Hilliard F. Seigler, M.D. Duke University 919-684-2137 FAX: 919-684-6070
9303-40 9408-82	Melanoma Prostate Renal cell	GM-CSF gene	MRV	Jonathan W. Simons, M.D. Johns Hopkins Oncology Center 410-614-1662 FAX: 410-614-3695
9406-80	Glioblastoma	IL-2 gene	MRV	Robert E. Sobol, M.D. San Diego Regional Cancer Center 619-450-5990 FAX: 619-450-3251
9312-63	Melanoma	B7-costimulatory molecule gene	Liposomes	Mario Sznol, M.D. NIH (Frederick) 301-846-1520 FAX: 301-846-1436

In Vivo Gene Transfer into Tumor Cells or Other Tissue[b]

9409-90	Mesothelioma	HS-*tk* gene	Adenovirus	Steven M. Albelda, M.D. University of Pennsylvania 215-662-3307 FAX: 215-349-5172
9511-135	Ovarian	HS-*tk* gene	Adenovirus	Ronald D. Alvarez, M.D. University of Alabama (Birmingham) 205-934-4986 FAX: 205-975-6174

RAC-Approved Gene Therapy Protocols for Cancer (*continued*)

RAC protocol approval number(s)	Cancers to be treated	Therapeutic genes to be transferred	Vector systems	Contact person, institution, telephone numbers

9508-115
 	
9508-120
	Melanoma, Colon, lymphoma
	Breast, Renal cell
	Non-Hodgkins lymphoma
		HLA-B7 + β_2-microglobulin genes	Liposomes	Alfred E. Chang, M.D.
				  University of Michigan[a]
				  Arizona Cancer Ctr. (Tuscon)
				  University of Chicago,
				  Stanford University
				  Wayne State University,
				  UCLA
				  Mayo Clinic
				  313-936-4392
				  FAX: 313-936-5830

9509-126	Prostate	Prostate-specific antigen gene	Vaccina[b]	Alice P. Chen, M.D.
				  National Naval Medical Ctr.
				  (Bethesda, MD)
				  301-496-0901
				  FAX: 301-496-0047

9412-96	Head and neck squamous cell carcinoma	Wild-type p53 gene	Adenovirus	Gary L. Clayman, D.D.S., M.D.
				  MD Anderson Cancer Center
				  713-792-6920
				  FAX: 713-794-4662

9510-128	Adenocarcinomas of the GI tract, Breast, Lung	Prostate-specific antigen gene	Vaccinia[b]	David Cole, M.D.
				  Medical University of South
				  Carolina
				  803-792-3276
				  FAX: 803-792-2048

9509-125	Metastatic colon carcinoma of the liver	Cytosine deaminase gene	Adenovirus	Ronald G. Crystal, M.D.
				  Cornell Medical Center
				  212-746-2250
				  FAX: 212-746-8383

9406-73	Colon	CEA gene	DNA[b]	David T. Curiel, M.D.
				  University of Alabama (Birmingham)
				  205-934-8627
				  FAX: 205-975-7476

9509-124	Ovarian	Anti-*erbB*-2 single-chain antibody gene	Adenovirus	David T. Curiel, M.D.
				  University of Alabama (Birmingham)
				  205-934-8627
				  FAX: 205-975-7476

9408-89	Primary and metastatic brain tumors	HS-*tk* gene	Adenovirus	Stephen L. Eck, M.D., Ph.D.
				  University of Pennsylvania
				  215-898-8359
				  FAX: 215-349-8623

9502-99	Anaplastic astrocytoma and glioblastoma	HS-*tk* gene	MRV	Michael Fetell, M.D.
				  Columbia-Presbyterian
				    Medical Center[a]
				  University of Cincinnati
				  M.D. Anderson Cancer
				    Center
				  University of Florida
				  University of Virginia
				  University of California (SF)
				  Tel Aviv University
				  212-305-5571
				  FAX: 212-305-7365

RAC-Approved Gene Therapy Protocols for Cancer (*continued*)

RAC protocol approval number(s)	Cancers to be treated	Therapeutic genes to be transferred	Vector systems	Contact person, institution, telephone numbers
9508-121	Renal cell	HLA-B7 + β_2-microglobulin genes	Liposomes	Robert A. Figlin, M.D. UCLA 310-825-5788 FAX: 310-206-5414
9506-108	Melanoma Renal cell	HLA-B7 + β_2-microglobulin genes	Liposomes	Bernard A. Fox, Ph.D. Providence Portland Medical Center 503-230-6311 FAX: 503-230-6182
9512-142	Head/Neck	HLA-B7+ β-2-microglobulin genes	Lipsomes	Jack L. Gluckman, M.D. University of Cincinnati 513-558-4152 FAX: 513-558-5203
9412-98	Primary and metastatic brain tumors	HS-*tk* gene	Adenovirus	Robert G. Grossman, M.D. Baylor College of Medicine 713-798-4696 FAX: 713-798-3739
9508-122	Breast Colon Lung Ovarian Pancreatic Stomach	CEA gene	Canarypox[b]	Michael J. Hawkins, M.D. Georgetown University 202-687-2103 FAX: 203-687-4429
9403-72	Melanoma	HLA-B7 + β_2-microglobulin genes	Liposomes	Evan M. Hersh, M.D. Arizona Cancer Center (Tucson) 602-626-2250 FAX: 602-626-2225
9412-95	Breast Colon Melanoma Non-Hodgkin's lymphoma Renal cell	IL-2 gene	Liposomes	Evan M. Hersh, M.D. Arizona Cancer Center (Tucson)[a] Scott and White Clinic 606-626-2250 FAX: 602-626-2225
9409-84	Breast	Anti-sense c-*fos* or antisense c-*myc* gene	MRV	Jeffrey T. Holt, M.D. Vanderbilt University 615-343-4730 FAX: 615-343-4539
9602-148	Ovarian	BRCA-1 gene	MRV	Jeffrey T. Holt, M.D. Johns Hopkins University 615-343-4730 FAX: 615-343-4539
9512-137	Breast Ovarian	E1A gene	Liposomes	Gabriel Hortobagyi, M.D. MD Anderson Cancer Center 713-792-2933 FAX: 713-794-4535
9309-55	Recurrent pediatric brain tumors	HS-*tk* gene	MRV	Larry E. Kun, M.D. St. Jude Children's Research Hospital 901-522-0604 FAX: 901-525-2690
9503-100	Ovarian	HS-*tk* gene	MRV	Charles J. Link, Jr., M.D. Iowa Methodist Medical Center 515-241-8787 FAX: 515-241-8788

RAC-Approved Gene Therapy Protocols for Cancer (*continued*)

RAC protocol approval number(s)	Cancers to be treated	Therapeutic genes to be transferred	Vector systems	Contact person, institution, telephone numbers
9202-13 9306-45	Breast Solid tumors	HLA-B7 $\pm$ -β_2- microglobulin genes	Liposomes	Gary J. Nabel, M.D., Ph.D. University of Michigan 313-747-4798 FAX: 313-747-4730
9206-19 9312-59	Primary and metastatic brain tumors Leptomeningeal carcinomatosis	HS-*tk* gene	MRV	Edward H. Oldfield, M.D. NIH 301-496-5728 FAX: 301-496-0380
9603-149	Head/neck	HS-*tk* gene	Adenovirus	Bert W. O'Malley, M.D. Johns Hopkins University 410-955-8409 FAX: 410-955-0035
9309-50	Recurrent pediatric brain tumors	HS-*tk* gene	MRV	Corey Raffel, M.D., Ph.D. Mayo Clinic[a] Children's Hospital of Los Angeles University of Washington Children's National Medical Center (Washington, D.C.) 507-284-2511 FAX: 507-284-5206
9512-140	Melanoma	MART-1 melanoma antigen	Adenovirus[b]	Steven A. Rosenberg, Ph.D., M.D. NIH 301-496-4164 FAX: 301-402-1738
9209-31 9406-79	Non-small-cell lung cancer	Wild-type p53 or antisense k-*ras* gene	MRV or adenovirus	Jack A. Roth, M.D. M.D. Anderson Cancer Center[a] University of Alabama (Birmingham) 713-792-6932 FAX: 713-794-4901
9312-64	Metastatic colon cancer in the liver	HLA-B7 + β_2- microglobulin genes	Liposomes	Joseph Rubin, M.D. Mayo Clinic 507-284-3902 FAX: 507-284-1803
9601-144	Prostate	HS-*tk* gene	Adenovirus	Peter T. Scardino, M.D. Baylor University 713-798-6153 FAX: 713-798-7900
9601-145	Bladder	Retinoblastoma gene	Adenovirus	Eric J. Small, M.D. University of Calif., San Diego 619-597-0177 FAX: 619-623-2032
9509-123	Prostate	Antisense c-*myc* gene	MRV	Mitchell S. Steiner, M.D. Vanderbilt University[a] University of Tennessee 901-448-5868 FAX: 901-448-8758

RAC-Approved Gene Therapy Protocols for Cancer (*continued*)

RAC protocol approval number(s)	Cancers to be treated	Therapeutic genes to be transferred	Vector systems	Contact person, institution, telephone numbers
9303-37	Glioblastoma	HS-*tk* gene	MRV	John C. Van Gilder, M.D. University of Iowa[a] University of California (SF) University of Washington University of Cincinnati Southwestern Medical School-Dallas 319-356-2772 FAX: 319-353-6605
9412-97	Hepatoma and colon cancer metastases in the liver	Wild-type p53 gene	Adenovirus	Alan P. Venook, M.D. University of California (SF) 415-476-3745 FAX: 415-476-0467
9403-71	Renal cell	HLA-B7 + β_2- microglobulin genes	Liposomes	Nicholas J. Vogelzang, M.D. University of Chicago 312-702-6743 FAX: 312-702-3163

RAC-Approved Gene Therapy Protocols for HIV Infection

RAC protocol approval number(s)	Gene transferred	Cells altered	Vector system	Contact person, institution, telephone number
9504-113	HIV envelope (*env*) and *rev* genes	Intramuscular injection	MRV	Marcus Conant, M.D. Conant Medical Group (San Francisco) 415-661-2613 FAX: 415-661-6275
9510-131	CD4-zeta gene	T-cells	MRV	Elizabeth Connick, M.D. University of Colorado[a] University of California (SF) 303-270-7233 FAX: 303-270-8681
9306-48	HIV envelope (*env*) and *rev* genes	Intramuscular injection	MRV	Jeffrey E. Galpin, M.D. Shared Medical Research Foundation 818-345-2172 FAX: 818-345-2542
9511-134	PolyTAR and RRE-polyTAR	T-cells	MRV	Mark Gilbert, M.D. Fred Hutchinson Cancer Res. Ctr 206-667-6097 FAX: 206-667-7983
9202-17	HS-*tk* gene	CD8(+) HIV- specific T cells	MRV	Philip D. Greenberg, M.D. University of Washington 206-543-8306 FAX: 206-685-3128

RAC-Approved Gene Therapy Protocols for HIV Infection (*continued*)

RAC protocol approval number(s)	Gene transferred	Cells altered	Vector system	Contact person, institution, telephone number
9312-62	HIV envelope (*env*) and *rev* genes	Intramuscular injection	MRV	Richard Haubrich, M.D. University of California—San Diego 619-543-8080 FAX: 619-298-0177
9602-147	RRE decoy	HSC	MRV	Donald B. Kohn, M.D. Childrens Hospital of Los Angeles 213-669-2546 FAX: 213-660-1904
9506-112	Intracellular antibody gene to the HIV *env*	T cells	MRV	Wayne A. Marasco, M.D., Ph.D. Dana-Farber Cancer Institute 617-632-2153 FAX: 617-632-3889
9503-103	Antisense TAR and trans-dominant *Rev* genes	T cells	MRV	Richard A. Morgan, Ph.D. NIH 301-402-1830 FAX: 301-402-1921
9306-49	Transdominant negative mutant *rev* gene	T cells	MRV or particle bombard-ment	Gary J. Nabel, M.D., Ph.D. University of Michigan 313-747-4798 FAX: 313-747-4730
9503-105	HIV envelope (*env*) anf *rev* genes	Intramuscular injection	MRV	David F. Paenti, M.D. George Washington University[a] University of California—San Diego Keely Ave. Clinic (Portland, OR) University of Cincinnati Washington University (St. Louis) 202-994-2715 FAX: 202-994-0465
9512-141	Anti-Rev Single Chain Antibody	T-cells	MRV	Roger Pomerantz, M.D. Thomas Jefferson University 215-955-8575 FAX: 215-923-1956
9508-119	HS-*tk* gene	CD8+ HIV-specific T cells	MRV	Stanley R. Riddell, M.D. Fred Hutchinson Cancer Research Center 206-667-5249 FAX: 206-667-7983
9508-117	Anti-HIV RNA ribozyme gene	Hematopoietic progenitor cells	MRV	Joseph D. Rosenblatt, M.D. UCLA 310-825-2745 FAX: 310-825-6192
9403-69	CD4-zeta HIV targeting gene	T cells	MRV	Robert E. Walker, M.D. NIH 301-402-0564 FAX: 301-402-4097
9309-57	Anti-HIV RNA ribozyme gene	T cells	MRV	Flossie Wong-Staal, Ph.D. University of California-San Diego 619-534-7957 FAX: 619-534-7743

RAC-Approved Gene Therapy Protocols for Autoimmune and Cardiovascular Diseases

RAC protocol approval number(s)	Gene transferred	Cells altered	Vector system	Contact person, institution, telephone number
	Ex Vivo Gene Transfer for Rheumatoid Arthritis			
9406-74	Interleukin-1 receptor antagonist protein (IRAP) gene	Synoviocytes	MRV	Chris H. Evans, M.D. University of Pittsburgh 412-648-1090 FAX: 412-648-8412
	In Vivo Gene Transfer for Vascular Disease			
9409-88 9508-118	Vascular endothelial growth factor (VEGF) gene	Direct injection	DNA	Jeffrey M. Isner, M.D. Tufts University 617-789-2392 FAX: 617-789-5029

REFERENCE LIST OF PUBLISHED CLINICAL TRIAL PROTOCOLS FROM THE U.S. AND EUROPE

Marking Clinical protocols (United States)

Brenner, M., Mirro, Jr.J., Hurwitz, C., Santana, V., Ihle, J., Krance, R., Ribeiro, R., Roberts, W.M., Mahmoud, H., Schell, M., and Garth, K. (1991): Autologous bone marrow transplant for children with acute myelogenous leukemia in first remission: Use of marker genes to investigate the biology of marrow reconstitution and the mechanism of relapse. Hum. Gene Ther. 2:137-159.

Brenner, M., Santana, V.M., Bowman, L.C., Furman, W., Heslop, H., Krance, R., Mahmoud, H., Boyett, J., Moss, T., Moen, R.C., and Mills, B. (1993c): Use of marker genes to investigate the mechanism of relapse and the effect of bone marrow purging in autologous transplantation for stage D neuroblastoma. Hum. Gene Ther. 4:809-820.

Brenner, M., Krance, R., Heslop, H.E., Santana, V., Ihle, J., Ribeiro, R., Roberts, W.M., Mahmoud, H., Boyett, J., Moen, R.C., and Klingemann. (1994b): Assessment of the efficacy of purging by using gene marked autologous marrow transplantation for children with AML in first complete remission. Hum. Gene Ther. 5:481-499.

Cornetta, K., Tricot, G., Brown, E.R., Hromas, R., Srour, E., Hoffman, R., Anderson, W.F., Moen, R.C., and Morgan, R.A. (1992): Retroviral-mediated gene transfer of bone marrow cells during autologous bone marrow transplantation for acute leukemia. Hum. Gene Ther. 3:305-318.

Deisseroth, A.B., Kantarjian, H., Talpaz, M., Champlin, R., Reading, C., Andersson, B., and Claxton, D. (1991): Autologous bone marrow transplantation for chronic myelogenous leukemia in which retroviral markers are used to discriminate between relapse which arises from systemic disease remaining after preparative therapy versus relapse due to residual leukemic cells in autologous marrow: A pilot trial. Hum. Gene Ther. 2:359-376.

Deisseroth, A.B., Kantarjian, H., Talpaz, M., Champlin, R., Reading, C., Andersson, B., and Claxton, D. (1993a): Use of two retroviral markers to test relative contribution of marrow and peripheral blood autologous cells to recovery after preparative therapy. Hum. Gene Ther. 4:71-85.

Deisseroth, A.B., Kantarjian, H., Champlin, R., Cabanillas, F., Keating, M., Reading, C., Andersson, B., Claxton, D., Robertson, B., Escudier, S., Andreeff, M., O'Brien, S., Kornblau, S., Ellerson, D., Hanania, E., and Fu, S. (1993b): Use of retroviral markers to identify efficacy of purging and origin of relapse following autologous bone marrow and peripheral blood cell transplantation in indolent B cell neoplasms (follicular non-hodgkin's lymphoma or chronic lymphocytic leukemia (CLL) patients). Hum. Gene Ther. 4:821-834.

Dunbar, C.E., Nienhuis, A.W., Stewart, F.M., Quesenberry, P., O'Shaughnessy, J., Cowan, K., Cottler-Fox, M., Leitman, S., Goodman, S., Sorrentino, B.P., McDonagh, K., Young, N.S., Donahue, R., Bodine, D., and Cassell, A. (1993): Gene marking with retroviral vectors to study the feasibility of stem cell gene transfer and the biology of hematopoietic reconstitution after autologous transplantation in multiple myeloma, chronic myelogenous leukemia, or metastatic breast cancer. Hum. Gene Ther. 4:205–222.

Economou, J.S., Belldegrun, A., Figlin, R.A., Holmes, E.C., Jacobs, E., Kohn, D., Golub, S., Shau, H., DeKernion, J., McBride, W.H., and Moen, R.C. (1992): The treatment of patients with metastatic melanoma and renal cell cancer using in vitro expanded and genetically-engineered (neomycin phosphotransferase) bulk, CD8(+) and/or CD4(+)tumor infiltrating leukocytes and bulk, CD8(+) and/or CD4(+) peripheral blood leukocytes in combination with recombinant interleukin-2 alone, or with recombinant interleukin-2 and recombinant alpha interferon. Hum. Gene Ther. 3:411–430.

Heslop, H.E., Brenner, M.K., Rooney, C.M., Krance, R.A., Roberts, W.M., Rochester, R., Smith, C.A., Turner, V., Sixbey, J., Moen, R.C., and Boyett, J.M. (1994): Administration of neomycin resistance gene marker EBV specific cytotoxic T lymphocytes to recipients of mismatched-related or phenotypically similar unrelated donor marrow grafts. Hum. Gene Ther. 5:381–397.

Lotze, M.T., Rubin, J.Y., Edington, H.D., Posner, M.G., Wolmark, N., Herberman, R.B., Whiteside, T.L., Elder, E., Dudjak, L., Snyder, J., Chelluri, L., Hayes, K., Kirkwood, J.M., Ernstoff, M., Vlock, D.R., Lembersky, B., Glorioso, J., Futrell, W., Yousem, S., Moen, R.C., Anderson, W.F. and Day, R. (1992): The treatment of patients with melanoma using interleukin-2, interleukin-4 and tumor infiltrating lymphocytes. Hum. Gene Ther. 3:167–177.

O'Shaughnessy, J.A., Cowan, K.H., Wilson, W., Bryant, G., Goldspiel, B., Gress, R., Nienhuis, A.W., Dunbar, C., Sorretino, B., Stewart, F.M., Moen, R., Fox, M., and Leitman, S. (1993): Pilot study of high dose ICE (ifosfamide, carboplatin, etoposide) chemotherapy and autologous bone marrow transplant (ABMT) with neo^R-transduced bone marrow and peripheral blood stem cells in patients with metastatic breast cancer. Hum. Gene Ther. 4:331–354.

Rosenberg, S.A., Blaese, R.M., Culver, K.W., Anderson, W.F., Cornetta, K., and Freeman, S.M. (1990): The N2-TIL human gene transfer clinical protocol. Hum. Gene Ther. 1:73–92.

Santana, V., Brenner, M.K., Ihle, J., Krance, R., Ribeiro, R., Hurwitz, C., Mahmoud, H., Moen, R.C., and Anderson, W.F. (1991a): A phase I/II trial of high dose carboplatin and etoposide with autologous marrow support for treatment of stage D neuroblastoma in first remission: Use of marker genes to investigate the biology of marrow reconstitution and the mechanism of relapse. Hum. Gene Ther. 2:257–272.

Santana, V., Brenner, M., Path, R., Ihle, J., Krance, R., Ribeiro, R., Hurwitz, C., Furman, W., Mahmoud, H., Bowman, L., Moen, R.C., and Anderson, W.F. (1991b): A phase II trial of high dose carboplatin and etoposide with autologous marrow support for treatment of relapse/refractory neuroblastoma without apparent bone marrow involvement. Hum. Gene Ther. 2:273–286.

Schuening, F., Miller, A.D., Torok-Storb, B., Bensinger, W., Storb, R., Reynolds, T., Fisher, L., Buckner, C.D., and Appelbaum, F.R. (1994): Study on contribution of genetically marked peripheral blood repopulating cells to hematopoietic reconstitution after transplantation. Hum. Gene Ther. 5:1523–1534.

Therapeutic Clinical Protocols (United States)

Berns, A.J.M., Clift, S., Cohen, L.K., Donehower, R.C., Dranoff, G., Hauda, K.M., Jaffee, E.M., Lazenby, A.J., Levitsky, H.I., Marshall, F.F., Mulligan, R.C., Nelson, W.G., Owens, A.H., Jr., Pardoll, D.M., Parry, G., Partin, A.H., Piantadosi, S., Simons, J.W., and Zabora, J.R. (1995): Phase I study of non-replicating autologous tumor cell injections using cells prepared with or without GM-CSF gene transduction in patients with metastatic renal cell carcinoma. Hum. Gene Ther. 6:347–368.

Brenner, M.K., Furman, W.L., Santana, V.M., Bowman, L., and Meyer, W. (1992): Phase I study of cytokine-gene modified autologous neuroblastoma cells for treatment of relapsed/refractory neuroblastoma. Hum. Gene Ther. 3:665–676.

Cassileth, P.A., Podack, E., Sridhar, K., and Savaraj, N. (1995): Phase I study of transfected cancer cells expressing the interleukin-2 gene product in limited stage small cell lung cancer. Hum. Gene Ther. 6:369–383.

Chang, A.E., Sondak, V.K., Bishop, D.K., Nickoloff, B.J., Mulligan, R.C., and Mulé, J.J. (1996): Adoptive immunotherapy of cancer with activated lymph node cells primed in vivo with autologous tumor cells transduced with the GM-CSF gene. Hum. Gene Ther. 7:773–792.

Conry, R.M., LoBuglio A.F., and Curiel, D.T. (1996): Phase Ia trial of a polynucleotide anti-tumor immunization to human carinoembryonic antigen in patients with metastatic colorectal cancer. Hum. Gene Ther. 7:755–772.

Culver, K.W., Van Gilder, J., Link, C.J., Jr., Carlstrom, T., Buroker, T., Yuh, W., Koch, K., Schabold, K., Doornbas, S., and Wetjen, B. (1993): Gene therapy for the treatment of malignant brain tumors with in vivo tumor transduction with the herpes simplex thymidine kinase gene/ganciclovir system. Hum. Gene Ther. 5:343–377.

Deisseroth, A.B., Holmes, F., Hortobagyi, G., and Champlin, R. (1996): Use of safety-modified retroviruses to introduce chemotherapy resistance sequences into normal hematopoietic cells for chemoprotection during the therapy of breast cancer: A pilot trial. Hum. Gene Ther. 7:401–416.

Deisseroth, A.B., Holmes, F., Hortobagyi, G., and Champlin, R. (1994): Use of safety-modified retroviruses to introduce chemotherapy resistance sequences into normal hematopoietic cells for chemoprotection duing the therapy of breast cancer: A pilot trial. Gum. Hene Ther. 5:1507-1522.

Douer, D., Levine, A., Anderson, W.F., Gordon, M., Groshen, S., Khan, A., Mohrbacher, A., Muggia, F., and Shibata, D. (1996): High-dose chemotherapy and autologous bone marrow plus peripheral blood stem cell transplantation for patients with lymphoma or metastatic breast cancer: Use of marker genes to investigate hematopoietic reconstitution in adults. Hum. Gene Ther. 7:669-684.

Fenton, R.T., Sznol, M., Luster, D.G., Taub, D.D., and Longo, D.L. (1995): A phase I trial of B7-transfected or parental lethally irradiated allogeneic melanoma cell lines to induce cell-mediated immunity against tumor-associated antigen presented by HLA-A2 or HLA-A1 in patients with stage IV melanoma. Hum. Gene Ther. 6:87-106.

Freeman, S.M., McCune, C., Robinson, W., Abboud, C.N., Abraham, G.N., Angel, C., and Marrogi, A. (1995): The treatment of ovarian cancer with a gene modified cancer vaccine: A phase-I study. Hum. Gene Ther. 6:927-939.

Gansbacher, B., Houghton, A., and Livingston, P. (1992a): A pilot study of immunization with HLA-A2 matched allogeneic melanoma cells that secrete interleukin-2 in patients with metastatic melanoma. Hum. Gene Ther. 3:677-690.

Gansbacher, B., Motzer, R., Houghton, A., and Bander, N. (1992b): A pilot study of immunization with interleukin-2 secreting allogeneic HLA-A2 matched renal cell carcinoma cells in patients with advanced renal cell carcinoma. Hum. Gene Ther. 3:691-703.

Hersh, E.M., Akporiaye, E., Harris, D., Stopeck, A.T., Unger, E.C., and Warneke, J.A. (1994): Clinical protocol: Phase I study of immunotherapy of malignant melanoma by direct gene transfer. Hum. Gene Ther. 5:1371-1384.

Hesdorfer, C., Antman, K., Bank, A., Fetell, M., Mears, G., and Begg, M. (1994): Human MDR gene transfer in patients with advanced cancer. Hum. Gene Ther. 5:1151-1160.

Heslop, H.E., Brenner, M.K., Krance, R.A., Bowman, L., Cunningham, J.M., Richardson, S., Alexander, B., and Heideman, R. (1996): Use of double marking with retroviral vectors to determine rate of reconstitution of untreated and cytokine expanded CD34+ selected marrow cells in patients undergoing autologous bone marrow transplantation. Hum. Gene Ther. 7:655-667.

Kun, L.E., Gajjar, A., Muhlbauer, M., Heideman, R.L., Sanford, R., Brenner, M., Walter, A., Langston, J., Jenkins, J., and Facchini, S. (1995): Stereotactic injection of herpes simplex thymidine kinase vector producer cells (PA317-G1Tk1SvNa.7) and intravenous ganciclovir for the treatment of progressive or recurrent primary supratentorial pediatric malignant brain tumors. Hum. Gene Ther. 6:1231-1255.

Lotze, M.T., Rubin, J., Carty, S., Edington, H., Fersen, P., Landreneau, R., Pippin, B., Posner, M., Rosenfelder, D., Watson, C., Carlos, T., Kirkwood, J., Lembersky, B., Logan, T., Rosenstein, M., Rybak, M.E., Whiteside, T., Elder, E., Moen, R.C., Jacob, W., Chiang, Y., Pinkus, R.L., and Bryant, J. (1994): Gene therapy of cancer: A pilot study of IL-4 gene-modified fibroblasts admixed with autologous tumor to elicit an immune response. Hum. Gene Ther. 5:41-55.

Nabel, G.J., Chang, A., Nabel, E.G., and Plautz, G. (1992): Immunotherapy of malignancy by in vivo gene transfer into tumors. Hum. Gene Ther. 3:399-410.

Nabel, G.J., Chang, A.E., Nabel, E.G., Plautz, G.E., Ensminger, W., Fox, B.A., Felgner, P., Shu, S., and Cho, K. (1994): Immunotherapy for cancer by direct gene transfer into tumors. Hum. Gene Ther. 5:57-77.

Oldfield, E.H., Ram, Z., Culver, K.W., Blaese, R.M., and DeVroom, H.L. (1993): Gene therapy for the treatment of brain tumors using intra-tumoral transduction with the thymidine kinase gene and intravenous ganciclovir. Hum. Gene Ther. 4:39-69.

Oldfield, E.H., Ram, Z., Chiang, Y., and Blaese, R.M. (1995): Intrathecal gene therapy for the treatment of leptomeningeal carcinomatosis. Hum. Gene Ther. 6:55-85.

O'Shaughnessy, J.A., Cowan, K.H., Nienhuis, A.W., McDonagh, K.T., Sorrentino, B.P., Dunbar, C.E., Chiang, Y., Wilson, W., Goldspiel, B., Kohler, D., Cottler-Fox, M., Leitman, S., Gottesman, M., Pastan, I., Denicoff, A., Noone, M., and Gress, R. (1994): Retroviral mediated transfer of the human multidrug resistance gene (MDR-1) into hematopoietic stem cells during autologous transplantation after intensive chemotherapy for metastatic breast cancer. Hum. Gene Ther. 5:891-911.

Raffel, C., Culver, K.W., Kohn, D., Nelson, M., Siegel, S., Gillis, F., Link, C.J., Jr., and Villablanca, J.G. (1994): Gene therapy for the treatment of recurrent pediatric malignant astrocytomas using in vivo tumor transduction with the herpes simplex thymidine kinase gene/ganciclovir system. Hum. Gene Ther. 5:863-890.

Rosenberg, S.A., Kasid, A., Anderson, W.F., Blaese, R.M., Aebersold, P., Yang, J., Topalian, S., Kreigler, M., Maiorella, B., Moen, R., and Chiang, Y. (1990): TNF/TIL human gene therapy clinical protocol. Hum. Gene Ther. 1:443-462.

Rosenberg, S.A., Anderson, W.F., Blaese, R.M., Ettinghausen, S.E., Hwu, P., Karp, S.E., Kasid, A., Mule, J.J., Parkinson, D.R., Salo, J.C., Schwartzentruber, D.J., Topalian, S.L., Weber, J.S., Yanneli, J.R., Yang, J.C., and Linehan, W.M. (1992a): Immunization of cancer patients using autologous cancer cells modified by insertion of the gene for interleukin-2. Hum. Gene Ther. 3:75-90.

Rosenberg, S.A., Anderson, W.F., Asher, A.L., Blaese, R.M., Ettinghausen, S.E., Hwu, P., Kasid, A., Mule, J.J., Parkinson, D.R., Schwartzentruber, D.J., Topalian, S.L., Weber, J.S., Yanneli, J.R., Yang, J.C., and Linehan, W.M. (1992b): Immunization of cancer patients using autologous cancer cells modified by insertion of the gene for tumor necrosis factor. Hum. Gene Ther. 3:57–73.

Roth, J.A. (1996): Modification of tumor suppressor gene expression in non-small cell lung cancer (NSCLC) with retroviral vector expressing wildtype (normal) p53. Hum. Gene Ther. 7:861–874.

Roth, J.A. (1996): Modification of mutant K-ras gene expression in non-small cell lung cancer (NSCLC). Hum. Gene Ther. 7:875–889.

Rubin, J., Charboneau, J.W., Reading, C., and Kovach, J.S. (1994): Phase I study of immunotherapy of hepatic metastases of colorectal carcinoma by direct gene transfer. Hum. Gene Ther. 5:1385–1399.

Seigler, H.F., Darrow, T.L., Abdel-Wahab, Z., Gangavalli, R., and Barber, J. (1994): A phase I trial of human gamma interferon transduced autologous tumor cells in patients with disseminated malignant melanoma. Hum. Gene Ther. 5:761–777.

Sobol, R.E., Royston, I., Fakhrai, H., Shawler, D.L., Carson, C., Dorigo, O., Gjerset, R., Gold, D.P., Koziol, J., Mercola, D., van Beveren, C., and Wilson, D. (1995): Injection of colon carcinoma patients with autologous irradiated tumor cells and fibroblasts genetically modified to secrete interleukin-2 (IL-2): A phase-I study. Hum. Gene Ther. 6:195–204.

Tahara, H., Lotze, M.T., Robbins, P.D., Storkus, W.J., and Zitvogel, L. (1995): IL-12 gene therapy using direct injection of tumors with genetically engineered autologous fibroblasts. Hum. Gene Ther. 6:1607–1624.

Vogelzang, N.J., Lestingi, T.M., and Sudakoff, G. (1994): Phase I study of immunotherapy of metastatic renal cell carcinoma by direct gene transfer into metastatic lesions. Hum. Gene Ther. 5:1357–1370.

Whitley, C.B., McIvor, R.S., Aronovich, E.L., Berry, S.A., Blazar, B.R., Burger, S.R., Kersey, J.H., King, R.A., Faras, A.J., Latchaw, R.E., McCullough, J., Pan, D., Ramsay, N.K.C., and Stroncek, D.F. (1996): Retroviral-mediated transfer of the iduronidase-2-sulfatase gene into lymphocytes for treatment of mild Hunter syndrome (mucopolysaccharidosis type II). Hum. Gene Ther. 7:537–549.

Marking Protocols (Non-United States)

Björkstrand, B., Gahrton, G., Dilber, M.S., Ljungman, P., Smith, C.I.E., and Xanthopoulos, K.G. (1994): Retroviral-mediated gene transfer of CD34-enriched bone marrow and peripheral blood cells during autologous stem cell transplantation for multiple myeloma. Hum. Gene Ther. 5:1279–1286.

Favrot, M.C., Philip, T., Merrouche, Y., Negrier, S., Mercatello, A., Coronel, B., Clapisson, G., Lanier, F., Heilman, M.O., Ranchere, J.Y., Philip, I., Moskovtchenko, J.F., Tolstoshev, P., Moen, R.C., and Franks, C.R. (1992): Treatment of patients with advanced cancer using tumor infiltrating lymphocytes transduced with the gene of resistance to neomycin. Hum. Gene Ther. 3:533–542.

Stewart, A.K., Dubé, I.D., Kamel-Reid, S., and Keating, A. (1995): A phase I study of autologous bone marrow transplantation with stem cell gene marking in multiple myeloma. Hum. Gene Ther. 6:107–119.

Therapeutic Clinical Protocols (Non-United States)

Bordignon, C., Bonini, C., Verzeletti, S., Nobili, N., Maggioni, D., Traversari, C., Giavazzi, R., Servida, P., Zappone, E., Benazzi, E., Bernadi, M., Porta, F., Ferrari, G., Mavilio, F., Rossini, S., Blaese, R.M., and Candotti, F. (1995): Transfer of the HSV-tk gene into donor peripheral blood lymphocytes for in vivo modulation of donor antitumor immunity after allogeneic bone marrow transplantation. Hum. Gene Ther. 6:813–819.

Cascinelli, N., Foà, R., Parmiani, G., Arienti, F., Belli, F., Bernengo, M.G., Clemente, C., Colombo, M.P., Guarini, A., Illeni, M.T., Mascheroni, L., Melani, C., Prada, A., and Sulé-Suso, J. (1994): Active immunization of metastatic melanoma patients with interleukin-4 transduced, allogeneic melanoma cells. A phase I-II study. Hum. Gene Ther. 5:1059–1064.

Klatzmann, D., Philippon, J., Malery, C.A., and Bensimon, G. (1996): Gene therapy for glioblastoma in adult patients: Safety and efficacy evaluation of an in situ injection of recombinant retroviruses producing cells carrying the thymidine kinase gene of the herpes simplex type I virus, to be followed with the administration of ganciclovir. Hum. Gene Ther. 7:109–126.

Klatzmann, D., Herson, S., Cherin, P., Chosidow, O., Baillet, F., Bensimon, G., and Boyer, O. (1996): Gene therapy for metastatic malignant melanoma: Evaluation of tolerance to intratumoral injection of cells producing recombinant retroviruses carrying the herpes simplex virus type I thymidine kinase gene, to be followed by ganciclovir administration. Hum. Gene Ther. 7:255–267.

Mackiewicz, A., Gorny, A., Laciak, M., Malicki, J., Murawa, P., Nowak, J., Wiznerowicz, M., Hawley, R.G., Heinrich, P.C., and Rose-John, S. (1995): Gene therapy of human melanoma. Immunization of patients with autologous tumor cells admixed with allogeneic melanoma cells secreting interleukin-6 and soluble interleukin-6 receptor. Hum. Gene Ther. 6:805–811.

Mertelsman, R., Lindemann, A., Boehm, T., Brennscheidt, U., Franke, B., Kulmburg, P., Lahn, M., Mackensen, A., Rosenthal, F.M., and Veelken, H. (1995): Pilot study for the evaluation of T-cell-mediated tumor immunotherapy by cytokine gene transfer into patients with malignant tumors. J. Mol. Med. 73:205–206.

Osanto, S., Brouwenstÿn, N., Vaessen, N., Figdor, C.G., Melief, C.J.M., and Schrier, P.I. (1993): Immunization with interleukin-2 transfected melanoma cells. A phase I–II study in patients with metastatic melanoma. Hum. Gene Ther. 4:323–330.

Schadendorf, D., Czarnetzki, B.M., and Wittig, B. (1995): Interleukin-7, interleukin-12, and GM-CSF gene transfer in patients with metastatic melanoma. J. Mol. Med. 73:473–477.

Schmidt-Wolf, I.G.H., Huhn, D., Neubauer, A., and Wittig, B. (1994): Interleukin-7 gene transfer in patients with metastatic colon carcinoma, renal cell carcinoma, melanoma, or with lymphoma. Hum. Gene Ther. 5:1161–1168.

Stingl, G., Bröcker, E.-B., Mertelsmann, R., Wolff, K., Schreiber, S., Kämpgen, E., Schneeberger, A., Dummer, W., Brennsheid, U., Veelken, H., Birnsteil, M.L., Zatloukal, K., Schmidt, W., Maass, G., Wagner, E., Buschle, M., Giese, M., Kempe, E.-R., Weber, H.A., and Voigt, T. (1996): Phase I study to the immunotherapy of metastatic malignant melanoma by a cancer vaccine consisting of autologous cancer cells transfected with the human IL-2 gene. Hum. Gene Ther. 7:551–563.

Glossary

Adeno-associated virus.   A single-stranded DNA parvovirus that is endogenous to humans. This virus is not associated with disease in humans and is currently being investigated as a possible clinical gene transfer vector.

Adenosine deaminase (ADA) deficiency.   A rare autosomal recessive disorder that results in failure of the maturation of T lymphocytes. Children with ADA deficiency have severe combined immunodeficiency and typically die within 2 years of birth in the absence of immune system reconstitution.

Anergy.   Lack of a delayed-type hypersensitivity (DTH) response to skin testing with antigens to which the individual has been previously exposed (e.g., tetanus vaccination, streptococcus in the environment).

Antisense.   The mirror image of a DNA or RNA sequence. Antisense genes are commonly used to bind the targeted "sense" gene to block its ability to produce a gene product, effectively shutting off expression of the targeted gene.

Apoptosis.   A process of genetically programmed cell death in which the cell nucleus becomes segmented, its cytoplasm condenses, the cell membrane develops blebs, and the DNA fragments. This process is distinctly different from necrosis where damaged cells swell and rupture due to increased membrane permeability. Gene transfer is being developed as a means to selectively induce programmed cell death to eliminate specific cell populations.

Artificial chromosome.   A vector that is constructed from telomeric, centromeric, and replication of origin sequences needed for replication in eukaryotic cells, plus the DNA fragment of interest.

Autosome.   Any chromosome other than the X and Y sex chromosomes.

Base pair (bp).   Two nitrogenous bases (adenine and thymidine or guanine and cytosine). The two strands of DNA are held together in the shape of a double helix due to the hydrogen bonding between base pairs.

Chromosome.   A supercoiled strand of DNA and protein that contains genes. Human somatic cells each have 46 chromosomes.

Cloning.   Laboratory production of multiple, identical copies of a gene or a cell.

Cloning vector.   DNA molecules originating from a virus, plasmid, or cells of a higher organism into which a different DNA fragment can be inserted without loss of the capacity for replication. Vectors are vehicles for the transfer of foreign DNA into cells where the vector genes or gene products can be produced in large quantities.

Coding sequence. The portion of a gene that is transcribed into mRNA.

Cytokines. Small glycoproteins that function as intercellular messengers that are commonly thought of as factors that alter immune function.

DNA (deoxyribonucleic acid). A string of deoxyribonucleotides that forms chromosomes and comprises the genetic material in cells.

Enhancer. A DNA regulatory element that acts to boost the level of gene expression.

E1A and E1B genes. Regulatory genes in the human adenovirus that can be deleted to produce a replication-defective adenoviral vector.

Exogenous DNA. DNA originating from outside an organism.

Exon. A piece of DNA encoding a gene that is transcribed into mRNA and then translated into protein.

Ex vivo. Occurring outside the body.

FISH (fluorescence in situ hybridization). A physical mapping technique that uses fluorescein tags to detect hybridization of probes in metaphase chromosomes.

Ganciclovir (Cytovene). An antiherpes drug that is currently approved by the FDA for the treatment of cytomegalovirus (CMV) retinitis.

Gene. The smallest unit of hereditary information, or DNA, that encodes the production of a specific protein product.

Gene expression. The process by which genetic information is converted into the structures present in the cell and molecules necessary for cellular metabolism. Expressed genes are those that are transcribed into mRNA and then translated into protein and those transcribed into RNA but not translated into protein (e.g., transfer and ribosomal RNAs).

Gene mapping. Determination of the relative positions of genes in a chromosome or plasmid.

Gene product. The biochemical material, either RNA or protein, resulting from expression of a gene.

Genome. The total DNA contained in all the chromosomes within a cell. The genome comprises the entire complement of genes for an individual.

Germline cells. The reproductive cells of the body (i.e., cells contained in the testis and ovary). See also Somatic cells.

Herpes simplex–thymidine kinase gene. This gene encodes an enzyme that will phosphorylate the antiherpes drugs acyclovir (Zovirax) and ganciclovir (Cytovene) to toxic derivatives that kill the cell in which the gene resides.

HIV. The human immunodeficiency virus; the known cause of acquired immunodeficiency syndrome (AIDS).

Homologous recombination. A process by which a gene with a partially identical sequence is substituted for another embedded in the chromosome. This switch has been used in the laboratory to replace a defective gene with a normal copy of the gene.

Human leukocyte antigen (HLA). Cell-surface proteins that determine human tissue type.

Insertional mutagenesis. The process by which a retroviral vector inserts adjacent to an oncogene and induces its expression, or inserts within a tumor suppressor gene, disrupting its function, increasing the possibility that the cell will become malignant.

Intron. A piece of DNA of unknown function that is interspersed between exons.

In situ. Literally "in position," this term refers to processes or substances occurring in their natural site inside the body.

***In situ* hybridization.** Use of a DNA or RNA probe to detect the presence of complementary DNA.

In vitro (ex vivo). Literally "in glass," this term refers to reactions occurring in an artificial environment outside the body.

In vivo. Literally "in the living," this term refers to processes occurring within the body.

Interleukins. One group of cytokines that functions as intercellular messengers within the immune system and between the immune system and other tissues.

Isohemagglutinins. Antibodies to blood group antigens that are spontaneously produced by immunocompetent individuals by age 3 at a titer of $\geq$ 1:16.

Karyotype. An enumeration of chromosomes removed from an individual cell; in the case of humans, the normal karyotype consists of 22 pairs of autosomes plus 2 sex chromosomes.

Kilobase (kb). DNA fragments equal to 1,000 nucleotides.

k-*ras*. An oncogene that is overexpressed in a variety of cancers including lung cancer.

Liposomes. A gene delivery system based on the production of lipid bodies that contain pieces of DNA. These lipid–DNA complexes fuse with the cell surface and are internalized by phagocytosis, depositing the encapsulated DNA into the target cell.

Megabase (Mb). DNA fragments equal to 1 million nucleotides.

mRNA. RNA that is produced by transcription of DNA. This genetic material leaves the nucleus and moves to the cytoplasm, where a protein strand is generated based on the nucleotide sequence encoded by the RNA.

***NeoR* gene.** This bacterial gene encodes the neomycin phosphotransferase II enzyme. Insertion of this enzyme into mammalian cells confers protection against the cytotoxic effects of the neomycin analogue, Geneticin (G418). Most gene transfer systems incorporate this gene into the vector or plasmid as a dominant selectable marker, allowing the selective growth of gene modified cells *in vitro.*

Nucleotide. Building blocks of DNA and RNA comprised of a base, a deoxyribose or ribose sugar, and a phosphate.

Oligonucleotide. A short piece of DNA, usually less than 100 nucleotides in length.

Oncogene. A gene that is normally tightly regulated. When its regulatory pathway is disrupted and the gene is overexpressed, the cell becomes premalignant or malignant.

p53. A tumor suppressor gene that protects cells from DNA-damaging agents, preventing these cells from becoming malignant. Deletion or damage of one or both copies of these genes increases the likelihood of a cell becoming malignant.

Plasmid. A circular, self-replicating piece of DNA naturally found in bacteria and yeast. Plasmids are commonly used to carry foreign genes into cells for the production of recombinant DNA pharmaceuticals and in gene expression studies.

Polyadenylation (Poly-A). A series of adenines added to the end of mRNA after transcription. The series of adenines is believed to function in the movement of the mRNA from the nucleus and to retard its degradation in the cytoplasm.

Polymerase. An enzyme that adds nucleotides to a chain creating a strand of DNA or RNA.

Polymerase chain reaction (PCR). A laboratory method by which a small fragment of DNA can be quickly amplified, or reproduced, millions of times.

Promoter. A regulatory element in DNA that functions to induce transcription of a gene.

Protein. A large molecule composed of one or more chains of amino acids. The amino acid order is determined by the base sequence of nucleotides in the expressed gene.

Recombinant DNA. The process by which DNA from different organisms is "spliced" or ligated together to form a "new" heterologous piece of DNA.

Recombination. A process by which a piece of genetic material is combined with a piece of genetic material from another location in the chromosome by the processes of crossing-over and independent assortment. The result is a new combination of genes.

Restriction endonuclease. An enzyme that will cut a piece of DNA at a specific nucleotide sequence.

Retroviral vector. A disabled retrovirus, usually murine, containing exogenous genes that will infect target cells and insert the vector DNA into the target cell chromosomes.

Rev. An HIV regulatory protein involved in the transport of HIV RNA from the nucleus of a cell into its cytoplasm, where it is packaged into an infectious virus.

Ribozymes. RNA molecules that specifically degrade other RNA molecules.

RNA (ribonucleic acid). A string of ribonucleotides that is similar in structure to DNA. There are several classes of RNA including messenger RNA (mRNA), transfer RNA (tRNA), and ribosomal RNA (rRNA).

Sense.   The normal sequence of a gene that is transcribed.

Sequence.   The relative order of nucleotide pairs whether in a fragment of DNA, a gene, or a chromosome.

Severe combined immunodeficiency (SCID).   A rare genetic disorder that results in profound failure of the humoral and cellular components of the immune system.

Somatic cells.   The nonreproductive cells of the body (e.g., muscle, skin, endothelial cells, hepatocytes, etc.). See also Germline cells.

Tat.   An HIV regulatory protein involved in HIV replication.

Transcript.   The mRNA template that is produced as a result of transcription of DNA (a gene).

Transcription.   The process of conversion of DNA into RNA.

Transdominant negative.   A gene product that competitively binds another intracellular factor blocking transcription or translation through competitive inhibition.

Transduction.   A virus-mediated method for gene transfer.

Transfection.   A non-virus-mediated method for gene transfer.

Transgenic.   Transgenic plants and animals are created by the insertion of a foreign gene into the germline (reproductive) cells. When the organism develops and matures, each of the cells of the plant or animal will contain the foreign gene.

Translation.   The process of conversion of mRNA into an amino acid sequence.

Tumor-infiltrating lymphocyte (TIL).   T lymphocytes derived from deposits of tumor, usually melanoma. Tumors are resected and grown in culture in high concentrations of interleukin-2 to stimulate T lymphocyte growth, where they destroy the malignant cells.

Tumor necrosis factor (TNF).   A cytokine that appears to be involved in mediating tumor cell destruction and in inflammatory responses such as rheumatoid arthritis. It has been purified and injected into mice and humans in an effort to cure cancer.

Vector.   A disabled virus or DNA structure used as a vehicle to transfer genes into cells.

Virus.   A noncellular biologic entity that can reproduce only within host cells. Viruses consist of nucleic acid (RNA or DNA) covered by protein or by a membrane. Once the virus infects the cell, the virus uses the synthetic capacity of the cell to produce more infectious virus.

INDEX OF HEALTH DISORDERS AND CHROMOSOME LOCATIONS

Alphabetical Index of Health Disorders and Chromosome Location*

Disorder	Location	Disorder	Location
3-beta-hydroxysteroid dehydrogenase, type II, deficiency (3)	1p13.1	Amyloidosis, Finnish type, 105120 (3)	9q34
3-hydroxyacyl-CoA dehydrogenase deficiency (1)	Chr.7	Amyloidosis, hereditary renal, 105200 (3)	4q28
3-ketothiolase deficiency (3)	**11q22.3–q23.1**	Amyloidosis, Iowa type, 107680.0010 (3)	11q23
Aarskog-Scott syndrome (3)	Xp11.21	Amyloidosis, renal, 105200 (3)	Chr.12
Abetalipoproteinemia (3)	2p24	{?Amyloidosis, secondary, susceptibility to} (1)	1q21-q23
[Acanthocytosis, one form] (3)	17q21-q22	Amyloidosis, senile systemic (3)	18q11.2-q12.1
Acatalasemia (3)	11p13	Amyotrophic lateral sclerosis, juvenile (2)	2q33-q35
Acetyl-CoA carboxylase deficiency (1)	17q21	Amytrophic lateral sclerosis, due to SOD1 deficiency, 105400 (3)	21q22.1
Achondrogenesis-hypochondrogenesis, type II (3)	12q13.11-q13.2	?Anal canal carcinoma (2)	11q22-qter
Achondroplasia, 100800 (3)	4p16.3	Analbuminemia (3)	4q11-q13
?Acrocallosal syndrome (2)	12p13.3-p11.2	**Androgen insensitivity, several forms (3)**	**Xq11-q12**
?Acrofacial dysostosis, Nager type (2)	9q32	?Anemia, megaloblastic, due to DHFR deficiency (1)	5q11.2-q13.2
ACTH deficiency (1)	2p25	Anemia, pernicious, congenital, due to deficiency of intrinsic factor (1)	Chr.11
Acyl-CoA dehydrogenase, long chain, deficiency of (3)	2q34-q35	?Anemia, sideroblastic, with spinocerebellar ataxia (2)	Xq13
Acyl-CoA dehydrogenase, medium chain, deficiency of (3)	1p31	Anemia, sideroblastic/hypochromic (3)	Xp11.21
Acyl-CoA dehydrogenase, short-chain, deficiency of (3)	12q22-qter	Aneurysm, familial, 100070 (3)	2q31
Adenylosuccinase deficiency (3)	22q13.1	Angelman syndrome (2)	15q11-q13
Adhalinopathy, primary (1)	**17q12-q21.33**	Angioedema, hereditary (3)	11q11-q13.1
Adrenal hyperplasia, congenital, due to 11-beta-hydroxylase deficiency (3)	8q21	Anhidrotic ectodermal dysplasia (2)	Xq12.2-q13.1
Adrenal hyperplasia, congenital, due to 17-alpha-hydroxylase deficiency (3)	10q24.3	Aniridia (3)	11p13
Adrenal hyperplasia, congenital, due to 21-hydroxylase deficiency (3)	6p21.3	?Anophthalmos-1 (2)	Xq27-q28
Adrenal hypoplasia, congenital, with hypogonadotropic hypogonadism (3)	**Xp21.3-p21.2**	Anterior segment mesenchymal dysgenesis (2)	4q28-q31
Adrenocortical carcinoma, hereditary, 202300 (2)	11p15.5	Antithrombin III deficiency (3)	1q23-q25
Adrenoleukodystrophy (3)	Xq28	**Apert syndrome, 101200 (3)**	**10q26**
Adrenoleukodystrophy, pseudoneonatal (2)	**17q25**	Apnea, postanesthetic (3)	3q26.1-q26.2
Adrenomyeloneuropathy (2)	Xq28	ApoA-I and apoC-III deficiency, combined (3)	11q23
[AFP deficiency, congenital] (1)	4q11-q13	Apolipoprotein B-100, ligand-defective (3)	2p24
Agammaglobulinemia, type 1, X-linked (3)	Xq21.3-q22	[Apolipoprotein H deficiency] (3)	17q23-qter
Agammaglobulinemia, type 2, X-linked (2)	Xp22	Argininemia (3)	6q23
Aicardi syndrome (2)	Xp22	Argininosuccinicaciduria (3)	7cen-q11.2
Alagille syndrome (2)	20p11.2	**Arrhythmogenic right ventricular dysplasia (2)**	**14q23-q24**
Albinism, brown, 203290 (1)	9p23	Aspartylglucosaminuria (3)	4q32-q33
Albinism, ocular, autosomal-recessive (3)	15q11.2-q12	**Ataxia with isolated vitamin E deficiency, 277460 (3)**	**8q13.1-q13.3**
Albinism, oculocutaneous, type IA (3)	11q14-q21	Ataxia-telangiectasia (2)	11q22.3
Albinism, oculocutaneous, type II (3)	15q11.2-q12	**{Atherosclerosis, susceptibility to} (2)**	**1q23-q25**
Albinism-deafness syndrome (2)	Xq26.3-q27.1	{Atherosclerosis, susceptibility to} (2)	19p13.3-p13.2
?Albright hereditary osteodystrophy 2 (2)	15q11-q13	?{Atherosclerosis, susceptibility to} (3)	8p21-p12
Alcohol intolerance, acute (3)	12q24.2	Atopy (2)	11q12-q13
Aldolase A deficiency (3)	16q22-q24	Atransferrinemia (1)	3q21
Aldosteronism, glucocorticoid-remediable (3)	8q21	Atrial septal defect, secundum type (2)	6p21.3
Alkaptonuria (3)	3q2	**Atrophia areata (2)**	**11p15**
Allan-Herndon syndrome (2)	Xq21	Autism, succinylpurinemic (3)	22q13.1
?{Allergy and asthma susceptibility} (2)	**5q31.1**	**{Autoimmune lymphoproliferative syndrome} (3)**	**10q24.1**
Alpha-1-antichymotrypsin deficiency (3)	14q32.1	Autoimmune polyglandular disease, type I (2)	21q22.3
Alpha-ketoglutarate dehydrogenase deficiency (1)	7p13-p11.2	**B**ardet-Biedl syndrome 1 (2)	**11q13**
Alpha-thalassemia/mental retardation syndrome, type 1 (1)	16pter-p13.3	Bardet-Biedl syndrome 2 (2)	16q21
Alpha-thalassemia/mental retardation syndrome, type 2, 301040 (3)	Xq13	Bardet-Biedl syndrome 3 (2)	3p13-p12
Alport syndrome, 301050 (3)	Xq22	Bardet-Biedl syndrome 4 (2)	15q22.3-q23
Alport syndrome, autosomal-recessive, 203780 (3)	**2q36**	Bare lymphocyte syndrome, type I, due to TAP2 deficiency (1)	6p21.3
Alport syndrome, autosomal-recessive, 203780 (3)	**2q36-q37**	Barth syndrome (2)	Xq28
?Alport syndrome, X-linked, type 2 (1)	Xq22	?Basal cell carcinoma (2)	9q31
Alzheimer disease, APP-related (3)	21q21.3-q22.05	Basal cell carcinoma (3)	5q13.3
Alzheimer disease 2, late onset (2)	19cen-q13.2	Basal cell nevus syndrome (2)	9q31
Alzheimer disease 3 (3)	14q24.3	Batten disease (2)	16p12.1
Alzheimer disease 4 (3)	**Chr. 1**	Becker muscular dystrophy (3)	Xp21.2
Amelogenesis imperfecta (3)	Xp22.3-p22.1	Beckwith-Wiedemann syndrome (2)	11pter-p15.4
?Amelogenesis imperfecta 3, hypoplastic type (2)	Xq22-q28	**Benign recurrent intrahepatic cholestasis (2)**	**18q21-q22**
[AMP deaminase deficiency, erythrocytic] (3)	11pter-p13	Bernard-Soulier syndrome (1)	17pter-p12
Amyloid neuropathy, familial, several allelic types (3)	18q11.2-q12.1	**Bernard-Soulier syndrome, type B (2)**	**22q11.2**
Amyloidosis, cerebroarterial, Dutch type (3)	21q21.3-q22.05		

Italics indicate genes recently repositioned on chromosomes—June 1994 to September 1995.
Boldface indicates recently located disorders—June 1994 to September 1995.
*©1995. The Journal of NIH Research, Washington, DC. Reprinted with permission.

Disorder	Location
Bernard-Soulier syndrome, variant form (3)	**Chr.3**
{Beryllium disease, chronic, susceptibility to} (3)	6p21.3
Biotinidase deficiency (1)	**3p25**
Bladder cancer, 109800 (3)	**13q14.1-q14.2**
Bleeding disorder due to defective thromboxane A2 receptor (3)	**19p13.3**
Blepharophimosis, epicanthus inversus and ptosis (2)	3q22-q23
Bloom syndrome (2)	15q26.1
Borjeson-Forssman-Lehmann syndrome (2)	Xq26-q27
Bornholm eye disease (2)	Xq28
?Brachydactyly type E (2)	**2q37**
Brachydactyly-mental retardation syndrome (2)	**2q37**
Branchiootorenal dysplasia (2)	8q13.3
?Breast cancer (1)	**17p13.3**
Breast cancer (1)	6q25.1
Breast cancer 1, early onset (3)	17q21
Breast cancer 2, early onset (2)	**13q12.3**
Breast cancer 3 (2)	**11q23**
Breast cancer, ductal (2)	1p36
Breast cancer, ductal (2)	Chr.13
Breast cancer, male, with Reifenstein syndrome (3)	**Xq11-q12**
Brody myopathy (1)	Chr.16
Brunner syndrome (3)	Xp11.23
Burkitt lymphoma (3)	8q24.12-q24.13
Butterfly dystrophy, retinal (3)	**6p21.1-cen**
Byler disease (2)	**18q21-q22**
?C1q deficiency (1)	1p36.3-p34.1
C1r/C1s deficiency, combined (1)	12p13
C2 deficiency (3)	6p21.3
C3 deficiency (3)	19p13.3-p13.2
C3b inactivator deficiency (1)	4q25
C4 deficiency (3)	6p21.3
C5 deficiency (1)	9q34.1
C6 deficiency (1)	5p13
C7 deficiency (1)	5p13
C8 deficiency, type I (2)	1p32
C8 deficiency, type II (3)	1p32
C9 deficiency (1)	5p13
Campomelic dysplasia with autosomal sex reversal (3)	17q24.3-q25.1
Canavan disease (3)	17pter-p13
Carbamoylphosphate synthetase I deficiency (3)	2q33-q36
Carbohydrate-deficient glycoprotein syndrome (2)	**16p13.3-p13.2**
Carboxypeptidase B deficiency (1)	Chr.13
?Cardiomyopathy (1)	2q35
Cardiomyopathy, dilated, X-linked (3)	Xp21.2
Cardiomyopathy, dilated, X-linked fatal infantile (2)	**Xq28**
Cardiomyopathy, familial dilated, with conduction defect (2)	**1p11-q11**
Cardiomyopathy, familial hypertrophic, 1, 192600 (3)	14q12
Cardiomyopathy, familial hypertrophic, 2, 115195 (3)	1q3
Cardiomyopathy, familial hypertrophic, 3, 115196 (3)	15q22
Cardiomyopathy, familial hypertrophic, 4 (3)	11p13-q13
?Carnitine acetyltransferase deficiency (1)	**9q34.1**
?Carnitine palmitoyltransferase I deficiency (1)	**11q**
Carnitine palmitoyltransferase II deficiency (3)	**1p32**
Carpal tunnel syndrome, familial (3)	18q11.2-q12.1
Cartilage-hair hypoplasia (2)	9p13-q11
Cat eye syndrome (2)	22q11
?Cataract, anterior polar, I (2)	14q24-qter
?Cataract, congenital (2)	15q15
Cataract, congenital, cerulean type (2)	**17q24**
?Cataract, congenital total (2)	Xp
Cataract, congenital, with late-onset corneal dystrophy (3)	**11p13**
Cataract, congenital, with microphthalmia (2)	16p13.3
Cataract, Coppock-like (3)	2q33-q35
Cataract, Marner type (2)	16q22.1
Cataract, zonular pulverulent 1 (2)	1q2
Cavernous angiomatous malformations (2)	**7q11-q22**
CD3, zeta chain, deficiency (1)	1q23-q25
[CD4(+) lymphocyte deficiency] (2)	**12pter-p12**
CD59 deficiency (3)	11p13
Central core disease, 117000 (3)	19q13.1
?Central core disease, one form (3)	14q12
Centrocytic lymphoma (1)	11q13
Cerebellar ataxia, paroxysmal acetazolamide-responsive (2)	**19p13**
Cerebellar ataxia with retinal degeneration (2)	**3p21.1-p12**
Cerebral amyloid angiopathy (3)	20p11
Cerebral arteriopathy with subcortical infarcts and leukoencephalopathy (2)	19q12
Cerebrotendinous xanthomatosis (3)	2q33-qter
Cerebrovascular disease, occlusive (3)	**14q32.1**
Ceroid lipofuscinosis, neuronal-1, infantile (2)	1p32
Ceroid-lipofuscinosis, neuronal, variant late infantile form (2)	**13q21.1-q32**
Cervical carcinoma (2)	11q13
[CETP deficiency] (3)	16q21
Charcot-Marie-Tooth disease, type II (2)	1p36-p35
Charcot-Marie-Tooth disease, type IVA (2)	8q13-q21.1
Charcot-Marie-Tooth neuropathy, slow nerve conduction type Ia (3)	17p11.2
Charcot-Marie-Tooth neuropathy, slow nerve conduction type Ib, 118200 (3)	1q22
Charcot-Marie-Tooth neuropathy, X-linked-1, dominant, 302800 (3)	Xq13.1
Charcot-Marie-Tooth neuropathy, X-linked-2, recessive (2)	Xp22.2
Chloride diarrhea, congenital (2)	7q31
Cholesteryl ester storage disease (3)	10q24-q25
?Chondrodysplasia punctata, rhizomelic (2)	4p16-p14
Chondrodysplasia punctata, X-linked dominant (2)	Xq28
Chondrodysplasia punctata, X-linked recessive, 302940 (3)	Xp22.3
Choroideremia (3)	Xq2
Chronic granulomatous disease, autosomal, due to deficiency of CYBA (3)	16c
Chronic granulomatous disease due to deficiency of NCF 1 (3)	7q11
Chronic granulomatous disease due to deficiency of NCF 2 (1)	1c
Chronic granulomatous disease, X-linked (3)	Xp2
{Chronic infections, due to opsonin defect} (3)	10q11.2-c
Citrullinemia (3)	9c
Cleft palate, X-linked (2)	Xq21.1-q21
Cleidocranial dysplasia (2)	6p
CMO II deficiency (3)	8c
Cockayne syndrome 2, late onset, 216410 (2)	10c
Coffin-Lowry syndrome (2)	Xp22.2-p2
Cohen syndrome (2)	**8q22-q**
?Colon cancer (1)	7q22-q3
Colon cancer, familial nonpolyposis, type 1 (3)	2p16-p
Colorblindness, blue monochromatic (3)	Xc
Colorblindness, deutan (3)	Xc
Colorblindness, protan (3)	Xc
Colorblindness, tritan (3)	7q31.3-c
Colorectal adenoma (1)	12p1
Colorectal cancer (1)	12p1
Colorectal cancer, 114500 (3)	17p1
Colorectal cancer (3)	18q2
Colorectal cancer (3)	5c
Colorectal cancer (3)	5q21-c
Colorectal cancer, familial nonpolyposis type 2 (3)	**3p2**
Colton blood group (3)	**7p**
Combined C6/C7 deficiency (1)	5
Combined hyperlipemia, familial (3)	**8p**
Combined immunodeficiency, X-linked, moderate, 312863 (3)	**Xq**
?Combined variable hypogammaglobulinemia (1)	14q32
Cone-rod retinal dystrophy 1 (2)	**18q21.1-q2**
Cone-rod retinal dystrophy 2 (2)	**19q13.1-q1**
Congenital bilateral absence of vas deferens (3)	7q3
?Conotruncal cardiac anomalies (2)	22c
Contractural arachnodactyly, congenital (3)	5q23-
Coproporphyria (3)	3c
Cornea plana congenita, recessive (2)	**12q**
Corneal dystrophy, combined granular/lattice type (2)	5q22-q3
Corneal dystrophy, Groenouw type I (2)	5q22-q5
Corneal dystrophy, lattice type I, 122200 (2)	5q22-q3
?Cornelia de Lange syndrome (2)	3q2
{Coronary artery disease, susceptibility to} (1)	6c
Cortisol resistance (3)	5c
CR1 deficiency (1)	1c
?Craniofrontonasal dysplasia (2)	Xpter-p2
Craniosynostosis, Adelaide type (2)	**4p**
Craniosynostosis, type 1 (3)	7p21.3-p2
Craniosynostosis, type 2 (3)	5q34-c
[Creatine kinase, brain type, ectopic expression of] (3)	14c
Creutzfeldt-Jakob disease, 123400 (3)	20pter-
Crigler-Najjar syndrome, type I, 218800 (3)	2c
Crouzon craniofacial dysostosis, 123500 (3)	**10c**
?Cryptorchidism (2)	Xc
?Cutis laxa, marfanoid neonatal type (1)	7q31.1-q3
[Cystathioninuria] (1)	Ch
Cystic fibrosis (3)	7q2
Cystinosis (2)	
Cystinuria, 220100 (3)	2p
Darier disease (keratosis follicularis) (2)	12q23-q2
Deafness 4, congenital sensorineural (2)	**Xp2**
Deafness 3, conductive, with fixed stapes, 304400 (3)	Xq2
Deafness, autosomal-dominant 1 (2)	5q31-
Deafness, autosomal-dominant 2 (2)	1c
Deafness, autosomal-recessive 1 (2)	13
Deafness, autosomal-recessive 2 (2)	11q
Deafness, autosomal-recessive 3 (2)	17p12-
Debrisoquine sensitivity (3)	22c
Dejerine-Sottas disease, myelin P(0)-related, 145900 (3)	1
Dejerine-Sottas disease, PMP22 related, 145900 (3)	17p
?Dent disease, 310468 (2)	**Xp11**
Dentatorubro-pallidoluysian atrophy (3)	12pter-
Dentinogenesis imperfecta-1 (2)	4q13-
Denys-Drash syndrome (3)	11c
Diabetes insipidus, nephrogenic (3)	X
Diabetes insipidus nephrogenic, autosomal-recessive (3)	12
Diabetes insipidus, neurohypophyseal, 125700 (3)	20
?Diabetes mellitus, insulin-dependent, 1 (2)	6p2
Diabetes mellitus, insulin-dependent, 2 (2)	11p
Diabetes mellitus, insulin-dependent, 3 (2)	**15c**
Diabetes mellitus, insulin-dependent, 4 (2)	**11c**
Diabetes mellitus, insulin-dependent, 5 (2)	**6q24-c**
?Diabetes mellitus, insulin-dependent, 7 (2)	**2c**
?Diabetes mellitus, insulin-dependent, neonatal (2)	**Ch**
Diabetes mellitus, insulin-resistant, with acanthosis nigricans (3)	19p
Diabetes mellitus, rare form (1)	11p
Diastrophic dysplasia (3)	5q31-
?Dicarboxylicaminoaciduria, 222730 (1)	9
DiGeorge syndrome (2)	22
Diphenylhydantoin toxicity (1)	1p11-
{Diphtheria, susceptibility to} (1)	5
Disinhibition-dementia-Parkinsonism-amyotrophy complex (2)	**17q21-c**
Distal arthrogryposis 1 (2)	**9p21-c**

...A ligase I deficiency (3)	19q13.2-q13.3
...pamine-beta-hydroxylase deficiency (1)	**9q34**
...wn syndrome (1)	**21q22.3**
...bin-Johnson syndrome (2)	13q34
...chenne muscular dystrophy (3)	Xp21.2
...ysalbuminemic hyperthyroxinemia] (3)	4q11-q13
...ysalbuminemic hyperzincemia] (3)	4q11-q13
...autonomia, familial (2)	9q31-q33
...serythropoietic anemia, congenital, type III (2)	15q21
...sfibrinogenemia, alpha types (3)	4q28
...sfibrinogenemia, beta types (3)	4q28
...sfibrinogenemia, gamma types (3)	4q28
...skeratosis congenita (2)	Xq28
...slexia, specific, 2 (2)	**6p21.3**
...splasminogenemic thrombophilia (1)	6q26
...sprothrombinemia (1)	11p11-q12
...stonia, DOPA-responsive, 128230 (3)	14q22.1-q22.2
...stransthyretinemic hyperthyroxinemia] (3)	18q11.2-q12.1
...?EEC syndrome (2)	7q11.2-q21.3
Ehlers-Danlos syndrome, type III (3)	**2q31**
Ehlers-Danlos syndrome, type IV, 130050 (3)	2q31
...lers-Danlos syndrome, type unspecified (3)	**9q34.2-q34.3**
...ers-Danlos syndrome, type VI, 225400 (3)	1p36.3-p36.2
...ers-Danlos syndrome, type VIIA1, 130060 (3)	17q21.31-q22.05
...ers-Danlos syndrome, type VIIA2, 130060 (3)	7q22.1
...lers-Danlos syndrome, type X (1)	2q34
...liptocytosis, Malaysian-Melanesian type] (3)	17q21-q22
...ptocytosis 1 (3)	1p36.2-p34
...ptocytosis 2 (3)	1q21
...ptocytosis 3 (3)	14q22-q23.2
...ery-Dreifuss muscular dystrophy (3)	Xq28
...physema (3)	14q32.1
...physema due to alpha-2-macroglobulin deficiency (1)	12p13.3-p12.3
...physema-cirrhosis (3)	14q32.1
...docardial fibroelastosis 2 (2)	Xq28
...dometrial carcinoma (3)	**16q22.1**
...lase deficiency (1)	1pter-p36.13
...terokinase deficiency (1)	**21q21**
...uresis, nocturnal, 1 (2)	**13q13-q14.3**
...sinophilic myeloproliferative disorder (2)	12p13
...dermolysis bullosa dystrophica, dominant, 131750 (3)	3p21.3
...dermolysis bullosa dystrophica, recessive, 226600 (3)	3p21.3
...dermolysis bullosa, Herlitz junctional type, 226700 (3)	1q25-q31
...dermolysis bullosa, Herlitz junctional type, 226700 (3)	**1q32**
...dermolysis bullosa, junctional, with pyloric atresia, 226730 (3)	**17q11-qter**
...dermolysis bullosa, Ogna type (2)	8q24
...dermolysis bullosa simplex, Dowling-Meara type, 131670 (3)	17q12-q21
...dermolysis bullosa simplex, Dowling-Meara type, 131760 (3)	12q11-q13
...dermolysis bullosa simplex, Koebner type, 131900 (3)	12q11-q13
...dermolysis bullosa simplex, Koebner type, 131900 (3)	17q12-q21
...dermolysis bullosa simplex, Weber-Cockayne type, 131800 (3)	17q12-q21
...dermolysis bullosa, Weber-Cockayne type, 131800 (3)	12q11-q13
...dermolytic hyperkeratosis, 113800 (3)	12q11-q13
...dermolytic hyperkeratosis, 113800 (3)	17q21-q22
...dermolytic palmoplantar keratoderma (3)	17q12-q21
...lepsy, benign neonatal, type I, 121200 (3)	20q13.2-q13.3
...lepsy, benign neonatal, type 2 (3)	8q
...lepsy, juvenile myoclonic (2)	6p21.3
...lepsy, nocturnal frontal lobe type (2)	**20q13.2**
...lepsy, partial (2)	10q
...lepsy, progressive myoclonus (3)	21q22.3
...lepsy, progressive, with mental retardation (2)	**8pter-p22**
...physeal dysplasia, multiple 1, 132400 (3)	**19p13.1**
...physeal dysplasia, multiple 2 (2)	**1p32**
...isodic ataxia/myokymia syndrome, 160120 (3)	**12p13**
...thelioma, self-healing, squamous 1, Ferguson-Smith type (2)	9q31
...ythremia (1)	7q21
...thremias, alpha- (3)	16pter-p13.3
...thremias, beta- (3)	11p15.5
...throblastosis fetalis (1)	1p36.2-p34
...rythrocytosis, familial], 133100 (3)	19p13.3-p13.2
...throkeratodermia variabilis (2)	1p36.2-p34
...trogen resistance (3)	**6q25.1**
...thyroidal hyper- and hypothyroxinemia] (1)	Xq22
...ing sarcoma (3)	22q12
...ertional myoglobinuria due to deficiency of LDH-A (3)	11p15.4
...ostoses, multiple, type 1 (2)	8q24.11-q24.13
...ostoses, multiple, type 2 (2)	11p11-q11
...ostoses, multiple, type 3 (2)	**19p**
...dative vitreoretinopathy, X-linked, 305390 (3)	Xp11.4
...abry disease (3)	Xq22
...Facioscapulohumeral muscular dystrophy 1A (2)	4q35
... Factor H deficiency (1)	1q32
...tor V deficiency (1)	1q23
...tor VII deficiency (3)	13q34
...tor X deficiency (3)	13q34
...tor XI deficiency (3)	4q35
...tor XII deficiency (3)	5q33-qter
...tor XIIIA deficiency (3)	6p25-p24
...tor XIIIB deficiency (3)	1q31-q32.1
...milial expansile osteolysis (2)	18q21.1-q22
...milial Mediterranean fever (2)	16p13
...nconi anemia (1)	1q42
Fanconi anemia 1 (2)	20q13.2-q13.3
Favism (3)	Xq28
[?Fetal alcohol syndrome] (1)	12q24.2
?Fetal hydantoin syndrome (1)	1p11-qter
?Fibrodysplasia ossificans progressiva (1)	20p12
Fibromuscular dysplasia of arteries, 135580 (3)	2q31
Fibrosis of the extraocular muscles, congenital (2)	**12q13.2-q24.1**
Fish-eye disease (3)	16q22.1
[Fish-odor syndrome] (1)	1q
Fletcher factor deficiency (1)	4q35
[Fluorouracil toxicity, sensitivity to] (1)	**1p22**
Focal dermal hypoplasia (2)	Xp22.31
Fragile X syndrome (3)	Xq27.3
Friedreich ataxia (2)	9q13-q21.1
Fructose intolerance (3)	9q22
Fucosidosis (3)	1p34
Fucosyltransferase-6 deficiency (3)	**19p13.3**
Fukuyama type congenital muscular dystrophy (2)	9q31-q33
Fumarase deficiency (3)	1q42.1
Fundus flavimaculatus with macular dystrophy (2)	**1p21-p13**
G6PD deficiency (3)	Xq28
Galactokinase deficiency with cataracts (3)	**17q24**
Galactose epimerase deficiency (1)	1p36-p35
Galactosemia (3)	9p13
Galactosialidosis (3)	20q13.1
[Gamma-glutamyltransferase, familial high serum] (2)	**22q11.12**
Gardner syndrome (3)	5q21-q22
Gaucher disease (3)	1q21
Gaucher disease, variant form (3)	10q21-q22
Generalized atrophic benign epidermolysis bullosa, 226650 (1)	**10q24.3**
Gerstmann-Straussler disease, 137440 (3)	20pter-p12
Gigantism due to GHRF hypersecretion (1)	20q11.2
?Gilbert syndrome, 143500 (1)	Chr.2
Glanzmann thrombasthenia, type A (3)	17q21.32
Glanzmann thrombasthenia, type B (3)	17q21.32
Glaucoma, primary open angle, adult-onset (3)	**1q21-q31**
Glaucoma, primary open angle, juvenile-onset (2)	1q21-q31
Glioblastoma multiforme (2)	10p12-q23.2
Glucocorticoid deficiency, due to ACTH unresponsiveness (1)	18p11.2
Glucose/galactose malabsorption (3)	22q11.2-qter
Glutaricacidemia, type I (3)	19p13.2
Glutaricacidemia, type IIC (3)	4q32-qter
Glutaricaciduria, type IIA (1)	15q23-q25
Glutaricaciduria, type IIB (3)	19q13.3
Glutathioninuria (1)	22q11.1-q11.2
Glycerol kinase deficiency (2)	Xp21.3-p21.2
Glycogen storage disease III (1)	1p21
Glycogen storage disease IV (1)	3p12
Glycogen storage disease I (3)	17q21
Glycogen storage disease II (3)	17q23
Glycogen storage disease VI (3)	14q21-q22
Glycogen storage disease VII (3)	1cen-q32
Glycogen storage disease, X-linked hepatic (2)	Xp22.2-p22.1
?Glycoprotein Ia deficiency (2)	5q23-q31
[Glyoxalase II deficiency] (1)	16p13
GM1-gangliosidosis (3)	3p21.33
GM2-gangliosidosis, AB variant (3)	5q31.3-q33.1
GM2-gangliosidosis, juvenile, adult (3)	15q23-q24
Goeminne TKCR syndrome (2)	Xq28
Goiter, adolescent multinodular (1)	8q24.2-q24.3
Goiter, congenital (3)	**2p25**
Goiter, nonendemic, simple (3)	8q24.2-q24.3
?Goldenhar syndrome (2)	7p
Gonadal dysgenesis, XY female type (2)	Xp22.11-p21.2
Gonadal dysgenesis, XY type (3)	Yp11.3
?Gonadotropin deficiency (2)	Xp21
Graves disease, 275000 (1)	14q31
Greig cephalopolysyndactyly syndrome, 175700 (3)	7p13
?Growth hormone deficient dwarfism (1)	7p15-p14
Gustavson syndrome (2)	Xq26
?Gynecomastia, familial, due to increased aromatase activity (1)	15q21.1
Gyrate atrophy of choroid and retina with ornithinemia, B6 responsive or unresponsive (3)	10q26
Hailey-Hailey disease (2)	**3q**
Harderoporphyrinuria (3)	3q12
Heart block, progressive familial, type I (2)	**19q13.2-q13.3**
Heinz body anemias, alpha- (3)	16pter-p13.3
Heinz body anemias, beta- (3)	11p15.5
Hemochromatosis (2)	6p21.3
Hemodialysis-related amyloidosis (3)	15q21-q22
Hemolytic anemia due to ADA excess (1)	20q13.11
Hemolytic anemia due to adenylate kinase deficiency (1)	9q34.1
Hemolytic anemia due to bisphosphoglycerate mutase deficiency (1)	7q31-q34
Hemolytic anemia due to G6PD deficiency (1)	Xq28
Hemolytic anemia due to glucosephosphate isomerase deficiency (3)	19q13.1
Hemolytic anemia due to glutathione peroxidase deficiency (1)	3q11-q12
Hemolytic anemia due to glutathione reductase deficiency (1)	8p21.1
Hemolytic anemia due to hexokinase deficiency (1)	10q22
Hemolytic anemia due to PGK deficiency (3)	Xq13
Hemolytic anemia due to phosphofructokinase deficiency (1)	21q22.3
Hemolytic anemia due to triosephosphate isomerase deficiency (3)	12p13
Hemophilia A (3)	Xq28
Hemophilia B (3)	Xq27.1-q27.2

Entry	Location
Hemorrhagic diathesis due to 'antithrombin' Pittsburgh (3)	14q32.1
Hemorrhagic diathesis due to PAI1 deficiency (1)	7q21.3-q22
Hemosiderosis, systemic, due to aceruloplasminemia (3)	**3q21-q24**
Hepatic lipase deficiency (3)	15q21-q23
Hepatocellular carcinoma (1)	11p14-p13
?Hepatocellular carcinoma (1)	2q14-q21
Hepatocellular carcinoma (1)	4q32.1
Hereditary hemorrhagic telangiectasia, 187300 (3)	9q34.1
Hereditary hemorrhagic telangiectasia, type II (2)	**3p22**
Hereditary hemorrhagic telangiectasia, type III (2)	**12p11-p12**
[Hereditary persistence of alpha-fetoprotein] (3)	4q11-q13
?Hereditary persistence of fetal hemoglobin (3)	11p15.5
?Hereditary persistence of fetal hemoglobin, heterocellular, Indian type (2)	7q36
?Hermansky-Pudlak syndrome, 203300 (2)	12q12-q13
?Hermansky-Pudlak syndrome, 203300 (1)	15q15
Heterocellular hereditary persistence of fetal hemoglobin, Swiss type (2)	Xp22.2
Heterotaxia, visceroatrial, autosomal-recessive (3)	**6q21-q23.2**
Heterotaxy, X-linked visceral (2)	Xq25-q26
[Hex A pseudodeficiency] (1)	15q23-q24
?HHH syndrome (2)	13q34
Hirschsprung disease, 142623 (3)	10q11.2
Hirschsprung disease 2, 600155 (3)	**13q22**
[Histidinemia] (1)	12q22-q23
HMG-CoA lyase deficiency (3)	**1pter-p33**
?Holoprosencephaly 1 (2)	18pter-q11
?Holoprosencephaly 2 (2)	2p21
Holoprosencephaly 3 (2)	7q36
?Holoprosencephaly 4 (2)	14q11.1-q13
Holt-Oram syndrome (2)	12q21.3-q22
Homocystinuria, B6-responsive and nonresponsive types (3)	21q22.3
Homocystinuria due to MTHFR deficiency (3)	1p36.3
[?Homosexuality, male] (1)	Xq28
HPFH, deletion type (3)	11p15.5
HPFH, nondeletion type A (3)	11p15.5
HPFH, nondeletion type G (3)	11p15.5
HPRT-related gout (3)	Xq26-q27.2
?Humoral hypercalcemia of malignancy (1)	12p12.1-p11.2
Huntington disease (3)	4p16.3
Hydrocephalus due to aqueductal stenosis, 307000 (3)	Xq28
Hydrops fetalis, one form (1)	19q13.1
Hyperbetalipoproteinemia (3)	2p24
Hypercalcemia, hypocalciuric, familial (3)	3q21-q24
Hypercholesterolemia, familial (3)	19p13.2-p13.1
Hyperchylomicronemia syndrome, familial (3)	**8p22**
Hyperglycinemia, isolated nonketotic, type I (3)	9p22
Hyperglycinemia, nonketotic, type II (3)	3p21.2-p21.1
?Hyperimmunoglobulin G1 syndrome (2)	14q32.33
Hyperkalemic periodic paralysis (3)	17q23.1-q25.3
?Hyperleucinemia-isoleucinemia or hypervalinemia (1)	12pter-q12
Hyperlipoproteinemia I (1)	8p22
Hyperlipoproteinemia, type Ib (3)	19q13.2
Hyperlipoproteinemia, type III (3)	19q13.2
Hyperoxaluria, primary, type 1 (3)	**2q36-q37**
Hyperphenylalaninemia due to pterin-4a-carbinolamine dehydratase deficiency, 264070 (3)	10q22
[Hyperphenylalaninemia, mild] (3)	12q24.1
[?Hyperproglucagonemia] (1)	2q36-q37
Hyperproinsulinemia, familial (3)	11p15.5
[Hyperproreninemia] (3)	**1q32**
Hypertension due to apparent mineralocorticoid excess (3)	**16q22**
{?Hypertension, essential} (1)	16p13.11
?Hypertension, essential, 145500 (1)	17q21-q22
{Hypertension, essential, susceptibility to} (3)	1q42-q43
Hyperthyroidism, congenital (3)	**14q31**
Hypertrichosis, congenital generalized (2)	**Xq24-q27.1**
Hypertriglyceridemia (3)	11q23
Hypertriglyceridemia, one form (3)	**11q23**
?Hypervalinemia or hyperleucine-isoleucinemia (1)	Chr.19
Hypoalphalipoproteinemia (3)	11q23
Hypobetalipoproteinemia (3)	2p24
Hypocalcemia, autosomal-dominant (3)	**3q21-q24**
Hypocalciuric hypercalcemia, type II (2)	19p13.3
[Hypoceruloplasminemia, hereditary] (1)	3q21-q24
Hypochondroplasia, 146000 (3)	4p16.3
Hypofibrinogenemia, gamma types (3)	4q28
?Hypoglycemia due to PCK1 deficiency (1)	20q13.31
Hypogonadism, hypergonadotropic (3)	19q13.32
?Hypogonadism, hypogonadotropic, due to GNRH deficiency, 227200 (1)	8p21-p11.2
Hypokalemic periodic paralysis, 170400 (3)	1q32
Hypomagnesemia, X-linked primary (2)	Xp22.2
Hypomelanosis of Ito (2)	15q11-q13
?Hypomelanosis of Ito (2)	9q33-qter
Hypoparathyroidism, autosomal-dominant(3)	**11p15.3-p15.1**
Hypoparathyroidism, autosomal-recessive (3)	**11p15.3-p15.1**
Hypoparathyroidism, familial (2)	3q13
Hypoparathyroidism, X-linked (2)	Xq26-q27
?Hypophosphatasia, adult, 146300 (1)	1p36.1-p34
Hypophosphatasia, infantile, 241500 (3)	1p36.1-p34
Hypophosphatemia, hereditary (2)	Xp22.2-p22.1
?Hypophosphatemia with deafness (2)	Xp22
Hypoprothrombinemia (3)	11p11-q12
?Hypospadias-dysphagia syndrome (2)	5p13-p12
Hypothyroidism, congenital (3)	**2p2**
Hypothyroidism, hereditary congenital (3)	8q24.2-q24
Hypothyroidism, nongoitrous (3)	1p
Hypothyroidism, nongoitrous, due to TSH resistance (3)	14q
Ichthyosis bullosa of Siemens, 146800 (3)	**12q11-q**
Ichthyosis, lamellar, autosomal-recessive 242100 (3)	**14q11**
?Ichthyosis vulgaris, 146700 (1)	1o
Ichthyosis, X-linked (3)	Xp22
[IgG receptor I, phagocytic, familial deficiency of] (1)	**1q21.2-q**
[Ii blood group, 110800] (1)	**9q**
?Immotile cilia syndrome (2)	
Immunodeficiency, X-linked, with hyper-IgM (3)	Xq
Incontinentia pigmenti, familial (2)	Xq
Incontinentia pigmenti, sporadic type (2)	Xp11
[Inosine triphosphatase deficiency] (1)	2
Insomnia, fatal familial (3)	20pter-p
Interferon, alpha, deficiency (1)	9p
Interferon, immune, deficiency (1)	12q24
Iris hypoplasia with glaucoma, autosomal-dominant (2)	**4q**
?Isolated growth hormone deficiency due to defect in GHRF (1)	20q1
Isolated growth hormone deficiency, Illig type with absent GH and Kowarski type with bioinactive GH (3)	17q22-q
Isovalericacidemia (3)	15q14-q
Jackson-Weiss syndrome, 123150 (3)	**10q**
?Jacobsen syndrome (2)	
Juberg-Marsidi syndrome (2)	Xq12-q
Junctional epidermolysis bullosa inversa (2)	**1q**
Kallmann syndrome (3)	Xp22
Kanzaki disease (3)	**22q**
[Kappa light chain deficiency] (1)	2p
Keratoderma, palmoplantar, nonepidermolytic (3)	**12q11-q**
Keratosis follicularis spinulosa decalvans (2)	Xp22.2-p21
[Kininogen deficiency] (3)	3q
?Klippel-Feil syndrome (2)	5q1
Kniest dysplasia (3)	12q13.11-q1
Kostmann neutropenia, 202700 (3)	1p35-p3
Krabbe disease (3)	14q24.3-q3
?Lactase deficiency, adult, 223100 (1)	2q
?Lactase deficiency, congenital (1)	2q
Lactic acidosis due to defect in iron-sulfur cluster of complex I (1)	2q33-q
?Lactoferrin-deficient neutrophils, 245480 (1)	3q21-c
Langer-Giedion syndrome (2)	8q24.11-q24
Laron dwarfism (3)	5p13-p
?Laryngeal adductor paralysis (1)	6p21.3-p2
{Lead poisoning, susceptibility to} (3)	9q
Leber congenital amaurosis I (2)	**17p**
?Leiomyomata, multiple hereditary cutaneous (2)	18p11
Leiomyomatosis, diffuse (1)	Xc
Leiomyomatosis-nephropathy syndrome, 308940 (1)	Xq
Leprechaunism (3)	19p1
Lesch-Nyhan syndrome (3)	Xq26-q27
?Letterer-Siwe disease (2)	13q14-q
Leukemia, acute lymphoblastic (1)	19p1
Leukemia, acute lymphoblastic (1)	9p22-p
?Leukemia, acute lymphocytic, with 4/11 translocation (3)	4q
Leukemia, acute myeloid (2)	**9q34**
Leukemia, acute myeloid (3)	21q2
Leukemia, acute myeloid, M2 type (1)	Xp22
Leukemia, acute nonlymphocytic (2)	**6p**
Leukemia, acute pre-B-cell (2)	1q
Leukemia, acute promyelocytic (1)	17q
Leukemia, acute promyelocytic (2)	15q
Leukemia, acute, T-cell (2)	11p
Leukemia, chronic lymphocytic, B-cell (2)	13q
Leukemia, chronic myeloid (3)	22q11
Leukemia, chronic myeloid (2)	9q3
Leukemia, myeloid/lymphoid or mixed-lineage (2)	11q
Leukemia, T-cell acute lymphoblastic (2)	11p
Leukemia, T-cell acute lymphoblastic (2)	9q3
Leukemia, T-cell acute lymphoblastoid (2)	19p13.2-p1
Leukemia, T-cell acute lymphocytic (2)	10q
?Leukemia, transient (1)	21q1
Leukemia-1, T-cell acute lymphoblastic (3)	1p
Leukemia-2, T-cell acute lymphoblastic (3)	9q
Leukemia/lymphoma, B-cell, 1 (2)	11q1
Leukemia/lymphoma, B-cell, 2 (2)	18q2
Leukemia/lymphoma, B-cell, 3 (2)	19q
Leukemia/lymphoma, T-cell (2)	14q3
Leukemia/lymphoma, T-cell (2)	2q
Leukemia/lymphoma, T-cell (3)	14q1
Leukocyte adhesion deficiency (1)	21q2
Leydig cell hypoplasia (3)	**2p**
Liddle syndrome (3)	**16p12**
Li-Fraumeni syndrome (3)	17p
Lipoamide dehydrogenase deficiency (3)	7q31-c
Lipoma (3)	**12q**
Lipoma, benign (3)	12c
Lipoprotein lipase deficiency (3)	**8p**
Liposarcoma (1)	19p13.2-q1
Long QT syndrome 1 (2)	11p1
Long QT syndrome 2 (3)	**7q35-q**
Long QT syndrome 3 (3)	**3p24-p**
Lowe syndrome (3)	Xq2

pus erythematosus, susceptibility to} (2)   **12pter-p12**
us erythematosus, systemic, 152700 (1)   1q23
phoma, B-cell (2)   3q27
phoma, diffuse large cell (3)   3q27
aphoma/leukemia, B-cell, variant (1)   **18q21.3**
phoproliferative syndrome, X-linked (2)   Xq25
ch cancer family syndrome II (2)   18q11-q12
osomal acid phosphatase deficiency (1)   11p12-p11
achado-Joseph disease (2)   14q24.3-q31
Macrocytic anemia of 5q- syndrome, refractory (2)   5q12-q32
Macrocytic anemia refractory, of 5q- syndrome, 153550 (3)   5q31.1
acrothrombocytopenia] (1)   7q11.2
cular dystrophy (3)   6p21.1-cen
cular dystrophy, atypical vitelliform (2)   8q24
cular dystrophy, dominant cystoid (2)   7p21-p15
cular dystrophy, North Carolina type (2)   6q14-q16.2
cular dystrophy, vitelliform type (2)   11q13
e germ cell tumor (2)   12q22
le infertility due to acrosin deficiency (2)   22q13-qter
le infertility, familial (1)   11p13
le pseudohermaphroditism due to defective LH (1)   19q13.32
ignant hyperthermia susceptibility 1, 145600 (3)   19q13.1
lignant hyperthermia susceptibility 2 (2)   **17q11.2-q24**
lignant hyperthermia susceptibility 3, 154276 (3)   **7q21-q22**
ignant melanoma, cutaneous (2)   1p36
nic-depressive illness, X-linked (2)   Xq28
nosidosis (1)   19cen-q12
le syrup urine disease, type Ia (3)   19q13.1-q13.2
ple syrup urine disease, type Ib (3)   **6p22-p21**
le syrup urine disease, type II (3)   1p31
fan syndrome, 154700 (3)   15q21.1
oteaux-Lamy syndrome, several forms (3)   5q11-q13
SA syndrome, 303350 (3)   Xq28
t cell leukemia (3)   4q12
urity-onset diabetes of the young, type III (2)   **12q22-qter**
rdle disease (3)   11q13
Cune-Albright polyostotic fibrous dysplasia, 174800 (3)   20q13.2
Leod phenotype (3)   Xp21.2-p21.1
lullary thyroid carcinoma, 155240 (3)   10q11.2
galocornea, X-linked (2)   Xq21.3-q22
elanoma (1)   **2p25.3**
lanoma (3)   **9p21**
anoma, cutaneous malignant (2)   9p21
elkersson-Rosenthal syndrome (2)   **9p11**
mbroproliferative glomerulonephritis (1)   **1q32**
ningioma, NF2-related (3)   22q12.2
ningioma, SIS-related (3)   22q12.3-q13.1
kes disease (3)   Xq12-q13
ntal retardation, Snyder-Robinson type (2)   Xp21
ntal retardation, X-linked, FRAXE type (2)   Xq28
ntal retardation, X-linked, FRAXF type (3)   **Xq28**
ntal retardation, X-linked nonspecific, with aphasia (2)   Xp11
ntal retardation, X-linked, syndromic 1, with
dystonic movements, ataxia, and seizures (2)   Xp2.2-p22.1
ntal retardation, X-linked, syndromic 2, with
dysmorphism and cerebral atrophy (2)   Xp11-q21
ntal retardation, X-linked, syndromic 3, with spastic diplegia (2)   Xp11-q21.3
ntal retardation, X-linked, syndromic 4, with
congenital contractures and low fingertip arches (2)   Xq13-q22
ntal retardation, X-linked, syndromic 5, with
Dandy-Walker malformation, basal ganglia disease, and seizures (2)   Xq25-q27
ntal retardation, X-linked, syndromic-6, with
gynecomastia and obesity (2)   Xp21.1-q22
ntal retardation, X-linked 1, non-dysmorphic (2)   Xp22
ntal retardation, X-linked 2, non-dysmorphic (2)   Xq11-q22
ntal retardation, X-linked 3 (2)   Xq28
ntal retardation-skeletal dysplasia (2)   Xq28
phenytoin poor metabolizer (3)   **10q24.1-q24.3**
achromatic leukodystrophy (3)   22q13.31-qter
achromatic leukodystrophy due to deficiency of SAP-1 (3)   10q21-q22
aphyseal chondrodysplasia, Murk Jansen type, 156400 (3)   **3p22-p21.1**
aphyseal chondrodysplasia, Schmid type (3)   6q21-q22.3
hemoglobinemia due to cytochrome b5 deficiency (3)   18q23
hemoglobinemia, type I (3)   **22q13.31-qter**
hemoglobinemia, type II (3)   **22q13.31-qter**
hemoglobinemia, type III (3)   **22q13.31-qter**
hemoglobinemias, alpha- (3)   16pter-p13.3
hemoglobinemias, beta- (3)   11p15.5
thylmalonicaciduria, mutase deficiency type (3)   6p21
valonicaciduria (1)   Chr.12
crophthalmia, dermal aplasia and sclerocornea (2)   **Xp22.31**
crophthalmia with linear skin defects (2)   Xp22.2
graine, hemiplegic 1 (2)   **19p13**
er-Dieker lissencephaly syndrome (2)   17p13.3
ochondrial complex I deficiency, 252010 (1)   11q13
DY, one form (3)   11p15.5
DY, type I (2)   20q13
DY, type II, 125851 (3)   7p15-p13
ebius syndrome (2)   13q12.2-q13
hr-Tranebjaerg syndrome (2)   **Xq22**
nocyte carboxyesterase deficiency (1)   16q13-q22.1
colipidosis II (1)   4q21-q23
colipidosis III (1)   4q21-q23

Mucopolysaccharidosis Ih (3)   4p16.3
Mucopolysaccharidosis Ih/s (3)   **4p16.3**
Mucopolysaccharidosis II (3)   Xq28
Mucopolysaccharidosis Is (3)   **4p16.3**
Mucopolysaccharidosis IVA (3)   16q24.3
Mucopolysaccharidosis IVB (3)   3p21.33
Mucopolysaccharidosis VII (3)   7q21.11
Multiple carboxylase deficiency, biotin-responsive (3)   **21q22.1**
Multiple endocrine neoplasia I (1)   11q13
Multiple endocrine neoplasia IIA, 171400 (3)   10q11.2
Multiple endocrine neoplasia IIB, 162300 (3)   10q11.2
?Multiple lipomatosis (2)   12q15
{?Multiple sclerosis, susceptibility to} (2)   18q22-qter
Muscle glycogenosis (3)   Xq13
Muscular dystrophy, congenital, merosin-negative (2)   **6q22-q23**
Muscular dystrophy, Duchenne-like, autosomal, type 1 (2)   13q12-q13
Muscular dystrophy, Duchenne-like, type 2 (3)   **17q12-q21.33**
Muscular dystrophy, limb-girdle, autosomal-dominant (2)   5q22.3-q31.3
Muscular dystrophy, limb-girdle, type 2A (2)   **15q15.1-q21.1**
Muscular dystrophy, limb-girdle, type 2B (2)   2p16-p13
Myelodysplasia syndrome 1 (3)   **3q26**
Myelodysplastic syndrome, preleukemic (3)   5q31.1
Myelogenous leukemia, acute (3)   5q31.1
Myeloid leukemia, acute, M4Eo subtype (2)   **16q22**
Myeloperoxidase deficiency (3)   17q21.3-q22
Myoadenylate deaminase deficiency (3)   1p21-p13
{Myocardial infarction, susceptibility to} (3)   17q23
Myoglobinuria/hemolysis due to PGK deficiency (3)   Xq13
?Myopathy, desminopathic (1)   2q35
Myopathy, distal (3)   **14q**
Myopathy due to phosphoglycerate mutase deficiency (3)   7p13-p12.3
?Myopathy due to succinate dehydrogenase deficiency (1)   **1p22.1-qter**
Myopia 1 (2)   Xq28
Myotonia congenita, atypical acetazolamide-responsive (3)   17q23.1-q25.3
Myotonia congenita, dominant, 160800 (3)   7q35
Myotonia congenita, recessive, 255700 (3)   7q35
Myotonia levior, recessive (3)   **7q35**
Myotonic dystrophy (3)   19q13.2-q13.3
Myotubular myopathy, X-linked (2)   Xq28
Myxoid liposarcoma (3)   12q13.1-q13.2
?N syndrome, 310465 (1)   Xp22.3-p21.1
Nail-patella syndrome (2)   9q34.1
Nance-Horan syndrome (2)   Xp22.3-p21.1
Nemaline myopathy 1, 161800 (3)   1q22-q23
Neonatal alloimmune thrombocytopenia (2)   5q23-q31
Neonatal hyperparathyroidism, 239200 (3)   3q21-q24
Nephrolithiasis 2, X-linked (2)   **Xp11.23-p11.22**
Nephrolithiasis, X-linked, with renal failure (2)   **Xp11.22**
Nephronophthisis, juvenile (2)   2q13
Nephrosis, congenital, Finnish (2)   19q12-q13.1
Neuroblastoma (2)   1p36.3-p36.2
?Neuroblastoma (2)   1p36.13-p36.11
Neuroepithelioma (2)   22q12
Neurofibromatosis, type I (3)   17q11.2
Neurofibromatosis, type 2 (3)   22q12.2
Neuropathy, recurrent, with pressure palsies, 162500 (3)   17p11.2
Neutropenia, immune (2)   1q23
Neutropenia, neonatal alloimmune (1)   Chr.4
Niemann-Pick disease, type A (3)   11p15.4-p15.1
Niemann-Pick disease, type B (3)   11p15.4-p15.1
Niemann-Pick disease, type C (2)   18q11-q12
Night blindness, congenital stationary, type I (2)   Xp11.3
Night blindness, congenital stationary, type 3, 163500 (3)   4p16.3
Night blindness, congenital stationery, rhodopsin-related (3)   3q21-q24
{Non-insulin dependent diabetes mellitus, susceptibility to} (2)   19q13.3
Noonan syndrome 1 (2)   **12q22-qter**
Norrie disease (3)   Xp11.4
Norum disease (3)   16q22.1
Nucleoside phosphorylase deficiency, immunodeficiency due to (3)   14q13.1
?Obesity (2)   7q31
?Ocular albinism, autosomal-recessive (2)   6q13-q15
Ocular albinism, Forsius-Eriksson type (2)   Xp11.4-p11.23
Ocular albinism, Nettleship-Falls type (2)   Xp22.3
Ocular albinism with sensorineural deafness (2)   Xp22.3
Oculopharyngeal muscular dystrophy (2)   **14q11.2-q13**
Oguchi disease, 258100 (3)   2q37.1
Optic atrophy 1 (2)   3q28-qter
Optic nerve coloboma with renal anomalies, 120330 (3)   **10q25**
Ornithine transcarbamylase deficiency (3)   Xp21.1
Orofacial cleft 1 (2)   6p24.3
Orofacial cleft 3 (2)   **19q13**
Oroticaciduria (1)   3q13
OSMED syndrome, 215150 (3)   **6p21.3**
Osteoarthrosis, precocious (3)   12q13.11-q13.2
Osteogenesis imperfecta, 4 clinical forms,
166200, 166210, 259420, 166220 (3)   17q21.31-q22.05
Osteogenesis imperfecta, 4 clinical forms,
166200, 166210, 259420, 166220 (3)   7q22.1
?Osteopetrosis, 259700 (3)   1p21-p13
Osteoporosis, idiopathic, 166710 (3)   17q21.31-q22.05
?Osteoporosis, involutional (1)   12q12-q14
Osteosarcoma, 259500 (3)   13q14.1-q14.2
Otopalatodigital syndrome, type I (2)   Xq28

Ovarian cancer, serous (2) 6q26-q27
Ovarian cancer, sporadic (3) **17q21**
Ovarian carcinoma, 167000 (2) 19q13.1-q13.2
Ovarian carcinoma (2) 9p24
Ovarian carcinoma (3) **16q22.1**
Ovarian failure, premature (2) Xq26-q27
Pachyonychia congenita, Jackson-Lawler type, 148069 (3) **17q12-q21**
 Pachyonychia congenita, Jackson-Lawler type (2) **17q12-q21**
 Pachyonychia congenita, Jadassohn-Lewandowsky type, 167200 (3) **17q12-q21**
Pachyonychia congenita, Jadassohn-Lewandowsky type (3) 12q12-q14
?Paget disease of bone (2) 6p21.3
?Pallister-Hall syndrome (2) 3p25.3
Palmoplantar keratoderma, Bothnia type (2) **12q11-q13**
Pancreatic cancer (3) **13q12.3**
Pancreatic lipase deficiency (1) 10q26.1
?Panhypopituitarism, X-linked (2) Xq21.3-q22
Paraganglioma (2) 11q22.3-q23.2
Paramyotonia congenita, 168300 (3) 17q23.1-q25.3
Paraneoplastic sensory neuropathy (1) 1p34
Parathyroid adenomatosis 1 (2) 11q13
?Parietal foramina (2) 11p12-p11.12
{?Parkinsonism, susceptibility to} (1) 22q13.1
Paroxysmal nocturnal hemoglobinuria (3) Xq22.1
Partington syndrome II (2) **Xp22-p21**
Pelizaeus-Merzbacher disease (3) Xq22
Pelviureteric junction obstruction (2) 6p
?Pendred syndrome (2) 8q24
PEO with mitochondrial DNA deletions (2) **10q**
Perineal hypospadias (3) **Xq11-q12**
Periodontitis, juvenile (2) 4q11-q13
Peroxisomal bifunctional enzyme deficiency (1) 3q26.3-q28
Persistent hyperinsulinemic hypoglycemia of infancy (1) **11p15.1**
Persistent hyperinsulinemic hypoglycemia of infancy (2) **11p15.1-p14**
Persistent Mullerian duct syndrome (3) 19p13.3-p13.2
Peters anomaly (3) 11p13
Pfeiffer syndrome, 101600 (3) **10q26**
Pfeiffer syndrome, 101600 (3) **8p12-p11.2**
Phenylketonuria (3) 12q24.1
Phenylketonuria, atypical, due to GCH1 deficiency, 233910 (1) **14q22.1-q22.2**
Phenylketonuria due to dihydropteridine reductase deficiency (3) 4p15.31
Phenylketonuria due to PTS deficiency (3) 11q22.3-q23.3
Pheochromocytoma (2) 1p
Phosphoribosyl pyrophosphate synthetase-related gout (3) Xq22-q24
?Phosphorylase kinase deficiency of liver and muscle, 261750 (2) 16q12-q13.1
Piebaldism (3) 4q12
Pituitary ACTH-secreting adenoma (3) **20q13.2**
Pituitary ACTH-secreting adenoma (3) **3p21**
Pituitary hormone deficiency, combined (3) 3p11
PK deficiency hemolytic anemia (3) 1q21
[Placental lactogen deficiency] (1) 17q22-q24
Placental steroid sulfatase deficiency (3) Xp22.32
Plasmin inhibitor deficiency (3) 17pter-p12
Plasminogen activator deficiency (1) 8p12
Plasminogen deficiency, types I and II (1) 6q26
Plasminogen Tochigi disease (1) 6q26
Platelet alpha/delta storage pool deficiency (1) 1q23-q25
Platelet glycoprotein IV deficiency (3) **7q11.2**
{Polio, susceptibility to} (2) 19q13.2-q13.3
Polycystic kidney disease, adult, type II (3) 4q21-q23
Polycystic kidney disease, autosomal-recessive (2) **6p21.1-p12**
Polycystic kidney disease, infantile severe, with tuberous sclerosis (3) **16p13.3**
Polycystic kidney disease 1 (3) 16p13.31-p13.12
Polyposis coli, familial (3) 5q21-q22
Porphyria, acute hepatic (3) 9q34
Porphyria, acute intermittent (3) 11q23.3
Porphyria, Chester type (2) 11q23.1
Porphyria, congenital erythropoietic (3) 10q25.2-q26.3
Porphyria cutanea tarda (3) 1p34
Porphyria, hepatoerythropoietic (3) 1p34
Porphyria variegata (2) 14q32
?Prader-Willi syndrome (1) 15q12
Prader-Willi syndrome (2) 15q11
Precocious puberty, male, 176410 (3) 2p21
{Preeclampsia, susceptibility to} (3) 1q42-q43
Progressive cone dystrophy (2) Xp11.3
Prolactinoma, hyperparathyroidism, carcinoid syndrome (2) **11q13**
Prolidase deficiency (3) 19cen-q13.11
Properdin deficiency, X-linked (3) Xp11.4-p11.23
Propionicacidemia, type I or pccA type (1) 13q32
Propionicacidemia, type II or pccB type (3) 3q21-q22
Prostate cancer, 176807 (3) **10q25**
Prostate cancer (3) **Xq11-q12**
Protein C cofactor deficiency (3) 1q23
Protein C inhibitor deficiency (3) 14q32.1
Protein S deficiency (3) 3p11.1-q11.2
Protoporphyria, erythropoietic (3) 18q21.3
Protoporphyria, erythropoietic, recessive, with liver failure (3) **18q21.3**
Pseudoachondroplasia, 177170 (3) 19p13.1
Pseudohermaphroditism, male, with gynecomastia (3) 9q22
Pseudohypoaldosteronism (1) 4q31.1
Pseudohypoparathyroidism, type Ia, 103580 (3) 20q13.2
Pseudovaginal perineoscrotal hypospadias (3) Chr.2
Pseudo-vitamin D dependency rickets 1 (2) 12q14

Pseudo-Zellweger syndrome (1) 3p2?
Psoriasis susceptibility (2)
Pulmonary alveolar proteinosis, congenital, 265120 (3) 2p12-p
Purpura fulminans, neonatal (1) **2q13**
Pycnodysostosis (2)
?Pyridoxine dependency with seizures (1)
Pyropoikilocytosis (3)
Pyruvate carboxylase deficiency (1) 11q13.4-q
Pyruvate dehydrogenase deficiency (3) Xp22.2-p
Rabson-Mendenhall syndrome (3) 19p
 ?Ragweed sensitivity (2) 6p
 Renal cell carcinoma (2) 3p
Renal cell carcinoma (3) 3p26
?Renal cell carcinoma, papillary, 1 (2)
Renal cell carcinoma, papillary, 2 (2) Xp
[Renal glucosuria] (2) 6p
?Renal glucosuria, 253100 (1) 16p
Renal tubular acidosis-osteopetrosis syndrome (3)
?Resistance/susceptibility to TB, etc. (1)
?Retinal cone dystrophy 1 (2) 6q25
Retinitis pigmentosa, autosomal-recessive (3) 3q2
Retinitis pigmentosa, digenic (3) **11**
Retinitis pigmentosa, digenic (3) **6p21.1**
Retinitis pigmentosa, peripherin-related (3) 6p21.1
Retinitis pigmentosa 1 (2) 8p1
Retinitis pigmentosa 2 (2) Xp
Retinitis pigmentosa 3 (2) Xp
Retinitis pigmentosa 4, autosomal-dominant (3) 3q2
?Retinitis pigmentosa 6 (2) Xp21.3-p
Retinitis pigmentosa 9 (2) 7p15.1
Retinitis pigmentosa 10 (2) 7q3
Retinitis pigmentosa 11 (2) **19q**
Retinitis pigmentosa 12, autosomal-recessive (2) **1q31-q**
Retinitis pigmentosa 13 (2)
Retinitis pigmentosa 14 (2) **6p**
Retinitis punctata albescens (3) 6p21.
Retinoblastoma (3) 13q14.1-q
?Retinol binding protein, deficiency of (1) 10q2?
Retinoschisis (2) Xp22.3-p
?Rett syndrome (2)
Rhabdomyosarcoma (2) 11p
Rhabdomyosarcoma, alveolar, 268200 (3) 13c
Rhabdomyosarcoma, alveolar, 268220 (3)
Rh-null disease (1) 3cen
?Rh-null hemolytic anemia (1) 1p36.2
Rickets, vitamin D-resistant (3) 12q12
Rieger syndrome (2) 4q25
Rippling muscle disease 1 (2)
Rod monochromacy (2) Ch
?Rothmund-Thomson syndrome (2) 6
Rubinstein-Taybi syndrome (2) 16p
Russell-Silver syndrome (2) 1
Sacral agenesis 1 (2) 7
 Saethre-Chotzen syndrome (2)
 Salivary adenoma (3) **12**
Salivary gland pleomorphic adenoma (2)
Salla disease (3) **6q14**
Sandhoff disease (3)
?Sanfilippo disease, type IIIC (2) Ch
Sanfilippo syndrome D (1) 12
Sarcoma, synovial (1) **18q**
Sarcoma, synovial (3) Xp
Schindler disease (3) 2
?Schizophrenia (2) 5q11.2-q
Schizophrenia, chronic (3) 21q21.3-q2
{?Schizophrenia, susceptibility to} (2) 3q
Schizophrenia 3 (2) **6**
Schwannoma, sporadic (2) 22q
Sclerotylosis (2) 4q28
SED congenita (3) 12q13.11-q
Segawa syndrome, recessive (3) **11p**
Selective T-cell defect (3) **2**
Severe combined immunodeficiency due to ADA deficiency (3) 20q1
Severe combined immunodeficiency due to IL2 deficiency (1) 4q26
Severe combined immunodeficiency,
 HLA class II-negative type, 209920 (2) 19p
?Severe combined immunodeficiency, type I (1) 8
Severe combined immunodeficiency, X-linked, 300400 (3) X
Short stature (2) Xpter-p2
?Sialidosis (2) 6p
Sickle cell anemia (3) 11p
Simpson-Golabi-Behmel syndrome (2)
?Situs inversus viscerum (2) 14
Sjogren-Larsson syndrome (2) **17q**
?SLE (1)
Small-cell cancer of lung (2) 3p23
SMED Strudwick type (3) 12q13.11-q
Smith-Lemli-Opitz syndrome (2) 7
Smith-Magenis syndrome (2) 17p
Somatotrophinoma (2) 11
Somatotrophinoma (3) 20q
Sorsby fundus dystrophy, 136900 (3) **22q12.1-q**
Sorsby fundus dystrophy (2) **22q13.1-**

astic paraplegia, 312900 (3) — Xq28
astic paraplegia 2, 312920 (3) — Xq22
stic paraplegia 3A (2) — 14q
astic paraplegia 4 (2) — 2p24-p21
astic paraplegia 5A (2) — 8p12-q13
astic paraplegia 6 (2) — 15q11.1
erocytosis, hereditary (3) — 17q21-q22
erocytosis, hereditary, Japanese type (3) — 15q15
erocytosis, recessive (3) — 1q21
erocytosis 1 (3) — 14q22-q23.2
erocytosis 2 (3) — 8p11.2
nal and bulbar muscular atrophy of Kennedy, 313200 (3) — Xq11-q12
nal muscular atrophy II (2) — 5q12.2-q13.3
nal muscular atrophy III (2) — 5q12.2-q13.3
inal muscular atrophy X-linked lethal infantile (2) — Xp
inocerebellar ataxia, infantile, with sensory neuropathy (2) — 10q23.3-q24.1
nocerebellar ataxia 1 (3) — 6p23
nocerebellar ataxia 3 (2) — 14q24.3-qter
inocerebellar ataxia, type 4 (2) — 16q
nocerebellar ataxia, type 5 (2) — 11p11-q11
nocerebellar atrophy II (2) — 12q24
it-hand/foot malformation, type 1 (2) — 7q21.2-q21.3
it hand/foot malformation, type 2 (2) — Xq26
ondyloepiphyseal dysplasia tarda (2) — Xp22.2-p22.1
argardt disease 2 (2) — 13q34
argardt disease 3 (2) — 6cen-q14
argardt macular dystrophy (2) — 1p21-p13
artle disease, autosomal-recessive (3) — 5q32
rtle disease/hyperekplexia, autosomal-dominant, 149400 (3) — 5q32
ickler syndrome, type I (3) — 12q13.11-q13.2
ickler syndrome, type II, 184840 (3) — 6p21.3
tiff skin syndrome (2) — Chr.15
omatocytosis I (1) — 9q34.1
crose intolerance (1) — 3q25-q26
pravalvar aortic stenosis, 185500 (3) — 7q11.2
Susceptibility to IDDM] (1) — 11q13
usceptibility to measles] (1) — 1q32
mphalangism, proximal (2) — 17q21-q22
ndactyly, type II (2) — 2q31
ay-Sachs disease (3) — 15q23-q24
Temperature-sensitive apoptosis (1) — 14q11-q12
Thalassemias, alpha- (3) — 16pter-p13.3
alassemias, beta- (3) — 11p15.5
anatophoric dwarfism, 187600 (3) — 4p16.3
oracoabdominal syndrome (2) — Xq25-q26.1
rombocytopenia, neonatal alloimmune (1) — 17q21.32
hrombocytopenia, Paris-Trousseau type (2) — 11q23
rombocytopenia, X-linked, 313900 (3) — Xp11.23-p11.22
hrombophilia due to elevated HRG (1) — 3q27
rombophilia due to excessive plasminogen activator inhibitor (1) — 7q21.3-q22
rombophilia due to heparin cofactor II deficiency (3) — 22q11
arombophilia due to protein C deficiency (3) — 2q13-q14
arombophilia due to thrombomodulin defect (3) — 20p12-cen
romboxane synthase deficiency (2) — 7q34
ymine-uraciluria (1) — 1p22
ayroid adenoma, hyperfunctioning (3) — 14q31
ayroid hormone resistance, 274300, 188570 (3) — 3p24.3
ayroid iodine peroxidase deficiency (1) — 2p25
ayroid papillary carcinoma (1) — 10q11-q12
ayrotropin-releasing hormone deficiency (1) — 3p
orsion dystonia (2) — 9q32-q34
orsion dystonia-parkinsonism, Filipino type (2) — Xq12-q13.1
otal anomalous pulmonary venous return (2) — 4p13-q12
ourette syndrome (2) — 18q22.1
ownes-Brocks syndrome (2) — 16q12.1
ranscobalamin II deficiency (3) — 22q11.2-qter

[Transcortin deficiency] (1) — 14q32.1
Treacher Collins mandibulofacial dysostosis (2) — 5q32-q33.1
Trichorhinophalangeal syndrome, type I (2) — 8q24.12
Triphalangeal thumb-polysyndactyly syndrome (2) — 7q36
Trypsinogen deficiency (1) — 7q32-qter
{?Tuberculosis, susceptibility to} (2) — 2q
Tuberous sclerosis 1 (2) — 9q34
Tuberous sclerosis 2 (2) — 16p13.3
Turcot syndrome with glioblastoma, 276300 (3) — 3p21.3
Turner syndrome (1) — Xq13.1
Tylosis with esophageal cancer (2) — 17q23-qter
Tyrosinemia, type I (3) — 15q23-q25
Tyrosinemia, type II (3) — 16q22.1-q22.3
Tyrosinemia, type III (1) — 12q14-qter
Urate oxidase deficiency (1) — 1p22
Urolithiasis, 2,8-dihydroxyadenine (3)   1 — 6q24
Usher syndrome, type 1A (2) — 14q32
Usher syndrome, type 1B (2) — 11q13.5
Usher syndrome, type 1C (2) — 11p15.1
Usher syndrome, type 2 (2) — 1q32
Usher syndrome, type 3 (2) — 3q21-q25
Uterine leiomyoma (3) — 12q15
Van der Woude syndrome (2) — 1q32
Velocardiofacial syndrome, 192430 (2) — 22q11
Venous malformations, multiple cutaneous and mucosal (2) — 9p
Virilization, maternal and fetal, from placental aromatase deficiency (3) — 15q21.1
Vitreoretinopathy, exudative, familial (2) — 11q13-q23
Vitreoretinopathy, neovascular inflammatory (2) — 11q13
{Vivax malaria, susceptibility to} (1) — 1q21-q22
von Hippel-Lindau syndrome (3) — 3p26-p25
von Willebrand disease (3) — 12p13.3
Waardenburg syndrome, type I (3) — 2q35
Waardenburg syndrome, type 2A, 193510 (3) — 3p14.1-p12.3
Waardenburg syndrome, type III, 148820 (3) — 2q35
Wagner syndrome, type II (3) — 12q13.11-q13.2
Waisman parkinsonism-mental retardation syndrome (2) — Xq28
?Walker-Warburg syndrome, 236670 (2) — 9q31-q33
Watson syndrome, 193520 (3) — 17q11.2
Werdnig-Hoffmann disease (3) — 5q12.2-q13.3
Werner syndrome (2) — 8p12-p11
{Wernicke-Korsakoff syndrome, susceptibility to} (1) — 3p14.3
Wieacker-Wolff syndrome (2) — Xq13-q21
Williams-Beuren syndrome, 194050 (3) — 7q11.2
Wilms tumor (3) — 11p13
Wilms tumor, type 2 (3) — 11p15.5
Wilson disease (3) — 13q14.3-q21.1
Wiskott-Aldrich syndrome (3) — Xp11.23-p11.22
?Wolf-Hirschhorn syndrome, 194190 (3) — 4p16.1
Wolf-Hirschhorn syndrome (2) — 4p16.3
Wolfram syndrome (2) — 4p
Wolman disease (3) — 10q24-q25
Wood neuroimmunologic syndrome (2) — Xq26-qter
Wrinkly skin syndrome (2) — 2q32
Xanthinuria (1) — 2p23-p22
?Xeroderma pigmentosum (1) — 1q42
Xeroderma pigmentosum, complementation group C (3) — 3p25
Xeroderma pigmentosum, group B (3) — 2q21
Xeroderma pigmentosum, group D, 278730 (3) — 19q13.2-q13.3
Xeroderma pigmentosum, group G (3) — 13q33
Xeroderma pigmentosum, type A (3) — 9q34.1
?Xeroderma pigmentosum, type F (2) — Chr.15
?XLA and isolated growth hormone deficiency, 307200 (3) — Xq21.3-q22
Zellweger syndrome 1 (2) — 7q11.23
Zellweger syndrome 2 (3) — 1p22-p21
Zellweger syndrome 3 (3) — 8q21.1

Points to Consider in the Design and Submission of Protocols for the Transfer of Recombinant DNA Molecules into the Genome of One or More Human Subjects

Appendix M applies to research conducted at or sponsored by an institution that receives any support for recombinant DNA research from the NIH. Researchers not covered by the *NIH Guidelines* are encouraged to use Appendix M.

The acceptability of human somatic cell gene therapy has been addressed in several public documents as well as in numerous academic studies. In November 1982, the President's Commission for the Study of Ethical Problems in Medicine and Biomedical and Behavioral Research published a report, *Splicing Life,* which resulted from a two-year process of public deliberation and hearings. Upon release of that report, a U.S. House of Representatives subcommittee held three days of public hearings with witnesses from a wide range of fields from the biomedical and social sciences to theology, philosophy, and law. In December 1984, the Office of Technology Assessment released a background paper, *Human Gene Therapy,* which concluded: civic, religious, scientific, and medical groups have all accepted, in principle, the appropriateness of gene therapy of somatic cells in humans for specific genetic diseases. Somatic cell gene therapy is seen as an extension of present methods of therapy that might be preferable to other technologies. In light of this public support, the Recombinant DNA Advisory Committee (RAC) is prepared to consider proposals for somatic cell gene transfer.

The RAC will not at present entertain proposals for germ line alterations but will consider proposals involving somatic cell gene transfer. The purpose of somatic cell gene therapy is to treat an individual patient, e.g., by inserting a properly functioning gene into the subject's somatic cells. Germ line alteration involves a specific attempt to introduce genetic changes into the germ (reproductive) cells of an individual, with the aim of changing the set of genes passed on to the individual's offspring.

In the interest of maximizing the resources of both the NIH and the Food and Drug Administration (FDA) and simplifying the method and period for review,

Amendment Effective March 1, 1996, Federal Register, March 12, 1996 (61 FR 10004)

research proposals involving the deliberate transfer of recombinant DNA or DNA or RNA derived from recombinant DNA into human subjects (human gene transfer) will be considered through a consolidated review process involving both the NIH and the FDA. Submission of human gene transfer proposals will be in the format described in Appendices M-I through M-V of the *Points to Consider*. Investigators must simultaneously submit their human gene transfer proposal to both the NIH and the FDA in a single submission format. This format includes (but is not limited to) the documentation described in Appendices M-I through M-V of the *Points to Consider*. NIH/ORDA and the FDA will simultaneously evaluate the proposal regarding the necessity for RAC review.

Factors that may contribute to the necessity for RAC review include: (i) new vectors/new gene delivery systems, (ii) new diseases, (iii) unique applications of gene transfer, and (iv) other issues considered to require further public discussion. Among the experiments that may be considered exempt from RAC review are those determined by the NIH/ORDA and FDA not to represent possible risk to human health or the environment (see Appendix M-VII, *Categories of Human Gene Transfer Experiments that May Be Exempt from RAC Review*). Whenever possible, investigators will be notified within 15 working days following receipt of the submission whether RAC review will be required. In the event that NIH/ORDA and the FDA require RAC review of the submitted proposal, the documentation described in Appendices M-I through M-V of the *Points to Consider,* will be forwarded to the RAC primary reviewers for evaluation. RAC meetings will be open to the public except where trade secrets and proprietary information are reviewed. The RAC and FDA prefer that information provided in response to Appendix M contain no proprietary data or trade secrets, enabling all aspects of the review to be open to the public. The RAC will recommend approval or disapproval of the reviewed proposal to the NIH Director. In the event that a proposal is contingently approved by the RAC, the RAC prefers that the conditions be satisfactorily met before the RAC's recommendation for approval is submitted to the NIH Director. The NIH Director's decision on the submitted proposal will be transmitted to the FDA Commissioner and considered as a *Major Action* by the NIH Director.

Public review of human gene transfer proposals will serve to inform the public about the technical aspects of the proposals as well as the meaning and significance of the research.

In its evaluation of human gene transfer proposals, the RAC, NIH/ORDA, and the FDA will consider whether the design of such experiments offers adequate assurance that their consequences will not go beyond their purpose, which is the same as the traditional purpose of clinical investigation, namely, to protect the health and well being of human subjects being treated while at the same time gathering generalizable knowledge. Two possible undesirable consequences of the transfer of recombinant DNA would be unintentional: (i) vertical transmission of genetic changes from an individual to his/her offspring, or (ii) horizontal transmission of viral infection to other persons with whom the individual comes in contact. Accordingly, Appendices M-I through M-V requests information that will enable the RAC, NIH/ORDA, and the FDA, to assess the possibility that the proposed experiment(s) will inadvertently affect reproductive cells or lead to infection of other people (e.g., medical personnel or relatives).

In recognition of the social concern that surrounds the subject of human gene transfer, the RAC, NIH/ORDA, and the FDA, will cooperate with other groups in assessing the possible long-term consequences of the proposal and related laboratory and animal experiments in order to define appropriate human applications of this emerging technology.

Appendix M will be considered for revisions as experience in evaluating proposals accumulates and as new scientific developments occur. This review will be carried out periodically as needed.

Appendix M-I. Submission Requirements—Human Gene Transfer Proposals.

Investigators must simultaneously submit the following material to both: (1) the Office of Recombinant DNA Activities, National Institutes of Health/MSC 7010, 6000 Executive Boulevard, Suite 302, Bethesda, Maryland 20892-7010, (301) 496-9838 (see exemption in Appendix M-IX-A, *Footnotes of Appendix M*); and (2) the Division of Congressional and Public Affairs, Document Control Center, HFM-99, Center for Biologics Evaluation and Research, 1401 Rockville Pike, Rockville, Maryland 20852-1448. Proposals will be submitted in the following order: (1) scientific abstract—1 page; (2) non-technical abstract—1 page; (3) Institutional Biosafety Committee and Institutional Review Board approvals and their deliberations pertaining to your protocol (the IBC and IRB may, at their discretion, condition their approval on further specific deliberation by the RAC); (4) Responses to Appendix M-II through M-V, *Description of the Proposal, Informed Consent, Privacy and Confidentiality, and Special Issues*—5 pages; (5) protocol (as approved by the local Institutional Biosafety Committee and Institutional Review Board)—20 pages; (6) Informed Consent document—approved by the Institutional Review Board (see Appendix M-III, *Informed Consent*); (7) appendices (including tables, figures, and manuscripts); (8) curricula vitae—2 pages for each key professional person in biographical sketch format; and (9) three 3 1/2 inch diskettes with the complete vector nucleotide sequence in ASCII format.

Appendix M-II. Description of the Proposal.

Responses to this appendix should be provided in the form of either written answers or references to specific sections of the protocol or its appendices. Investigators should indicate the points that are not applicable with a brief explanation. Investigators submitting proposals that employ the same vector systems may refer to preceding documents, relating to the vector sequence without having to rewrite such material.

Appendix M-II-A. Objectives and Rationale of the Proposed Research.

State concisely the overall objectives and rationale of the proposed study. Provide information on the specific points that relate to whichever type of research is being proposed.

Appendix M-II-A-1. Use of Recombinant DNA for Therapeutic Purposes.

For research in which recombinant DNA is transferred in order to treat a disease or disorder (e.g., genetic diseases, cancer, and metabolic diseases), the following questions should be addressed:

Appendix M-II-A-1-a. Why is the disease selected for treatment by means of gene therapy a good candidate for such treatment?

Appendix M-II-A-1-b. Describe the natural history and range of expression of the disease selected for treatment. What objective and/or quantitative measures of disease activity are available? In your view, are the usual effects of the disease predictable enough to allow for meaningful assessment of the results of gene therapy?

Appendix M-II-A-1-c. Is the protocol designed to prevent all manifestations of the disease, to halt the progression of the disease after symptoms have begun to appear, or to reverse manifestations of the disease in seriously ill victims?

Appendix M-II-A-1-d. What alternative therapies exist? In what groups of patients are these therapies effective? What are their relative advantages and disadvantages as compared with the proposed gene therapy?

Appendix M-II-A-2. Transfer of DNA for Other Purposes.

Appendix M-II-A-2-a. Into what cells will the recombinant DNA be transferred? Why is the transfer of recombinant DNA necessary for the proposed research? What questions can be answered by using recombinant DNA?

Appendix M-II-A-2-b. What alternative methodologies exist? What are their relative advantages and disadvantages as compared to the use of recombinant DNA?

Appendix M-II-B. Research Design, Anticipated Risks and Benefits.

Appendix M-II-B-1. Structure and Characteristics of the Biological System.

Provide a full description of the methods and reagents to be employed for gene delivery and the rationale for their use. The following are specific points to be addressed:

Appendix M-II-B-1-a. What is the structure of the cloned DNA that will be used?

Appendix M-II-B-1-a-(1). Describe the gene (genomic or cDNA), the bacterial plasmid or phage vector, and the delivery vector (if any). Provide complete nucleotide sequence analysis or a detailed restriction enzyme map of the total construct.

Appendix M-II-B-1-a-(2). What regulatory elements does the construct contain (e.g., promoters, enhancers, polyadenylation sites, replication origins, etc.)? From what source are these elements derived? Summarize what is currently known about the regulatory character of each element.

Appendix M-II-B-1-a-(3). Describe the steps used to derive the DNA construct.

Appendix M-II-B-1-b. What is the structure of the material that will be administered to the patient?

Appendix M-II-B-1-b-(1). Describe the preparation, structure, and composition of the materials that will be given to the patient or used to treat the patient's cells: (i) If DNA, what is the purity (both in terms of being a single DNA species and in terms of other contaminants)? What tests have been used and what is the sensitivity of the tests? (ii) If a virus, how is it prepared from the DNA construct? In what cell is the virus grown (any special features)? What medium and serum are used? How is the virus purified? What is its structure and purity? What steps are being taken (and assays used with their sensitivity) to detect and eliminate any contaminating materials (for example, VL30 RNA, other nucleic acids, or proteins) or contaminating viruses (both replication-competent or replication-defective) or other organisms in the cells or serum used for preparation of the virus stock including any contaminants that may have biological effects? (iii) If co-cultivation is employed, what kinds of cells are being used for co-cultivation? What steps are being taken (and assays used with their sensitivity) to detect and eliminate any contaminating materials? Specifically, what tests are being conducted to assess the material to be returned to the patient for the presence of live or killed donor cells or other non-vector materials (for example, VL30 sequences) originating from those cells? (iv) If methods other than those covered by Appendices M-II-B-1 through M-II-B-3, *Research Design, Anticipated Risks and Benefits,* are used to introduce new genetic information into target cells, what steps are being taken to detect and eliminate any contaminating materials? What are possible sources of contamination? What is the sensitivity of tests used to monitor contamination?

Appendix M-II-B-1-b-(2). Describe any other material to be used in preparation of the material to be administered to the patient. For example, if a viral vector is proposed, what is the nature of the helper virus or cell line? If carrier particles are to be used, what is the nature of these?

Appendix M-II-B-2. Preclinical Studies, Including Risk-Assessment Studies. Provide results that demonstrate the safety, efficacy, and feasibility of the proposed procedures using animal and/or cell culture model systems, and explain why the model(s) chosen is/are most appropriate.

Appendix M-II-B-2-a. Delivery System.

Appendix M-II-B-2-a-(1). What cells are the intended target cells of recombinant DNA? What target cells are to be treated *ex vivo* and returned to the patient, how will the cells be characterized before and after treatment? What is the theoretical and practical basis for assuming that only the target cells will incorporate the DNA?

Appendix M-II-B-2-a-(2). Is the delivery system efficient? What percentage of the target cells contain the added DNA?

Appendix M-II-B-2-a-(3). How is the structure of the added DNA sequences monitored and what is the sensitivity of the analysis? Is the added DNA extrachromosomal or integrated? Is the added DNA unrearranged?

Appendix M-II-B-2-a-(4). How many copies are present per cell? How stable is the added DNA both in terms of its continued presence and its structural stability?

Appendix M-II-B-2-b. Gene Transfer and Expression.

Appendix M-II-B-2-b-(1). What animal and cultured cell models were used in laboratory studies to assess the *in vivo* and *in vitro* efficacy of the gene transfer system? In what ways are these models similar to and different from the proposed human treatment?

Appendix M-II-B-2-b-(2). What is the minimal level of gene transfer and/or expression that is estimated to be necessary for the gene transfer protocol to be successful in humans? How was this level determined?

Appendix M-II-B-2-b-(3). Explain in detail all results from animal and cultured cell model experiments which assess the effectiveness of the delivery system in achieving the minimally required level of gene transfer and expression.

Appendix M-II-B-2-b-(4). To what extent is expression only from the desired gene (and not from the surrounding DNA)? To what extent does the insertion modify the expression of other genes?

Appendix M-II-B-2-b-(5). In what percentage of cells does expression from the added DNA occur? Is the product biologically active? What percentage of normal activity results from the inserted gene?

Appendix M-II-B-2-b-(6). Is the gene expressed in cells other than the target cells? If so, to what extent?

Appendix M-II-B-2-c. Retrovirus Delivery Systems.

Appendix M-II-B-2-c-(1). What cell types have been infected with the retroviral vector preparation? Which cells, if any, produce infectious particles?

Appendix M-II-B-2-c-(2). How stable are the retroviral vector and the resulting provirus against loss, rearrangement, recombination, or mutation? What information is available on how much rearrangement or recombination with endogenous or other viral sequences is likely to occur in the patient's cells? What steps have been taken in designing the vector to minimize instability or variation? What laboratory studies have been performed to check for stability, and what is the sensitivity of the analyses?

Appendix M-II-B-2-c-(3). What laboratory evidence is available concerning potential harmful effects of the transfer (e.g., development of neoplasia, harmful mutations, regeneration of infectious particles, or immune responses)? What steps will be taken in designing the vector to minimize pathogenicity? What laboratory studies have been performed to check for pathogenicity, and what is the sensitivity of the analyses?

Appendix M-II-B-2-c-(4). Is there evidence from animal studies that vector DNA has entered untreated cells, particularly germ-line cells? What is the sensitivity of these analyses?

Appendix M-II-B-2-c-(5). Has a protocol similar to the one proposed for a clinical trial been conducted in non-human primates and/or other animals? What were the results? Specifically, is there any evidence that the retroviral vector has recombined with any endogenous or other viral sequences in the animals?

Appendix M-II-B-2-d. Non-Retrovirus Delivery/Expression Systems.

If a non-retroviral delivery system is used, what animal studies have been conducted to determine if there are pathological or other undesirable consequences of the protocol (including insertion of DNA into cells other than those treated, particularly germ-line cells)? How long have the animals been studied after treatment? What safety studies have been conducted? (Include data about the level of sensitivity of such assays.)

Appendix M-II-B-3. Clinical Procedures, Including Patient Monitoring.

Describe the treatment that will be administered to patients and the diagnostic methods that will be used to monitor the success or failure of the treatment. If previous clinical studies using similar methods have been performed by yourself or others, indicate their relevance to the proposed study. Specifically:

Appendix M-II-B-3-a. Will cells (e.g., bone marrow cells) be removed from patients and treated *ex vivo*? If so, describe the type, number, and intervals at which these cells will be removed.

Appendix M-II-B-3-b. Will patients be treated to eliminate or reduce the number of cells containing malfunctioning genes (e.g., through radiation or chemotherapy)?

Appendix M-II-B-3-c. What treated cells (or vector/DNA combination) will be given to patients? How will the treated cells be administered? What volume of cells will be used? Will there be single or multiple treatments? If so, over what period of time?

Appendix M-II-B-3-d. How will it be determined that new gene sequences have been inserted into the patient's cells and if these sequences are being expressed? Are these cells limited to the intended target cell populations? How sensitive are these analyses?

Appendix M-II-B-3-e. What studies will be conducted to assess the presence and effects of the contaminants?

Appendix M-II-B-3-f. What are the clinical endpoints of the study? Are there objectives and quantitative measurements to assess the natural history of the disease? Will such measurements be used in patient follow-up? How will patients be monitored to assess specific effects of the treatment on the disease? What is the sensitivity of the analyses? How frequently will follow-up studies be conducted? How long will patient follow-up continue?

Appendix M-II-B-3-g. What are the major beneficial and adverse effects of treatment that you anticipate? What measures will be taken in an attempt to control or reverse these adverse effects if they occur? Compare the probability and magnitude of deleterious consequences from the disease if recombinant DNA transfer is not used.

Appendix M-II-B-3-h. If a treated patient dies, what special post-mortem studies will be performed?

Appendix M-II-B-4. Public Health Considerations.

Describe any potential benefits and hazards of the proposed therapy to persons other than the patients being treated. Specifically:

Appendix M-II-B-4-a. On what basis are potential public health benefits or hazards postulated?

Appendix M-II-B-4-b. Is there a significant possibility that the added DNA will spread from the patient to other persons or to the environment?

Appendix M-II-B-4-c. What precautions will be taken against such spread (e.g., patients sharing a room, health-care workers, or family members)?

Appendix M-II-B-4-d. What measures will be undertaken to mitigate the risks, if any, to public health?

Appendix M-II-B-4-e. In light of possible risks to offspring, including vertical transmission, will birth control measures be recommended to patients? Are such concerns applicable to health care personnel?

Appendix M-II-B-5. Qualifications of Investigators and Adequacy of Laboratory and Clinical Facilities.

Indicate the relevant training and experience of the personnel who will be involved in the preclinical studies and clinical administration of recombinant DNA. Describe the laboratory and clinical facilities where the proposed study will be performed. Specifically:

Appendix M-II-B-5-a. What professional personnel (medical and nonmedical) will be involved in the proposed study and what is their relevant expertise? Provide a two-page curriculum vitae for each key professional person in biographical sketch format (see Appendix M-I, *Submission Requirements—Human Gene Transfer Proposals*).

Appendix M-II-B-5-b. At what hospital or clinic will the treatment be given? Which facilities of the hospital or clinic will be especially important for the proposed study? Will patients occupy regular hospital beds or clinical research center beds? Where will patients reside during the follow-up period? What special arrangements will be made for the comfort and consideration of the patients. Will the research institution designate an ombudsman, patient care representative, or other individual to help protect the rights and welfare of the patient?

Appendix M-II-C. Selection of the Patients.

Estimate the number of patients to be involved in the proposed study. Describe recruitment procedures and patient eligibility requirements, paying particular attention to whether these procedures and requirements are fair and equitable. Specifically:

Appendix M-II-C-1. How many patients do you plan to involve in the proposed study?

Appendix M-II-C-2. How many eligible patients do you anticipate being able to identify each year?

Appendix M-II-C-3. What recruitment procedures do you plan to use?

Appendix M-II-C-4. What selection criteria do you plan to employ? What are the exclusion and inclusion criteria for the study?

Appendix M-II-C-5. How will patients be selected if it is not possible to include all who desire to participate?

Appendix M-III. Informed Consent.

In accordance with the Protection of Human Subjects (45 CFR Part 46), investigators should indicate how subjects will be informed about the proposed study and the manner in which their consent will be solicited. They should indicate how the Informed Consent document makes clear the special requirements of gene transfer research. If a proposal involves children, special attention should be paid to the Protection of Human Subjects (45 CFR Part 46), Subpart D, Additional Protections for Children Involved as Subjects in Research.

Appendix M-III-A. Communication About the Study to Potential Participants.

Appendix M-III-A-1. Which members of the research group and/or institution will be responsible for contacting potential participants and for describing the study to them? What procedures will be used to avoid possible conflicts of interest if the investigator is also providing medical care to potential subjects?

Appendix M-III-A-2. How will the major points covered in Appendix M-II, *Description of Proposal,* be disclosed to potential participants and/or their parents or guardians in language that is understandable to them?

Appendix M-III-A-3. What is the length of time that potential participants will have to make a decision about their participation in the study?

Appendix M-III-A-4. If the study involves pediatric or mentally handicapped subjects, how will the assent of each person be obtained?

Appendix M-III-B. Informed Consent Document.

Investigators submitting human gene transfer proposals must include the Informed Consent document as approved by the local Institutional Review Board. A separate Informed Consent document should be used for the gene transfer portion of a research project when gene transfer is used as an adjunct in the study of another technique, e.g., when a gene is used as a "marker" or to enhance the power of immunotherapy for cancer.

Because of the relative novelty of the procedures that are used, the potentially irreversible consequences of the procedures performed, and the fact that many of the potential risks remain undefined, the Informed Consent document should include the following specific information in addition to any requirements of the DHHS regulations for the Protection of Human Subjects (45 CFR 46). Indicate if each of the specified items appears in the Informed Consent document or, if not included in the Informed Consent document, how those items will be presented to potential subjects. Include an explanation if any of the following items are omitted from the consent process or the Informed Consent document.

Appendix M-III-B-1. General Requirements of Human Subjects Research.

Appendix M-III-B-1-a. Description/Purpose of the Study.

The subjects should be provided with a detailed explanation in non-technical language of the purpose of the study and the procedures associated with the conduct of the proposed study, including a description of the gene transfer component.

Appendix M-III-B-1-b. Alternatives.

The Informed Consent document should indicate the availability of therapies and the possibility of other investigational interventions and approaches.

Appendix M-III-B-1-c. Voluntary Participation.

The subjects should be informed that participation in the study is voluntary and that failure to participate in the study or withdrawal of consent will not result in any penalty or loss of benefits to which the subjects are otherwise entitled.

Appendix M-III-B-1-d. Benefits.

The subjects should be provided with an accurate description of the possible benefits, if any, of participating in the proposed study. For studies that are not reasonably expected to provide a therapeutic benefit to subjects, the Informed Consent document should clearly state that no direct clinical benefit to subjects is expected to occur as a result of participation in the study, although knowledge may be gained that may benefit others.

Appendix M-III-B-1-e. Possible Risks, Discomforts, and Side Effects.

There should be clear itemization in the Informed Consent document of types of adverse experiences, their relative severity, and their expected frequencies. For consistency, the following definitions are suggested: side effects that are listed as mild should be ones which do not require a therapeutic intervention; moderate side effects require an intervention; and severe side effects are potentially fatal or life-threatening, disabling, or require prolonged hospitalization.

If verbal descriptors (e.g., "rare," "uncommon," or "frequent") are used to express quantitative information regarding risk, these terms should be explained.

The Informed Consent document should provide information regarding the approximate number of people who have previously received the genetic material under study. It is necessary to warn potential subjects that, for genetic materials previously used in relatively few or no humans, unforeseen risks are possible, including ones that could be severe.

The Informed Consent document should indicate any possible adverse medical consequences that may occur if the subjects withdraw from the study once the study has started.

Appendix M-III-B-1-f. Costs.

The subjects should be provided with specific information about any financial costs associated with their participation in the protocol and in the long-term follow-up to the protocol that are not covered by the investigators or the institution involved.

Subjects should be provided an explanation about the extent to which they will be responsible for any costs for medical treatment required as a result of research-related injury.

Appendix M-III-B-2. Specific Requirements of Gene Transfer Research.

Appendix M-III-B-2-a. Reproductive Considerations.

To avoid the possibility that any of the reagents employed in the gene transfer research could cause harm to a fetus/child, subjects should be given information concerning possible risks and the need for contraception by males and females during the active phase of the study. The period of time for the use of contraception should be specified.

The inclusion of pregnant or lactating women should be addressed.

Appendix M-III-B-2-b. Long-Term Follow-Up.

To permit evaluation of long-term safety and efficacy of gene transfer, the prospective subjects should be informed that they are expected to cooperate in long-term follow-up that extends beyond the active phase of the study. The Informed Consent document should include a list of persons who can be contacted in the event that questions arise during the follow-up period. The investigator should request that subjects continue to provide a current address and telephone number.

The subjects should be informed that any significant findings resulting from the study will be made known in a timely manner to them and/or their parent or guardian including new information about the experimental procedure, the harms and benefits experienced by other individuals involved in the study, and any long-term effects that have been observed.

Appendix M-III-B-2-c. Request for Autopsy.

To obtain vital information about the safety and efficacy of gene transfer, subjects should be informed that at the time of death, no matter what the cause, permission for an autopsy will be requested of their families. Subjects should be asked to advise their families of the request and of its scientific and medical importance.

Appendix M-III-B-2-d. Interest of the Media and Others in the Research.

To alert subjects that others may have an interest in the innovative character of the protocol and in the status of the treated subjects, the subjects should be informed of the following: (i) that the institution and investigators will make efforts to provide protection from the media in an effort to protect the participants' privacy, and (ii) that representatives of applicable Federal agencies (e.g., the National Institutes of Health and the Food and Drug Administration), representatives of collaborating institutions, vector suppliers, etc., will have access to the subjects' medical records.

Appendix M-IV. Privacy and Confidentiality.

Indicate what measures will be taken to protect the privacy of patients and their families as well as to maintain the confidentiality of research data.

Appendix M-IV-A. What provisions will be made to honor the wishes of individual patients (and the parents or guardians of pediatric or mentally handicapped patients) as to whether, when, or how the identity of patients is publicly disclosed.

Appendix M-IV-B. What provisions will be made to maintain the confidentiality of research data, at least in cases where data could be linked to individual patients?

Appendix M-V. Special Issues.

Although the following issues are beyond the normal purview of local Institutional Review Boards, investigators should respond to the following questions:

Appendix M-V-A. What steps will be taken, consistent with Appendix M-IV, *Privacy and Confidentiality,* to ensure that accurate and appropriate information is made available to the public with respect to such public concerns as may arise from the proposed study?

Appendix M-V-B. Do you or your funding sources intend to protect under patent or trade secret laws either the products or the procedures developed in the proposed study? If so, what steps will be taken to permit as full communication as possible among investigators and clinicians concerning research methods and results?

Appendix M-VI. RAC Review—Human Gene Transfer Protocols.

Appendix M-VI-A. Categories of Human Gene Transfer Experiments that Require RAC Review.

Factors that may contribute to the necessity for RAC review include, but are not limited to: (i) new vectors/new gene delivery systems, (ii) new diseases, (iii) unique applications of gene transfer, and (iv) other issues considered to require further public discussion. Whenever possible, investigators will be notified within 15 working days following receipt of the submission whether RAC review will be required. In the event that RAC review is deemed necessary by the NIH and FDA, the proposal will be forwarded to the RAC primary reviewers for evaluation. In order to maintain public access to information regarding human gene transfer protocols, NIH/ORDA will maintain the documentation described in Appendices M-I through M-V (including protocols that are not reviewed by the RAC).

Appendix M-VI-B. RAC Primary Reviewers' Written Comments.

In the event that NIH/ORDA or the FDA recommend RAC review of the submitted proposal, the documentation described in Appendices M-I through M-V will be forwarded to the RAC primary reviewers for evaluation.

The RAC primary reviewers shall provide written comments on the proposal to NIH/ORDA. The RAC primary reviewers' comments should include the following:

Appendix M-VI-B-1. Emphasize the issues related to gene marking, gene transfer, or gene therapy.

Appendix M-VI-B-2. State explicitly whether Appendices M-I through M-V have been addressed satisfactorily.

Appendix M-VI-B-3. Examine the scientific rationale, scientific context (relative to other proposals reviewed by the RAC), whether the preliminary *in vitro* and *in vivo* data were obtained in appropriate models and are sufficient, and whether questions related to safety, efficacy, and social/ethical context have been resolved.

Appendix M-VI-B-4. Whenever possible, criticisms of Informed Consent documents should include written alternatives for suggested revisions for the RAC to consider.

Appendix M-VI-B-5. Primary reviews should state whether the proposal is: (i) acceptable as written, (ii) expected to be acceptable with specific revisions or after satisfactory responses to specific questions raised on review, or (iii) unacceptable in its present form.

Appendix M-VI-C. Investigator's Written Responses to RAC Primary Reviewers.

Appendix M-VI-C-1. Written responses (including critical data in response to RAC primary reviewers' written comments) shall be submitted to NIH/ORDA greater than or equal to 2 weeks following receipt of the review.

Appendix M-VI-D. Oral Responses to the RAC. Investigators shall limit their oral responses to the RAC only to those questions that are raised during the meeting. Investigators are strongly discouraged from presenting critical data during their oral presentations that was not submitted greater than or equal to 2 weeks in advance of the RAC meeting at which it is reviewed.

Appendix M-VI-E. RAC Recommendations to the NIH Director.

The RAC will recommend approval or disapproval of the reviewed proposal to the NIH Director. In the event that a proposal is contingently approved by the RAC, the RAC prefers that the conditions be satisfactorily met before the RAC's recommendation for approval is submitted to the NIH Director. The NIH Director's decision on the submitted proposal will be transmitted to the FDA Commissioner and considered as a *Major Action* by the NIH Director.

Appendix M-VII. Categories of Human Gene Transfer Experiments that May be Exempt from RAC Review.

A proposal submitted under one of the following categories may be considered exempt from RAC review unless otherwise determined by NIH/ORDA and the FDA on a case-by-case basis (see Appendix M-VI-A, *Categories of Human Gene Transfer Experiments that Require RAC Review*).

NOTE: For proposals that are exempt from RAC review, the documentation described in Appendices M-I through M-V will be maintained by NIH/ORDA for compliance with annual data reporting and adverse event reporting requirements (see Appendix M-VII, *Reporting Requirements—Human Gene Transfer Protocols*). Any subsequent modifications to proposals that were not reviewed by the RAC must be submitted to NIH/ORDA in order to facilitate data reporting requirements.

Appendix M-VII-A. Vaccines.

This category includes recombinant DNA vaccines not otherwise exempt from RAC review (see Appendix M-IX-A, *Footnotes of Appendix M,* for exempt vaccines).

Appendix M-VII-B. Lethally Irradiated Tumor Cells/No Replication-Competent Virus.

This category includes experiments involving lethally irradiated tumor cells and: (1) vector constructs that have previously been approved by the RAC (or with the incorporation of minor modifications), or (2) a different tumor cell target.

Appendix M-VII-C. New Site/Original Investigator.

This category includes the following: (1) initiation of a protocol at an additional site other than the site that was originally approved by the RAC, and (2) the investigator at the new site is the same as the investigator approved for the original study.

Appendix M-VII-D. New Site/New Investigator.

This category includes the following: (1) initiation of a protocol at an additional site other than the site that was originally approved by the RAC, and (2) the investigator at the new site is different than the investigator approved for the original site.

Appendix M-VII-E. "Umbrella" Protocols.

This category includes initiation of a RAC-approved protocol at more than one additional site (the Principal Investigator may be the same or different than the Principal Investigator approved for the original site).

Appendix M-VII-F. Modifications Related to Gene Transfer.

The category includes experiments involving a modification to the clinical protocol that is not related to the gene transfer portion of study.

Appendix M-VII-G. Gene Marking Protocols.

This category includes human gene marking experiments involving vector constructs that have previously been approved by the RAC and: (1) minor modifications to the vector constructs, or (2) a different tumor cell target.

Appendix M-VIII. Reporting Requirements—Human Gene Transfer Protocols.

Appendix M-VIII-A. Annual Data Reporting.

Investigators who have received approval from the FDA to initiate a human gene transfer protocol (whether or not it has been reviewed by the RAC) shall be required to comply with the annual data reporting requirements. Annual Data Report forms will be forwarded by NIH/ORDA to investigators. Data submitted in these reports will be evaluated by the RAC, NIH/ORDA, and the FDA and reviewed by the RAC at its next regularly scheduled meeting.

Appendix M-VIII-B. Adverse Event Reporting.

Investigators who have received approval from the FDA to initiate a human gene transfer protocol (whether or not it has been reviewed by the RAC) must report any serious adverse event immediately to the local IRB, IBC, NIH Office for Protection from Research Risks, NIH/ORDA, and FDA, followed by the submission of a written report filed with each group. Reports submitted to NIH/ORDA shall be sent to the Office of Recombinant DNA Activities, National Institutes of Health/MSC 7010, 6000 Executive Boulevard, Suite 302, Bethesda, Maryland 20892-7010, (301) 496-9838.

Appendix M-IX. Footnotes of Appendix M.

Appendix M-IX-A. Human studies in which the induction or enhancement of an immune response to a vector-encoded microbial immunogen is the major goal, such an immune response has been demonstrated in model systems, and the persistence of the vector-encoded immunogen is not expected, may be initiated without RAC review if approved by another Federal agency.

INDEX

Acquired diseases, gene transfer, 9
Acquired immunodeficiency syndrome (AIDS), 62–64
Adeno-associated virus, recombinant vectors, 30–31
Adenosine deaminase
  biochemical pathway, 49
  clinical treatment, 48
Adenosine deaminase deficiency (ADAD)
  cellular immunity, 52
  clinical results, 58
  economic impact, 12
  gene therapy, 2, 47–53
  genetics, 47–48
  humoral immunity, 52
Adenovirus vectors
  features, 29
  gene transfer, 28–30
  hepatocytes, 68
  wild-type, 28
Adult respiratory distress syndrome (ARDS), 71–72
Adverse events, reporting protocol, 191
Alpha-fetoprotein, 29
Alzheimer's disease, 79
Amgen, 10
Anemia. *See* Fanconi's anemia
Anergy, 157
Animals, transgenic, 3
Antibody genes, insertion trials, 121
Antiherpes drugs, 112
Antisense genes and oncogenes, 10, 121, 157
Antitrypsin deficiency, 2, 22, 67
Apolipoprotein E, 72
Apoptosis, 161
  cancer therapy, 122
  vesicles, 112
Arthritis, 9, 77
Artificial chromosomes, 23, 161
Asialoglycoproteins, gene transfer, 23–24
Atherosclerosis, 72
Autoimmune disorders, 155
Autopsy request, informed consent, 187
Autosomes, 161

Bacille Calmette-Guerin (BCG), genetically engineered, 66

Bacteria
  genes, 118
  recombinant, 3, 5
Base pairs, 161
Biological systems, structure and characteristics, 178–180
Biotechnology companies, 1, 10
Blindness, gene transfer, 81
Blood-clotting system, non-neoplastic disorders, 69–70
Bone disease, 76–77
Bone marrow
  gene marking, 101
  stem cells, 101, 103
  transplantation, 48
Brain tumors, 113–115
Breast cancer, gene marking, 101

Cancer
  apoptosis, 121
  clinical trials, 139
  gene marking, 100–103
  gene therapy, 97–100, 122–123, 145–151
  genes, 99–100
  hematopoietic stem cells, 100–103
  HS-tk therapies, 120
  liposome gene delivery, 110
  T-lymphocytes, 104–105
  trials and protocols, 98–103
  types and tissue, 99–100
Cancer Gene Therapy, 141
Candodate genes, positional cloning, 15
Carcinoembryonic antigen (CEA)
  cancer therapy, 98
  muscle cells, 112
  poxvirus vectors, 34
Carcinogenesis, genetic model, 97
Cardiac gene transfer, 74
Cardiovascular disease, 9, 155
Cardiovascular system, 72–74
Carolina Biological Supply Company, 144
Cells
  abnormalities, 17
  immunity, 52
  surface proteins, 17
  survival, 21

193

Center for Biologics Evaluation and Research (CBER), 138
Central nervous system (CNS), 79–81
Charcot-Marie-Tooth disease, 17
Chemical gene transfer, 20
Chemotherapy
    enhancement, 123
    gene experiments, 102
Chromosome locations, health disorders, 167–173
Chromosomes, artificial, 23, 161
Chronic granulomatous disease, 2
Clinical procedures, transfer protocols, 182
Cloning
    positional, 15
    vectors, 161
Clotting factor deficiency, 69–70
Coding sequence, 162
Colon cancer, genetic model, 97
Colorectal cancer, tumor vaccines, 107
Confidentiality, protocol consideration, 187
Cord blood, hematopoietic disorders, 59
Cystic fibrosis
    adenovirus vectors, 29
    economic impact, 12
    gene therapy, 2, 70
    positional cloning, 15
    transmembrane regulator, 70–71
Cystic Fibrosis Foundation, 12
Cytochrome P-450, gene transfer, 122
Cytokines, 162
    cancer therapy, 105
    clinical trials, 107
    gene transfer, 106–109
    recombinant forms, 4
    tumor cells, 105–109
    types, 107
Cytosine deaminase, sensitivity gene, 119

Databases, human genome, 15
Delivery systems
    gene transfer protocols, 180
    retrovirus and non-retrovirus, 181
Deoxyribonucleic acid (DNA)
    clinical diagnostics, 2
    direct injection, 66
    repair process, 17
    transfer purposes, 178
    see also Recombinant DNA
Diabetes mellitus, 9, 16, 78
Diseases
    gene mapping, 1–2
    see also Health disorders

Drugs
    approved, 4
    recombinant, 2, 4
    see also Pharmaceuticals
Duchenne's muscular dystrophy, 74–75
Dystrophin gene, 74–75

Endocrine system, gene therapy, 78
Enhancers, 162
Epidermal growth factor, cancer therapy, 98
Epilepsy, gene therapy, 80
Erythrocyte disorders, 60–62
Ethical issues, 136–137
European Working Group on Human Gene Transfer and Therapy, 141
Exons, 162
Eye disorders, gene therapy, 79–80

Facilities, adequacy, 183
Factor IX deficiency, 69–70
Familial hypercholesterolemia, 2, 72
Fanconi's anemia, 2, 61
Fibroblasts
    cytokines, 106–109
    gene therapy, 76, 145
    gene transfer, 106–109
    genetic alteration, 105
Food and Drug Administration (FDA), 4, 136, 175
Functional cloning, 15, 16
Fusion, gene transfer, 20

Ganciclovir, 112, 158
Gastrointestinal tract, gene therapy, 78
Gaucher's disease, 2, 12, 60
Gene expression, 162
    antisense down-regulation, 10
    protocols, 180–181
    regulating, 8
Gene therapy, xvi
    advisory committees, 141
    approved trials, 57
    aptosis, 121
    biotechnology, 10–11
    cancer applications, 97–100
    clinical results, 58, 139
    drug enhancement, 122
    economic impact, 11–12
    ethical issues, 138–139
    experiments, 1–2, 47–53
    historical perspective, xiii, 1–10
    journals and periodicals, 143

major events, xv
non-neoplastic disorders, 57
organizations, 143–144
potential applications, 9–10
protocols, xvii, 145–155
radiation enhancement, 122
recombinant DNA, 1–10
regulatory issues, 137–138
skin cells, 76–77
videotapes, 142
Gene Therapy, 141
Gene Therapy Advisory Committee, 143
Gene transfer
    biotechnology, 10–11
    CNS applications, 81
    cytokines, 106–109
    HIV strategies, 64
    in vitro methods, 20
    integration vs. nonintegration, 19, 20
    methods, 7–8, 19–24
    potential applications, 9
    proposals, 177–184
    protocols, 175–177
    receptor-mediated, 23
    recombinant viruses, 20
    vector types, 35
Genentech, 10
Genes
    applications, 1–5
    cloning, 15
    delivery methods, 7–8, 25–28
    human genome, 15–17
    identification, 1–5, 15–17
    mapping, 1, 15, 158
    marking, 101–103
    repair mechanisms, 36–37
    replacement methods, 35–37
Genetic diseases, 16–17
    clinical trials, 139
    economic impact, 12
    gene therapy, 1–2, 145–146
    gene transfer, 9
Genetic Engineering News, 141
Genetic Therapy Inc., 11
Genetics, 1
Genome. *See* Human Genome Project
Germline cells, xvi, 158
Glial fibrillary acidic protein (GFAP), 30
Glioblastoma multiforme, 114–116
Granulocyte-colony stimulating factor (G-CSF), 102, 103
Granulocyte disorders, gene therapy, 57–59
Granulomatous disease, chronic, 2

Health disorders, chromosome locations, 167–173
Heart disease. *See* Cardiovascular disease
Hematologic disorders, 60–62
Hematopoietic disorders, 57–62
Hematopoietic stem cells
    cancer, 100–103
    gene marking, 100–103
    therapy protocols, 100, 147
Hemophilia A and B, 9, 12, 67
Hemophilia Foundation, 12
Hepatic system, non-neoplastic disorders, 67–69
Hepatitis B, recombinant vaccine, 6
Hepatocytes, gene transfer, 24, 68
Herpes drugs, 112
Herpes simplex-thymidine kinase (Hs-tk)
    brain tumors, 113–115
    cancer therapy, 112–118
    sensitivity gene, 112–118
Herpes simplex virus (HSV)
    neurotropic vector, 79–80
    recombinant vectors, 32–33
Homologous recombination, 7, 162
    gene repair, 36–37
Housekeeping genes, 17, 47
Human Gene Therapy, 143, 175
Human genome
    gene identification, 15–17
    recombinant DNA, 175–177
    transfer protocols, 175–177
Human Genome Organization, 15
Human Genome Project, 1
Human growth hormone, recombinant form, 5
Human immunodeficiency virus (HIV)
    clinical trials, 139
    gene therapy, 62–64, 151–152
    gene transfer, 9, 22, 64
    life cycle, 65
    recombinant vectors, 34–35
Human leukocyte antigen (HLA), 159
Humoral immunity, 52
Hunter's syndrome. *See* Mucopolysaccharidosis type II
Huntington's disease, positional cloning, 15
Hypercholesterolemia, 67, 72
    familial, 2, 72
Hyperlipedemia, 72
Hypertension, gene transfer, 74

Immune Deficiency Foundation, 12, 142
Immune stimulatory genes, 107
Immunologic disorders, gene therapy, 57–59
Influenza virus, direct DNA injection, 65–66

Informed consent, 184–187
  alternative therapies, 185
  benefits and risks, 185–186
  document, 185–187
  financial costs, 186
  media interest, 187
  reproductive considerations, 186
  voluntary participation, 185
Insertional mutagenesis, 163
Insulin-dependent diabetes mellitus (IDDM), 78
Insulin gene, 16–17
Insulin-like growth factor (IGF), 111
Intercellular communication abnormalities, 17
Interleukins, 107, 163
International Society for the Advancement of Biotechnology, 143
Intracellular antibody genes, 121
Introns, 163
Investigational new drug (IND), 138
Investigators, qualifications, 183
Ischemia, gene transfer, 73
Isohemagglutinins, 163

Joints, gene therapy, 76–77

Karyotypes, 163
Keratinocytes, 76–77

Leukemia, gene marking, 100–101
Liposomes, 163
  gene delivery, 71, 110
  tumor cell injection, 109–110
Liver
  genetic alteration, 68–69
  see also Hepatic system
Low-density lipoprotein (HDL), receptor gene, 67, 72
Lung, gene delivery, 70–71
  see also Pulmonary disorders
Lyme disease, recombinant vaccine, 66
Lymphocyte disorders, 57–59
Lymphoma, gene marking, 101
Lysomal storage disorders, 60

Macrophage disorders, 60
Major histocompatibility complex (MHC), gene transfer, 108–111
Map of Life: Science, Society and the Human Genome Project (videotape), 144
Marfan syndrome, 73
Media interest, informed consent, 187
Megabase (Mb), 163

Melanin, 30
Melanoma
  liposome gene delivery, 110
  tumor vaccines, 107
  tyrosinase antigen, 105
Mental illness, gene transfer, 81
Microencapsulation, 21, 78
Microorganisms, genetically engineered, 66
Molecular biology
  gene therapy, 10–11
  recombinant techniques, 3–5
Molecular medicine, major events, xv
Molecular Miracles: Human Gene Therapy and the Future of Molecular Medicine (videotape), 144
Moloney murine leukemia virus (MoMLV), 25–28
Monocyte disorders, 60
Mucopolysaccharidosis type II, 2
Multiple myeloma, gene marking, 101
Multiple sclerosis, 80
Muscle cells, tumor antigen expression, 112
Muscle creatine kinase, 30
Muscle disorders, gene therapy, 74–75
Muscular dystrophy. See Duchenne's muscular dystrophy
Mutagenesis, insertional, 163
Myocardium, direct injection, 74

National Center for Human Genome Research, 144
National Institutes of Health (NIH), 16, 135, 175, 189
National Organization for Rare Disorders, 12, 141
Neo-organs, gene transfer, 21, 22
Nerve growth factor (NGF), 80
Neuroblastoma, gene marking, 100–101
Neurofibromatosis
  gene therapy, 79
  positional cloning, 15
Neurotropic vectors, 79–80
Non-neoplastic disorders, 57
Nucleotides, 164

Office of Recombinant DNA Activities (ORDA), 135, 143
Oligonucleotides, 10, 164
  see also Antisense genes and oncogenes
Ommaya reservoir, brain tumors, 115
Oncogenes, 2, 164
Oncogenesis, genetic model, 97
Organoids. See Neo-organs

Ornithine transcarbamylase deficiency, 2, 69
Osteoporosis, gene transfer, 77
Ovarian cancer
    gene marking, 104
    gene transfer, 117–118

Parkinson's disease, gene therapy, 79
Patient monitoring and selection, 182, 184
Peripheral blood stem cells, 101–103
Pharmaceuticals
    industry, 10–11
    production, 3–5
    recombinant, 2–5
Phenylalanine hydroxylase deficiency, 68
Phenylketonuria, gene therapy, 67, 68
Physical gene transfer, 20
Plants, recombinant techniques, 3
Plasmids, 164
Platelet disorders, 60–62
Polyadenylation, 164
Polycystic kidney disease
    gene therapy, 79
    positional cloning, 15
Polymerases, 164
Positional cloning, 15, 16
Poxvirus vectors, gene transfer, 33–34
Preclinical studies, gene transfer, 180–181
Premature birth, gene therapy, 71–72
Privacy, protocol consideration, 187
Prostate-specific antigen (PSA), 34, 112
Protocols
    cancer therapy, 100–103
    clinical procedures, 182
    delivery systems, 180
    design and submission, 175–177
    gene marking, 191
    gene therapy, 175
    informed consent, 184–187
    new sites, 190
    patient monitoring, 182
    potential participants, 184
    preclinical studies, 180–181
    privacy and confidentiality, 187
    qualifications of investigators, 183
    reporting requirements, 191
    research design, 178–183
    risks and benefits, 178–183
    special issues, 188
    umbrella, 190
    vaccines, 190–191
Public health, protocol consideration, 183
Pulmonary disorders, gene therapy, 70–72

Purine nucleotide phosphorylase deficiency, 2, 59

Rabies vaccines, 33, 67
Radiation therapy, gene enhancement, 123
Receptor-mediated gene transfer, 23–24
Recombinant DNA
    direct injection, 21–23
    expected benefits, xvi
    gene therapy, 1–10
    historical development, 1–10
    human genome, 175–177
    pharmaceuticals, 2–5
    regulatory issues, 135
    research, xvi
    therapeutic use, 178
    transfer protocols, 175–177
Recombinant DNA Advisory Committee (RAC)
    exempt experiments, 190
    gene transfer protocols, 175
    investigators responses, 189
    NIH recommendations, 189
    protocol review, 188–189
    reviewers' comments, 188–189
Regulatory genes
    abnormalities, 17
Regulatory issues, 135–136
Renal cell carcinoma
    gene marking, 104
    liposome gene delivery, 111
    tumor vaccines, 107
Reproductive considerations, informed consent, 186–187
Restenosis, angioplasty, 73
Restriction endonuclease, 164
Retroviral vectors, 164
    direct injection, 68
    disadvantages, 26
    HIV infection, 63
    MoMLV, 25–28
Retroviruses, delivery systems, 181
Rheumatoid arthritis, 77
Ribozymes, 164
    Marfan syndrome, 73
Risk assessment, gene transfer, 180–181

Salmonella microorganisms, genetically engineered, 66
Sensitivity enzymes, 119
Sensitivity genes
    cytosine deaminase, 119
    system diagram, 113
    types, 112–119

Severe combined immunodeficiency, 161
Sickle cell anemia, 61
Skin cells
    antigen expression, 112
    gene therapy, 76–77
Solid tumors, gene transfer, 118
Somatic cells, 165
    gene therapy, 136–137
    germline therapy, xvi
Splicing Life, 175
Stem cells
    bone marrow, 101
    gene marking, 61–62, 100–103
    genetic alteration, 63
    harvesting, 103
    intestinal, 78
Storage disorders, 60
Suicide genes, 35
Superoxide dismutase, 79
Surfactant deficiency, 71–72
Surfactant proteins, 30

T-lymphocytes
    gene marking, 104–105
    gene therapy, 104–105, 145
    gene transfer, 104–105
    genetic alteration, 62–64
    visible tumor, 111
Target cell, gene transfer, 19, 20
Thalassemias, 9, 60
Thrombocytopenia, 62
Tissue cells, therapy protocols, 148–151
Tissue plasminogen activator, 7
Tissue-specific promoters, 29, 30
Transdominant negative, 165
Transgenic animals, 3
Transmembrane regulators
    adenovirus vectors, 29
    cystic fibrosis, 70–71
Transplantation, bone marrow, 48
Trypsin. *See* Antitrypsin deficiency
Tumor cells
    antigen expression, 112
    cytokines, 106–109
    foreign genes, 109–111
    gene therapy, 150–155
    gene transfer, 106–111
    genetic alteration, 105
    immunization, 106

    infiltrating lymphocytes, 104
    lethally irradiated, 190
    liposome injection, 109–110
    skin and muscle, 112
    solid, 118
    visible, 111
Tumor necrosis factor (TNF), 165
    cancer therapy, 105
    clinical trials, 107
    recombinant form, 4–5
Tumor suppressor genes
    adenoviral, 119–120
    insertion trials, 120–121
Tumor vaccines, 107, 108
Tyrosinase, melanoma antigen, 105

Upper respiratory tract infections, 28
Urea cycle disorders, 69
Urinary system, gene therapy, 79

Vaccination, viral vectors, 67
Vaccines
    direct injection, 65–66
    FDA-approved, 4
    genetically engineered, 66
    hepatitis B, 6
    production, 108
    protocols, 190–191
    recombinant, 2, 4, 65–67
    tumor, 107
Vaccinia virus, 34–35
Vascular disease, 21
    occlusive, 73
Vascular endothelial growth factor, 73, 98
Vector producer cells
    implantation, 114
    motile type, 117
Vectors, 165
Vesicles, apoptotic, 112
Vesicular stomatitis virus (VSV), 28
Viagene, 11
Vical Inc., 11
Virus vectors
    recombinant, 25–35
    types, 35
    vaccination, 67

Yeast, recombinant vaccine, 6